PAST ERAS AWAKEN
I

The Grail Movement in the UK and Ireland
Suite F6, Flemington House,
Glasgow G21 4BF
www.grail-message.com
Email – info@grailmovement-uk.org
Telephone – 0141 558 7133

PAST ERAS
AWAKEN

Received in the proximity of Abd-ru-shin
through the special gift of
one Called for the purpose

I

GRAIL ACRES PUBLISHING CO. LTD.

LONDON

British Library Cataloguing in Publication Data.
A catalogue record for this book is available from
the British Library.

ONLY AUTHORIZED EDITION
ISBN 1-898853-06-1
© 1997 BY STIFTUNG GRALSBOTSCHAFT, STUTTGART

PUBLISHER'S FOREWORD

THIS VOLUME is one of the book-series entitled "Past Eras Awaken". In it are shown the direct helps and the spiritual guidance from the Light given to mankind from their early beginnings. The explanations embrace happenings both on earth and in the beyond.

The list of individual volumes and their contents at the end of the book gives a general survey of persons and events within this far-reaching cycle.

The origin of the writings is certainly unusual according to the present way of thinking. The contents of the books are "received", not thought out. To grasp this, it must be recognised that in Creation nothing is lost, that every living happening remains indelibly preserved. The ability to receive and record, however, was granted to Called persons in the proximity of Abd-ru-shin, the Bringer of the Grail Message, "In the Light of Truth". For this reason the name of the author is not mentioned.

What is received always follows specific threads in the development of events. For each of the receiving persons they are of a different kind. Therefore some of the same events are illumined from various aspects; while one description may view and report from the spiritual standpoint, thus seen from above downwards, another gives the same from the earthly point of view.

Every unprejudiced reader can experience within himself the rightness of what is offered. He will sense that it was not fantasy that guided the pen, but a genuine happening, evoked from mists of antiquity. Amazed, perhaps deeply moved, he will be able to perceive how the veils are lifted from a great, decisive past, whereby he can attain to spiritual far-sight, and to recognition of the connections right up to the closing of the cycle at the present time.

All the beyond-earthly happenings described in the aforesaid book-series are logically and completely substantiated by the Work "In the Light of Truth", in accordance with the Laws of Creation.

The differences of opinion about the teaching and work of the well-known prophets, even about the Word of Truth brought by Jesus the Son of God, call for a special comment: no reader need fear that he will become involved in the dissension of the various religious creeds.

In the way in which the teachings were once given by these wise men – beginning with Hjalfdar (the book "Ephesus"), to Krishna, Zoroaster, Lao-Tse, Buddha and Mohammed, and some others besides – lies a clear, uniform course of spiritual guidance from the Light for mankind on earth.

Abd-ru-shin writes about this in a bequest:

"If in the course of thousands of years men had not *always* acted as they still do *today*, if they had not time and again distorted everything that was intended to help them, in order to adapt it to their human way of thinking and their earthly desires, there would now be only *one uniform* teaching here on earth, issuing from the Will of God. There would not be so many kinds of denominations.

"All the teachings that have come to earth in the past would, *united*, form *a single flight of steps* to the pedestal on which the Truth is to stand, as it has so often been proclaimed to mankind in various promises.

"There would be no differences in the interpretations, much less differences in the teachings themselves!

"For all the teachings were at one time willed by God, precisely adapted to the individual peoples and countries, and formed in complete accord with their actual spiritual maturity and receptivity.

"... The bringers of all the individual teachings were Forerunners of the Word of Truth Itself."

6

A CALL FROM THE LIGHT REACHES THE EAR OF THE SEER.

HE OPENS WIDE THE EYE OF HIS SPIRIT

AND SEES HOW THE THREADS OF THE HAPPENINGS

EXTEND THROUGH THE WORLDS.

A bright ray pierces the mists of the past, and from it steps Krishna in order to put right all the wrong concepts that mankind have formed about him and his earth-life as Forerunner for the Light. Before the seer that epoch arises:

KRISHNA

A PURE HUMAN FLOWER had opened spiritually to a specially high incarnation.

This flower was Sita, Krishna's mother. She had blossomed forth like a still, pure lotus on sacred waters – natural, undistorted and clear, far away from the sultry atmosphere of the Indian South country. As a member of an upper caste, her childhood passed harmoniously in association with the high spiritual.

Isolated from the rest of the world by impassable mountain ranges, the country was of singular beauty and majesty.

Shimmering snow-capped giants, white and colossal, encircled the blessed plateau that extended in their midst for the space of many, many hours. Its position allowed the valley to receive the radiations of the stars in lawful rhythm.

Bubbling waters from the regions of ice flowed through it; clear, snow-laden breezes were warmed by mild southerly winds, so that the air spreading across the valley enriched the soil in equal measure with moisture and heat. The hot rays of the sun were tempered by the refreshing atmosphere, and the tall mountains warded off the harsh winds.

This small country was a blessed Middle Kingdom in the most beautiful sense of the word. Here human beings were able to develop freely and purely, for through their connection with the forces of Nature they had remained untouched by the confusing influence of the world.

There was no degeneracy of any kind here. The people were tall, well-built and supple; their hands and feet were long and slender.

Well-proportioned and natural, they were as they had been created, according to their Maker's Will. It was a matter of course for them to care for their bodies, which always moved and breathed in the right way, without constraints of any kind.

As a result their spirits received a continuous flow of Power from purest spheres, keeping their souls in perfect harmony, and consequently their bodies in good health.

Among these pure human beings there was such a powerful spiritual swinging as to afford their country spiritual protection like a pure ring of glowing rays, so that nothing base or alien was able to approach.

From this tribe rose Sita, the pure lotus blossom, who bore a fruit which was to be called Krishna, by decree of the "White Flame".

THE PALACE in which Krishna's father, the King, lived was surrounded by a sacred grove. A great variety of magnificent trees grew beside the clear waters that purled around it. Refreshing the air and the earth, these streams were formed by seven springs from seven cardinal points.

The palm-trees and overhanging foliage-plants rustled in the moist, warm winds; and in the strong sunbeams of midday the waterfalls sprayed rainbow colours through the air. Then the palms and broad leaves glistened in emerald green, exuding strong fragrances.

Across velvety meadows a narrow path led gradually upwards to ever more beautiful gardens.

At the highest point was a mango grove which was particularly sacred to the lineage of Kings. Great stones, like benches, invited the wayfarer to sit there in quiet contemplation. In this spot anyone could easily open himself to the Light from Above by relaxing naturally. It induced receptivity, and awakened in the soul the longing for the White Halls which offered spiritual purification and refreshment.

Thus the visitor was prepared for the sudden appearance before him of a high, broad wall, gleaming like snow and rising from the emerald belt of sunlit leafy treetops.

The Castle itself rose above these walls like a huge square block. Its stone was literally one with the white cliff, as though chiselled from it.

Only he who strove earnestly for purity and beauty was permitted to walk through the gate. His body seemed to him lighter and fresher than before. He bowed his head devoutly and removed his shoes.

From the houses of the settlements the rhythmic sound of joyful work was carried up to the Castle. All the activity of this small people was a prayer of gratitude!

Krishna's father was Sovereign over these pure human beings, whose purpose in life was to serve the Creator and Preserver. He also performed the Service before the Holy of Holies in the Temple, to which he dedicated his life. He alone, with twelve Knights of the purest spiritual volition, was allowed to guard the Sanctuary of the "White Flame".

This Service had been entrusted to them by their forefathers as the most sacred treasure. Through the Power of the Flame the spirit of these men shone forth and influenced all Its servants. It bore within It the Power of Life.

"The White Flame" was to radiate across the tall mountains to the very depths of the lowlands, to help and strengthen all human beings. Therefore it was the greatest treasure for everyone. But none knew of it save this small chosen tribe.

The Hours of Worship were completely linked with Nature, and thus full of life.

Hidden from all eyes, on the second storey behind the huge Temple-Hall, was the Holiest Room. With its upward-striving tower it seemed to reach into the azure sky. It was here that the Twelve Knights gathered at the appointed hour.

Enveloped in white mantles, they stood in a circle round a table upon which a White Stone shone forth. It lay in the centre of a huge silver mirror which faced east and revolved with the orbit of the sun, catching all the rays and reflecting them intensified. It gathered heat and luminosity, and a particular type of radiation containing hidden power-sources. This Stone was the earthly light-dispenser of the lustrous Castle. Moreover it was the guardian and bearer of the Holiest that these human beings possessed, for it provided the connection with the White Flame!

Once again the Knights were assembled for worship. The highest Servant, called the Wise Knight, stepped forth from the circle. He raised his hands towards the east and prayed. His eyes took on a strange radiance, for the Prince was blessed with the ability to open his spi-

15

ritual eyes and ears to lofty Powers. For a long time he remained in silent prayer.

The other initiates waited devoutly in the adjoining hall, their souls opened wide.

A Power arose in the circular hall, so great that its pressure threatened to split the walls. With growing intensity the silver mirror gathered the light-rays falling into the room. At first they were reflected in yellow, then in brilliant white, until at the apex of the Stone appeared a tremulous, reflecting lustre that made contact with the White Light from Above.

Suddenly a huge White Flame leapt up, and at the same moment a Voice spoke out of the Wise Knight:

"*I am*, and I call you! Sita is to bear a son, and through him the world will hear My Truth. Guard the Treasure that I send you: *Krishna, the Hero!*"

A FEW WEEKS LATER, when Sita was in the gardens with her female attendants, an unfamiliar lassitude overcame her. She longed to escape from the singing and playing of the dancing maidens. Her dark eyes looked about uneasily. The sound of the harps was almost painful to her.

Her first lady-in-waiting and friend approached her, and with an understanding look the two women walked towards the Palace. Sita rested, and only hours later awoke from a deep sleep. She found herself alone and was grateful to her friend, who never failed to do what was right.

Thus she was able to enjoy the peace which she found so beneficial today. She mused quietly, and hummed a soft tune. Then a bright light filled the room, and everything around her was lit by a roseate glow.

The luminous figure of a Knight was approaching her. He was garbed in white, with a golden cuirass. In his hand he held a sword.

"Hear me, Sita. On this day the spirit whom you are to call Krishna will enter into you."

Thus the incarnation of Krishna, one of the Spirit-Envoys, came to pass.

16

THE YEARS WENT BY, and the child Krishna, who romped merrily in the gardens with his playmates, became a thoughtful lad. He had learned how to handle weapons, and was skilled at their use in hunting and in noble tournaments. But the time of children's games and youthful exercises soon passed, and wise teachers now cultivated his gifts in the knowledge of the Laws and fine art, in poetry, writing, and in music.

But Krishna longed particularly to learn more about the entities whom he knew and loved, who seemed to him to bring tidings and rich gifts from a distant, familiar land.

Forces of a wondrous kind often approached him, and he understood them. Everyone around him knew of this, for they too were aware of those great connections in Creation; in silence, they experienced with the awakening boy the development of his lofty destiny.

Each in his own way loved and guided him, from his wise, priestly father, who stood above them all, to the humblest servants. Each subordinated his own person, and looked only to the great goal which lay before the youth.

Soon the forces of Nature began to make a more powerful impression on Krishna, especially the sun, which awakened him in the morning with its first rays. He heard the rush of its singing light approaching, as soon as its first glimmer flitted across the night sky, even before its orb had emerged on the horizon. Just as the singing of these rays elicited the soft twitter of the birds, so the sound always thrilled through Krishna's sleeping body.

With this sound an entity appeared to him, one whose coming he never wished to miss, for it bestowed upon the break of day an inconceivable solemnity and power.

It was a female figure with a curved golden vessel, formed like the horn of a huge bull, and filled with a soft rosy light.

She was the herald of the approaching day. Sometimes she rode in a golden arc on a luminous animal. The animal changed its form with the ascending orbit of the sun. On a succession of days she always appeared upon the same animal.

For a long time Krishna was unable to account for this phenomenon, but he observed, reflected and probed all the more eagerly. As soon as

17

the rosy figure appeared, indeed, as soon as the singing of the light-rays began, he mounted the tower above the Temple which received the first touch of the sunbeams.

For a time the image of a great bull appeared in the eastern sky, afterwards that of a crab, and then in turn that of a ram. Krishna began to note the days on which he saw these images, and then he thought of engraving in stone the days when the images did not change. To his delight he perceived that a definite number of days always recurred, while the moon changed its shape four times.

He began to divine the rhythm of Creation; in devout wonder he looked up to the heavens, which revealed to him the Magnitude and Might of their Creator.

All that transpired in the firmament seemed to Krishna like a cycle, in which beginning and end became merged. At the same time he perceived again and again his own position as the focal point of his observations.

The Spirit guided him, so that he added stroke upon stroke, sign upon sign to his white stone-tablets, thereby discovering fundamental concepts of unity and multiplicity, which enabled him to investigate further. It was not the investigating of dogged, one-sided intellectual curiosity working only in one direction, becoming rigid and lifeless in the process; it was worshipful recognition of the Grace, Might and Goodness of the Most High, Whom he still thought of as being in the light of the sun.

That was how Krishna worked as a boy at the age of twelve.

One thing fell into place beside another. His young life was like a chain of bright gems, precious and lustrous, pearl upon pearl, jewel upon jewel, forming an exquisite necklace. He was granted one picture after another of the world's wonderful mysteries.

Sun and moon, and the shape of whole groups of stars were revealed to him as active energies – formed and forming. They were of singular beauty. The numbers which he derived from the concepts, the tones which he sought to express in definite characters, united in turn in a wonderfully mysterious way with the rays and vibrations that he began to receive from the celestial lights.

The world, as he now recognised it, appeared to be a glorious web, extending from the heavens down to the earth, and he felt immensely rich in this knowledge. He was filled with indescribable bliss, and often he clasped his hands while profound happiness, which he could not put into words, welled up in him. At such moments he saw a great white light, whose origin was unknown to him.

Those around him observed with joyous admiration the boy's quiet, eager nature, and they did not interfere with his development.

Sita loved her son above all else. Her solicitude and love were solely for him. Music united them in beautiful, though rare, hours. She strove to understand him, yet she was unable to follow the lofty flight of his spirit.

And so the time came when the son gradually slipped from the mother's caring hands into the strict guidance of fatherly love. With his father he liked to discuss his innermost, earnest thoughts. Together they undertook long rides, accompanied only by two trusted servants. The paths led them high up into the beautiful woodlands of the mountains.

And there, on a wind-swept mountain-top, the son told his father, who listened attentively, about his experiences with the sun, moon and the many stars, about the tones and colours that he had perceived, and about the calculation derived from his pictures. His father nodded with satisfaction and understanding, and said:

"This is only the beginning. You must probe still more deeply within you, then your eyes will be opened to all things, and you will experience what is in the world and above the worlds. My son, soon you will have the maturity to receive the wisdom of your forefathers. Only a few years yet separate you from your fulfilment. The holy Laws are preparing you wisely, so that you may stand secure. When the time of physical maturity sets in, your spirit too will spread its wings for the flight into the Realm ordained for you. Your present experience is but the preparation."

Krishna marvelled at his father's words. This glorious, sublime experiencing was to be only the beginning of his development? He, who was capable of grasping in such depth, was almost overwhelmed by the fullness of this promise, and he was seized with apprehension.

For the first time he vaguely sensed a great responsibility. How much is demanded of him to whom so much is given! His spirit, awakening more and more, firmly resolved always to do justice to this demand.

It was as though this talk with his father had matured him by many years. The exuberant joy derived from his investigations gave way to calm, as with a lake whose waves are stilled by the cool of evening. Anticipation spread almost wistfully over his joy. The gravity of being Called filled his opened soul with foreboding. Again a silent entreaty arose within him to undreamed-of heights, to a destination as yet unknown.

As soon as Krishna began to recognise the high entities of Nature, a wonderful harmony with them evolved. Love grew steadily stronger within him, and through Love, which in him bore Justice in natural, undistorted purity, his spirit stood in the Law of Balance and Harmony.

Love and Justice radiated from him, attracting the forces of good, and since there was nothing in his environment to oppose this purity, Love, Justice and Purity were increasingly attracted.

Those around him first noticed it in his association with animals. Krishna could no longer bring himself to hunt. The pursuit of game, which he had cultivated as a noble sport, was now repugnant to him. Out of love he gave up hunting; out of love the animals now came to him. As with the animals, so also with the elements. After he had recognised the life of the animistic sphere and was able to communicate with the beings of air, water, fire and earth, they were to him serving friends with whom he was on good terms. But he never made use of them for his own ends.

Serenity and simplicity formed the first step on the way to perfection. Krishna strove to attain to these virtues.

Thus it came to pass that the gate of wisdom was opened to him, and he realised that he could overcome space and time. Through this recognition his spiritual eyes opened; he gazed upon more luminous planes,

20

and became ever stronger in his humility before the magnitude of the Law.

In the night, lofty beings appeared to him; or else his spirit, his true ego, set out on a journey which took it far upwards. There too everything was alive as it was on earth, and he encountered wonderful beings.

The animistic being which he beheld in the garb of the earthly sun appeared to him as his special friend. Yet it was soon apparent that this being did not draw its power from itself. All that he experienced in the way of radiation, movement, formation, transformation, all that he saw in the heavenly bodies and their entities suddenly seemed to him subsequently formed and subsequently created. The world of the senses became strangely empty to him; all the more firmly did he strive to grasp that which lies beyond the realm of the senses.

Thus he lived simultaneously in his body and above the World of Matter. As spirit, he journeyed through Primordial Creation, and found there his actual home.

Subsequent Creation seemed to him like a reflection of Primordial Creation. He experienced its different kind of density and its ever-increasing crystallisation.

At first it was not possible for him to find his way about, and the beings of the spirit-sphere became visible to him only by degrees. At the same time, however, the miraculous happened, in that he found himself in a circle of kindred spirits. Although unable to grasp this with his intellect, he knew that it was actually so.

He believed in the Creative Power, and revered it. He knew that it was to be found above the sun and the stars, but now he recognised that the Power of Life, Whose origin he was seeking beyond the deity of his people and beyond the solar system, was enthroned even above Primordial Creation. At that he was overwhelmed by the feeling of smallness, and sank to his knees in prayer.

Krishna's body had become sick, for during his spirit's long journey to its homeland a ray had penetrated it which was to transform the body, the earthly cloak, and enable it to endure the radiation of his spirit continuously. At first, however, the ray paralysed his physical body.

Thus by Divine Decree, at not quite fourteen years of age, the way had been prepared in Krishna for his solemn initiation.

The White Flame had spoken: his father was to admit him to the circle of Guardians.

When after eight days and nights Krishna awakened from a deep sleep, he could not move at first, for the power from Primordial Creation exerted an enormous pressure on the physical body, to which this body had to become slowly accustomed.*

---

* The explanation of such processes in accordance with the Laws of Creation can be found in the Work "In the Light of Truth", The Grail Message by Abd-ru-shin.

The gross material earthly body of a human being can only be linked harmoniously with a developed human spirit of Subsequent Creation, so that the spirit is enabled to work through it in the World of Gross Matter. Where there is a direct connection between the physical body and a higher plane, in this instance with a spirit from Primordial Creation, thus with a Primordial Being, a natural restraint in the connection is bound to occur. This restraint can only be diminished through help and careful preparation from the Light. Without help from the Light such a connection would be quite impossible and would result in a kind of short-circuit that is fatal to the body. The immense pressure breaks the connection with the physical body through the short-circuit, which amounts to physical death.

Anyone who would object that, according to the account, the Primordially-created spirit of Krishna had already entered the developing body at incarnation, and should therefore have caused the short-circuit even at that time, should read the lecture "Generative Power" in the Work of Abd-ru-shin, where he will find the explanation.

Until puberty, the incarnated Primordial Being lacked the connection with the outside world through his physical body. The spirit was not able to radiate through the body, because during childhood the body acts as an insulating layer. Only the onset of the *generative power* lowers the bridge to the outside world, establishing the connection that enables the incarnated spirit to radiate through the physical body from within.

This was the moment when Krishna was bound to make direct contact with Primordial Creation again, and when he had the inner experience of the visit to Primordial Creation. His spirit was able to radiate through the body and receive radiations from Primordial Creation. With that the body was for the first time set aglow by the exceptional pressure, to which it was not equal. Since in Krishna's case, however,

Everyone was deeply concerned about him; Sita did not leave his bedside. But he did not speak to them of his experience, for even they would not yet have been able to absorb the knowledge of Primordial Creation. This awareness was engraved upon his soul like a Command uttered from On High, and it had to be observed.

A new life, long dormant, had awakened within him: he now saw with the eyes of his spirit.

Krishna had also changed as a human being; he was no longer a boy. Tall and slender, he towered even above the men of his tribe. But his face had retained its childlike grace and beauty, suffused by goodness and wisdom. The clarity of his powerful will stamped it with severity. He was imperious, and his presence was regal; after his recovery his bearing was stately and calm.

IN THE PALACE of Krishna's parents everything was prepared for the Festival of Initiation. The rooms were richly adorned with flowers. Fragrant oil was lit, and rose upwards in colourful flames into the blue sky.

Wonderfully peaceful nights lay over the land of white mountains, and the stars shone forth in special size and beauty.

Thus there was sublime joy in the gardens of the Castle, and the people too participated with all their heart in the Festival in Krishna's honour. With reverence and love they looked to the young Prince; and everything that concerned Krishna received close attention.

careful preparation had been made by decree of the Divine Will, only temporary un-consciousness and paralysis of the gross material body resulted.

When physical bodies are to fulfil such a rare task, a special connecting layer is developed through higher animistic helpers. This layer is also perceptible *gross-materially*, and is capable of absorbing the exceptional pressure and of thus protecting the body.

This explains to the reader the exact fulfilment of the Creation-Laws, also in the process experienced by Krishna at the age of fourteen, since that was the time of his earthly maturity. This maturity had been hastened by a few years through the higher pressure exerted by the incarnated spirit of the Primordial Being.

Krishna himself approached the day of his initiation with inner calm. He devoted himself to his studies and his work with the same quiet perseverance as ever. With great zeal he again pursued his physical exercises, as well as his studies of the many Indian languages. He was to be acquainted with conditions in the country as well. A picture of India was shown to him, and a voice spoke:

"Behold, everything awaits you, for you are to be a guidepost for the straying children of this people. You are to lead them out of the utter chaos of spiritual Darkness to the clear path that takes them to the Truth. The way is far, and the work difficult, which the Most High enjoins upon you. Go forth as a shining light in the Darkness!"

Often now there appeared to him a great White Light, with radiant beams on either side, thus forming a Cross; and in this form he recognised the expression of completeness, of the highest Law and Perfection. Always he thought of this Light, Whose image he carried within him.

And he set to work still more eagerly to perfect himself in the earthly, for he recognised the effect of all the Laws and saw how the slightest deviation or clouding was perpetuated in the gossamer fabric that men wove around themselves ethereally.

Then again a luminous spirit approached him, saying:

"You have seen the bonds woven by your people in the realm of your ancestors. But now a different time has come, and you shall see the webs in which the majority of the human race have entangled themselves. This is the beginning of your task."

And it was as if a grey veil rose up from below, shrouding all that was light and pure. He himself felt as though weighed down, and he seemed to sink slowly.

Krishna heard the voice say: "It is thus that the greater density and heaviness seizes the originally pure spirit as soon as it allows itself to be densified. Soon you will see the beings that live in those planes."

And a wild commotion arose in the grey, nebulous forms; faces and figures in strange shapes emerged from them. Krishna had never seen anything like it, and he did not know what to make of it. To his astonishment he only beheld that they were really alive, and that they lived in

24

groups, in nests, where they multiplied, and from which they emanated. They wriggled like serpents. Their clustered mass was disgusting.

These strange forms sought to approach him. But they soon reached a boundary that halted their progress. This infuriated them. But the more they raved, the more they swelled up and multiplied, and where such an ugly form grew especially large, similar forms thronged to it from all directions, seeking to feed upon it.

Krishna shuddered with horror. Nevertheless he now consciously sent out thoughts of defence. There, it was as if rays of Light were rushing at the dark vermin. Red flames shot up, and limb upon limb was severed; one snake-body after another crumbled away and shrivelled up. From this, Krishna perceived the power of pure thoughts against the effects of evil. He resolved to seek out evil and destroy it.

In spirit he was conducted to places on earth where evil was raging. There Krishna saw terrible things. It seemed to him that human beings were wallowing in a deep mire.

Ever more fervently the desire began to glow within him to intervene helpfully, so that the downward-hurtling wheel might finally come to a stop, and be able to turn again in the other direction. In spirit he placed himself with all the strength of his loving volition in the mechanism of the Ethereal World.

But human beings seemed to perceive nothing of it.

And so there ripened in Krishna the will to descend to them, to leave the pure luminous realm of his mountains in order to help them in their turbid lowlands as a man among men. He made this resolve on the morning of his initiation.

THE CLEAR TONE of the silver bells rang from the white towers, and the deep tones of huge gongs vibrated in between. It rang through the blue, sunlit morning like a mighty festal hymn. The waves of sound re-echoed thunderously from the white mountain-giants. To the music of their golden lyres, singing maidens moved slowly through the gates of the Palace, through the gardens and streets, asking for the protection of the Light.

Dressed in white, wearing the decorations of their ranks and offices, the men assembled, each caste separately. Everyone thronged towards the great Temple-Hall, in which they prayed to the White Flame. There was a pure swinging in these human beings, and circle joined circle harmoniously. Thus did the people await the initiation of their young future King.

Krishna gazed down from the Palace on the undulating palms in the gardens. He wore a long white silk robe which reached to his ankles, and was held together by a broad gold-embroidered belt. Round his neck hung strings of exquisite pearls; sapphires and emeralds embellished the broad armlets. A golden coronet, with a gleaming emerald the size of a hazelnut, adorned his head. A dagger of singular beauty was fastened in his belt.

Krishna was alone. Serenity and peace filled his soul. Musing, he surveyed the years of his development, recalling with joy the merry games and beautiful hours near his beloved mother, his teachers and companions.

Now he stood before an important, incisive hour. But he knew that already long ago he had entered into the sacred Covenant with the Most High.

THE GATE SWUNG OPEN. Garbed in white, nine men of the highest rank awaited Krishna, and strode with him across the golden mosaic of the long hall into the Temple-Room, which was filled with pale violet light.

The wall of the innermost room shone in translucent white, and the movement of rays evoked by the silver mirror flooded the whole room with Living Light.

Krishna seated himself at the highest place upon a raised chair, and everyone gazed up at him in diffident love. Standing, they awaited the beginning of the Festival. All was hushed in the room.

When the Wise Knight joined them and raised his hand, the other eleven Knights followed him into the innermost room.

Then began the resounding strains of harps, mingled with jubilant, clear voices. The deep resonant tones of the men responded. Sacred hymns came surging down from Above.

Krishna's spirit was raised On High; he experienced all that took place on earth as though in a dream. As spirit, his actual ego stood in a sea of flames, and a radiant Figure handed him a Sword.

"*I am He* Who is to come, the First and the Last, He Who judges the human spirits. Be thou faithful unto Me!

"Flames of Enlightenment, move through Creation, I send you ahead!"

With that a blue Light-Flame descended into Krishna. He rose to his feet, and at the Call of the Mighty, Radiant One he entered the Sanctuary. There he heard the voice of his father, who stood in the circle of Knights before the White Stone:

"Krishna, you are Called to come before the Countenance of the Mighty One Who bears within Him the White Flame. He is our Father. Bear His Light, which He bestows upon you today, into the world of pain and sorrow, and use it for victory. As a sign that you are one with us, I give you this Sword and the Ring. Be faithful! You stand high above all when you remain in the Will of the White Flame. Wisdom has been granted to you. Now you will enter fully into the Power!"

Praying, he spread wide his arms. Krishna did likewise. Then a white ray descended with a thunderous sound, and Krishna stood in a white glow.

"Thus I baptise you with My Fire!" resounded the Word of the White Flame.

Krishna received Power from the Ray of God, and the pure Light remained in him. His figure shone, and his eyes were like bright flames when he stepped before the assembled people.

The music of the harps rang out, and in chorus the singers praised the Holiness of the Light.

With hands raised, Krishna, the Warrior for the Light, blessed human beings for the first time.

AFTER THE FESTIVAL of Initiation, Krishna quietly withdrew.

On the uppermost floor of the Palace his father had set apart for him a dwelling-place surrounded by roof-gardens. There he was also near the tower which was the first to receive the power of the sun.

The servants assigned to him attended to all his needs, and did not disturb his peace.

Again he became engrossed in the observation of the stars, and discovered important connections between their rays and the plants, the animals and the characteristics of all created things. And again the star-entities appeared to him.

When he was absorbed in prayer during the night, the Ray of the White Flame shone for him. His prayer was not a request with words; rather it was a quiet opening of himself to higher power-currents. In a natural attitude, silent and turned inward, he allowed intellect and feeling to be completely silenced. Everything that had occupied him, whether serious or cheerful, fell from him, and he was in a state of perfect tranquillity. Then the longing for the familiar luminous goal came of itself, and the longing was strengthened by the tremendous influx of the purity that was over him. At such moments he was in contact with the Light.

And the Power remained with him while he wrote, investigated, calculated. In spirit he traversed vast worlds. As he did so he was often accompanied by the luminous figure of a woman. She was transparent as mist, and fine as a moonbeam gliding over the waters. She led him into a silver-blue light-sphere, whose worlds were as luminous and delicate as herself.

Full of goodness, she inclined towards him. She was the female animistic mediator of Purity and Love, the guardian of woman and of fertility: Astarte, as in truth she is. That she was worshipped by some peoples as the goddess of the moon was related to the clear light of the celestial sphere in which she reigned. Her realm was above the World of Matter, and she carried out the will of Mercury. She was sacred to all peoples who aspired to the purity of woman. But no human being knew her actual lofty vocation.

She was attracted by Krishna's pure volition to free mankind from all dark ties.

It was as he investigated the radiations, in which he was striving to perceive the transitions from the spirit into the World of Matter, that she appeared to him. Astarte was filled with sorrow as she related what the human beings had made of the concept of "Purity". She lamented that she no longer found any connection with earth-woman.

"They worship only the forms produced by their own delusions," she said. "Mainly these are demons and phantoms. Once you have crossed the borders of your homeland, Krishna, you will see the horror of these aberrations. Until then, none of it can approach you."

With that Krishna knew that the time had now come for him to leave the peace and purity of his mountains, in order to bring salvation to mankind.

He looked forward to it and would do it soon. But he had to await the signal to depart, since the point in time was determined by the Law of Radiations, not by human ideas.

KRISHNA OFTEN WALKED on lonely paths up into the forests and the white mountains. For days he remained at the summit, which offered a wide view over the land. He was absorbed in quiet contemplation, and always he did what seemed right to him, without asking about anything else. Untouched by any other thought, he followed the path prescribed by the spirit.

But sometimes a pressure weighed upon his soul like the foreboding of impending danger as yet unrecognised. He was to fight one more battle before leaving his homeland to journey to the human beings. In order to strengthen himself, he withdrew into complete solitude for forty days and forty nights in preparation.

There was deep sadness in him since he had gazed into the misery of mankind; with the desire to help, his recognition of their need grew. Filled with compassion, he wished to bring them salvation, even at the cost of suffering.

Thus he set out on a thorny path, and was aware of it, for he recognised the weak nature of the human spirit and its dire need of help. He sensed that men would not even accept the means of help offered by him. He knew that he would have to cut through the tangle of evil threads with a sharp knife, but that human beings would not understand.

Hence he found himself in an inner conflict between his task and the recognition of the state of those whom he wished to save. This conflict, and his spiritual need, increased from day to day.

It was the beginning of his struggle, which lay in the Will of the White Flame. This time, however, a bandage was placed before the eyes of Krishna, who was usually aware of everything, lest he should recognise the purpose of his suffering. He was to experience everything himself in order to mature through it. The human element in him, which hitherto had lived high above all humanity in the lowlands, and had associated only with mature human beings, was to harden. It was for this reason too that he had gone from them, because he realised that now their help would not be good for him. He had to separate from his own kind in order to become quite solitary, and to be left entirely to his own resources.

It was not easy for him, for he too had to overcome "the human being". Only then would he be mature for his task.

Krishna could not eat, his pain was too great. Nor was he able to sleep. He prayed continually for recognition, and his spirit sought the Light of the White Flame. But the White Flame did not reveal Itself to him. He did not see Its Light either by day or by night, nor did he hear the sonorous reverberation of Its Voice.

Krishna felt forsaken.

A cloud rose up from below, enveloping the top of the mountain, so that he found himself cut off from the earth in a dim twilight. The winds seemed to be asleep, the animistic forces were as though extinguished, and Krishna did not know what was happening to him. Had he offended against the Will of the White Flame? He strayed like a wanderer in the desert, lonely, starving, weak and full of anxiety, near to dying of thirst.

He sought his guilt, but could find it nowhere. And ever more fervent grew the strength of his prayer.

Krishna was suffering. The spiritual pain was far more terrible than all earthly affliction.

30

In this agony Maro (Lucifer) approached him. Enveloped in a strange light, he rose up from a grotto.

Krishna was startled. He had never seen this flickering glow before. The light glistened; it was far removed from the calm, pure light of the spirit. Krishna was wholly alert, with every nerve taut, yet he felt the pain of isolation. No sign, no comfort, no succour!

Where were his trusted friends? How happy he would have been if only an animal, a fly or a beetle had appeared to him, if only the quiet sparkle of the grass had brought him solace. It was as though he were deserted by everything, by all the lively weaving of Creation. Only now did he recognise how rich he had been, how empty life was without the spark of the White Flame.

Was he then dead? Or was it a new life, into which this glistening being was to lead him? Why now, after his initiation, at the height of his power, this spiritual affliction?

With a fawning, friendly smile Maro approached. He was handsome and mighty. Imperious, he stood before Krishna, to tell him that he ruled the world. Now that Krishna was about to go forth into the world, he would provide help if Krishna would submit to him.

Thus spoke Maro. He was seductive in the beauty and power of his sovereign will. And Krishna was apparently forsaken by all the high helpers. But then in the deepest pain he intuitively perceived the mighty resilience of his will, and in spirit he grasped the Sword which the White Flame had placed in his hand.

"Though Thy Countenance be turned from me, yet will I serve Thee in eternity! I hold to the strength of the Sword which Thou hast given me, that I may wield it victoriously!"

Like a jubilant cry, this awareness streamed through Krishna. Against it Maro's false volition was dashed to pieces.

A flash of lightning descended from heaven.

"Depart from me, Tempter!" said Krishna.

And Maro vanished in the gloomy cloud, just as he had come.

Soft winds blew from the east, parting the mists, and the light of the radiant sun gleamed upon the mountain-top. Blue sky arched over Krishna's shining head.

SLOWLY AND SOLEMNLY Krishna descended the steep path to his cave. He tied up in a cloth the few things that he had brought with him, and grasped his staff. With his hand he scooped a mouthful of water from the pure spring that gushed out of the ground near the cave; then with a quiet word of benediction he passed his hand over the sparse herbs and stones, and the low moss. Like pale shadows, earnest faces peered out of them. Lovely voices whispered in the fresh breeze blowing across the mountain-tops. A tinkling as of delicate ice-crystals quivered through the snowy air. Thus did the mountain-spirits take leave of him.

Across the steep slopes rolled stones loosened by chamois. The animals came leaping over the crags and pressed close to him. A pair of mighty eagles circled above him; with the rushing beat of wings the female came quite near, brushing against his shoulder. Thus did the mountain-world bid him farewell.

Around his head shone the light of blessing, and upon his brow, still radiant, was the Sign of his Consecration bestowed by his father.

Ever further Krishna descended the steep, often quite dangerous trail. Calm and confident, he followed the arduous track. When the snow-fields and rugged stony paths were behind him, he quickened his pace.

For a long time he gazed down upon the place that was his home. There rose the tower in which he had experienced the great mysteries of the heavens. There were the Brothers, the Guardians of the White Ray, and there his beloved parents.

But Krishna did not take the path that led back to his paradisal gardens. He did not wish to be escorted by a retinue, to depart in splendour and magnificence, acclaimed by his people.

He stretched out his hands to the east in greeting, towards the cupolas and towers of his homeland, then he turned away from them, no longer looking back. Wherever he went, he took with him his most precious possession, the Power of the White Flame, and it radiated from his pure cloak.

Linked in thought with the Light, Krishna continued on the new, unknown path. He would go alone, and appear among men unrecognised and poor. Without attracting undue attention, he would quietly bring the treasures of his spirit to human beings.

Those who then heard him and followed him he would have by his side; those he would teach. And he hoped that they would open their homes to the wayfarer so that he could go in and out among them, simply and without ceremony. Then he would come near to them, and recognise what they were really like.

Thus Krishna let himself be counselled by the spirit that spoke within him.

For a whole day he journeyed down rocky paths, until he reached a deserted valley. There was a small lake with many fish. Krishna caught one with his hand, made a fire between the stones and grilled it. Then he lay down by the lakeside and fell asleep.

After a brief, dreamless slumber he awakened and resumed his journey. The wide bed of the brook flowing from the lake offered the only way downwards for Krishna. The trees became taller and denser. He made his way into magnificent forests.

Here there were new forms of life: brightly coloured birds fluttered round him, squawking parrots took wing at sight of the man. Now and then bright faces peered from among the leaves, as if playing at hide-and-seek. Little monkeys approached, only to withdraw hastily, shy and screeching.

The weaving life of the wild was all about him. The luxuriant vegetation and marvellous fruits delighted his eyes. Iridescent lizards gazed from the trees, and herds of gazelles leapt through the tall, swaying grasses which extended eastwards for miles and miles.

Surrendering completely to the solitude, the rugged mountain-world and the forest, Krishna wandered on. The trumpeting of elephant-herds, the cracking and crackling of bushes, the snarling of panthers and the roaring of tigers – he experienced it all in his immediate proximity, and he lived with these creatures, with the weaving and whispering of the wild; he was in tune with the animistic in its pure, natural Laws, and was happy.

Nothing disturbed him, nothing threatened him. Every sound was a message from the world of beings around him.

Filled with gratitude, he sensed the life in and about him, the gift of the White Flame.

He only needed to show love to these beings; then he was able to control them with his will. But they did not need him, and so Krishna journeyed on. Now he was in search of human beings. The spirit within him urged him on.

And so he continued, arriving next day in a region of bountiful water. Here the atmosphere was sultry, the floor of the forest was marshy and covered with tall grass. Long, almost unbreakable coils of mighty aerial roots hung down from the trees. There were miles of jungle.

Only with difficulty could Krishna force his way through. Often he had to change direction, warned off by watery-airy elementals.

Krishna walked even during the night; he found no more peace, and hastened on, driven by a force that kept him awake and strengthened him, so that he felt no need for rest or food.

Heavy rain pattered down, but after a few moments the golden sunlight sparkled again through the shining green foliage. Red flower-cups with tall golden stamens exuded heady fragrances, and the splendour of the glorious blossoms of inconceivably iridescent orchids was all around him.

The beauty of these forests was enchanting; Krishna rejoiced at all their loveliness. How beautiful God had created the world! He always looked within when he was so happy, and he always remembered the One by Whom development and decay were ordained. In spirit he beheld the perfect form of the Cross, and he prayed to the Creator.

But still Krishna had not found man, over whom the spirits wept. What could he be like, he whom the Creator had placed in the midst of all this splendour, he to whom was given the opportunity to possess and make use of all this?

Krishna recalled the few strangers who had come to his people. They had found the way to the wisdom of his forefathers. Yet they had always remained a little strange to his people. But where were the human beings who, it was said, celebrated wild orgies when they engaged in prayer, who waged wars, plundered and murdered, who were full of

34

passions and contentions, and who entangled themselves in the evil webs of their deeds and volition? Where were they? Where were they?

The spirit drove Krishna to them.

THE MOONLIGHT flooded through the deep forest. All the animal world had gone to rest. Drops of water that had gathered in the cups of leaves and in cacti gleamed and glistened. Now and then birds' voices cooed softly, as in a dream. The palms rustled, and the tall grass whispered in the wind. From afar came the rumble of thunder – or was it the roaring of beasts of prey? It was as though the earth quaked gently, and every move of a nocturnal prowler, however cautious, could be heard in the jungle.

The physical senses of the wanderer, to whom Creation down to the deepest mysteries of the Ethereal and Animistic Worlds were open, grew ever keener. Day after day, night after night, the world revealed new wonders to him. How could he fail to be blissfully happy, increasingly enriched and grateful hour after hour?

He wanted to step before men and show them all these treasures in which to delight, if only they were regarded in the right way! How rich he would make human beings! Could there still be loneliness, fear, affliction, suffering of any kind, once man had found the pulsating life of God's Love in every radiation, every stone, every plant, every dewdrop? The whole world could become new.

But where was man? He still had not found him.

Yet what were those sounds penetrating the deep forest from afar? Was it the screeching of monkeys, the quarrelling of agitated birds? What was that drumming and whistling – those piercing sounds like the screeching of excited peacocks? Then there was silence again; afterwards the murmuring of many voices could be heard, and the plaintive tones of male singers. Over there in the jungle there must be human beings!

Occasionally he saw a reddish glow among the branches and through the moonlit leaves. Again Krishna heard drumming, and the shrill whine of a pipe. It was an unpleasant tune, producing vibrations of a very peculiar kind. Krishna strained his ears in close attention. What was in these sounds? Danger and temptation, stifling poison, that was it!

The sounds attracted variegated, iridescent threads in intoxicating colours, scents which, although imperceptible to the earthly senses, conspired to stimulate, allure and stupefy the ethereal receptive faculty.

What were those eyes with the look of ravenous serpents, and what were those glittering bodies moving across the ground, even through the air?

Krishna was standing at the edge of a moonlit clearing on which stood a wooden temple. Around it were gathered many people who had little appeal – indeed who appeared to him to be the scum of the earth. Enshrouded in a gloomy half-light sat a man with a long beard, covered in rags, a woollen cap on his head. From a long pipe he drew forth the sounds that Krishna had heard.

Attracted by the sounds, which influenced the lower ethereal planes, clusters of monstrosities gathered, wrapped in a greyish-yellow vapour. Everything was yellow and grey, venomous green and iridescent. Snake-eyes, snake-bodies, snake-teeth, and a sickly, repugnant smell of blood. Ethereal threads wove like creepers around the people, who, gripped with curiosity, watched spellbound what was taking place on the ground before them.

From a basket emerged gross-material snakes, which rose up, raised their heads and danced in time to the music, swaying their bodies to and fro. That was all. These people did not see the other, which was far more terrible, yet it was caught ethereally in their clothes, it hung in the women's hair and adhered to their hands; it coiled around their feet so that they dared not raise them, and it even mingled with their personal aura.

Krishna was overcome with horror. He nearly shouted a warning to them. But what good would it have done?

Meanwhile the moon had gone down further, the shadows had lengthened, and the fires had gone out. Peace reigned. Two dogs scoured the camp; the lean horses approached Krishna. Monkeys climbed from the branches and frolicked on the roof of the half-ruined temple.

An elephant rose ponderously, giving forth a trumpet-blast from its lifted trunk.

The animals were aware of Krishna's presence, but the human beings were not.

THE NEW DAY BEGAN. The fine mists rising from the swamps with the first rays of the sun took on a rosy hue.

Krishna saw that the temple was inhabited, and stepped inside the portal. The gloominess of the place settled on him oppressively. When his eyes had become accustomed to the darkness, he saw crude, blackish-brown walls and columns adorned with roughly-carved, sombre heads and figures. A large black wooden form with seven heads stood in the background. From the shoulders of the huge figure extended wildly-contorted arms and hands bearing symbols.

This was the crude earthly appearance of the place, which was all that most of the people were able to grasp. But woe betide those who were open or subject to the influences of the spiritual processes that had condensed here in the course of many decades.

A red glow as of steaming blood rose from the floor and the blood-smeared pedestals of the gruesome idols. A woeful moaning reached Krishna's ears, pale shadows flitted about. There were shapes of men and beasts, with accusing eyes and faces contorted with pain. White and green, with the pallid lustre of shells, they floated about like cobwebs – sticky, filthy and nauseating – then they dissolved again.

Such was the appearance of the temple, in which the columns were covered with the blood of animal and human sacrifices. But under the ground leered the awful skulls of the murdered, piled up like walls.

How could people sleep in a place that was filled with such ghastly things? Children, girls, women, dressed in brightly-coloured garments, crouched on the floor, preparing a meal that exuded odours far from tempting. Chewing on rubber and leafy plants, the men sat around – among them the snake-charmer and a dwarf with a tall cap and an ugly face.

Now they had caught sight of Krishna; they leapt up quickly and

37

crowded round him. He was offered food and wine. The latter he declined, but he took some of the food in order not to give offence. They immediately trusted the strange man, accepted him into their midst and overwhelmed him with questions and small gifts. They did not even notice that the stranger still had not uttered a word.

He calmly allowed the flow of words to pour forth. Although the language was unfamiliar to him he grasped the meaning of them. These creatures were stranger to him than the animals, which after all were not of his kind.

Between him and these people yawned an enormous gulf, which he must learn to bridge so that they could understand him. Yet this seemed almost impossible, and he instantly realised that he must regard them as children, as quite immature, ill-bred children. He felt sorry for them, and could not even be angry with them.

The women were shy; they felt ashamed before the quiet, earnest man. In his dark eyes there was such power and severity as they could hardly bear. They felt that here their cunning flattery would be out of place, even absurd, and they had nothing else to give. Never before had they felt so foolish and empty, and this sense of their poverty made the good ones shy, the bad wary and irritable.

The elephant-guide proved to be an intelligent, good man who had travelled much and could tell many stories about animals. He became increasingly communicative, and soon he was convinced that he must take Krishna to the King of the Jadava. He did not know why it was necessary, but when he saw Krishna this resolve had awakened in his soul, as though he had borne it within him long ago, and had merely forgotten it. Indeed at the sight of Krishna he had the extraordinary feeling that he ought to kneel down before this unknown wayfarer and say:

"Here I am, Master; do with me as you will!"

He had never experienced anything like it before. It was as if he had only been awaiting this stranger, of whom he really knew nothing at all. He was almost annoyed with himself, and then again he felt silly and childish.

Why should he force himself on the stranger who had so suddenly appeared in the wilderness, and was certainly different from himself. For that very reason he wanted to take him to the King, because "like belongs with like"; this he perceived to be an inner command.

The quiet, sad man would have liked to shout for joy. After the tiger had snatched his wife and child from him, he had nothing left but the love for Amba, his elephant. He was not pious, but good and simple, trusting as a child.

Quiet and withdrawn, he had neither friend nor foe, but if anyone was in need he would help to the best of his ability. Therefore everyone liked him. The money earned by him with Amba, who was a good, strong worker, he shared with others. Amba was alert and faithful, a good protection for him.

Soon his companions observed that the Hindu had taken a great liking to the stranger, who was kind, with a word for each one that compelled the hearer to reflect.

To the dwarf he said:

"You have borne your burden patiently, and will therefore carry it with greater ease than if you were to complain. When you return you will be free of it."

The dwarf was a cheerful fellow who had come to terms with his deformity, and led a simple vagrant life. His grotesque appearance aroused sympathy everywhere, and therefore he was never in need. Wherever he could, he helped his companions. Although he did not understand Krishna, he sensed inwardly that his words had a meaning that would help him on. He did not ponder it, but retained it in his spirit.

To the snake-charmer Krishna said:

"Throw away your pipe and follow me, otherwise the tangled web of your piping will lead you on to the end of the world."

The snake-charmer took this literally: he dogged Krishna's footsteps, but would not be separated from his pipe.

One of the girls was weeping bitterly; she refused to dance because she was afraid in the temple; for that, her father had beaten her.

"Weep not," said the stranger to her, "but rejoice that you cannot dance here, because your intuitive perception is pure. Therefore one day you shall kneel before the Throne of the Most High."

THE JUGGLERS SET out towards midday. It was a motley band that moved through the jungle: a few goats and horses, a small cart, children, women behind them, then the snake-baskets on long poles, the snake-charmer with his pipe beside the carriers, finally the Hindu and his elephant, with Krishna seated on its back.

The dwarf frisked about and jested. In the evening they stopped by a small lake. It was sultry and oppressive there. On the south shore were caves in which they caught snakes.

Krishna had no wish to stay. He told the Hindu, who merely nodded. They took leave of the others; the girl wept, the dwarf teased the Hindu, and the snake-charmer blew his pipe and remained behind.

Krishna, however, rode with his companion to Jadava.

THEY JOURNEYED FOR THREE DAYS. During the night they slept in the jungle, in waterproof plant-huts which the Hindu knew how to build. The nights were both beautiful and fearsome: the solitude of the wilderness surrounded them, tigers roared in the distance, and the sounds of animals hiding in the bush could be heard all the time. Only the children of this land are able to be at one with the mysterious world of the virgin forest, and to adapt completely to it.

The Hindu was both an excellent guide and a faithful, alert servant. The elephant supported its master to the best of its ability; it was the trail-blazer and the guide.

In the evening of the third day they reached a mountainous region, and the Hindu led Krishna to the temples, built in the rocks by a mighty prince to honour the gods.

At first sight the huge, grotesque figures of gods barely stood out against the rugged, sombre rocks. The longer the eye rested on the rocks, however, the more figures could be discerned. But the ethereal picture offered to Krishna by this temple-entrance probably had not been seen by any human being, nor could anyone have borne it. For he would have been shaken by horror, as with fever-spasms, at the sight.

At the entrance to the cave stood a colossal dark idol, from whose stone-hewn body stared faces. Terrified, overstrained human faces, covered with blood, were permanently held captive there. Sweat and blood ran down from the stones of this idol created by human beings, in trembling fear of the tormentors who vented their power on them.

The king who had ordered this monument of his idol worship to be built was himself held fast in eternal torment until he should come to recognition. But his wretched victims, bloodied by the scourgings of his slave-owners, clung to him and his work.

Could such a work gather the faithful for the edification and ascent of their spirits? Products of fear generated in this place roamed about, saturating the whole neighbourhood with their nature. Fear surged from the gates of this temple, fear and unrest, feverish inner agitation, mental anguish and brutality.

Krishna stood under the small square door which was surrounded by stone gargoyles, and took a deep breath before entering the temple.

Green light came to meet him, and glowing, hate-filled eyes stared anxiously at him wherever he turned. Krishna hardly noticed the stone idols, which to some people might appear like works of art. What was moving around them in green, iridescent murderousness, full of fear and bloodlust, was terrible. Gruesome forms like dogs, monkeys, vultures, frogs and hyenas flew at him. But they were forced to keep a considerable distance; this seemed to surprise and alarm them.

The Hindu, standing in quiet devotion, saw only the externals of the temple; he attributed his eerie mood to the influence of the gods. "Durga" was powerful, and always wanted blood-sacrifices.

Krishna now entered the grotto of the beggars, and was stunned. The brutalised figures he saw aroused a loathing which surpassed even that evoked in him by the demons. Filled with wrath, he went among these people, who sat or stood in forced ecstasy like figures of stone, plastered with filth and hung with rags. Dense ethereal walls surrounded them.

These people had dealt cruelly with the flame bestowed upon them by God as a living light, and they even took pride in violently tormenting the poor earthly body to death in order to attain to salvation. The light burning in them was but a partly-burned wick, with neither oil for sustenance nor oxygen to maintain its flame. Dim and flickering, it struggled not to die out altogether, for it had literally nothing to feed on!

Krishna stood among them like a blazing torch. One of them was unable to move. For years he had stood motionless with one arm raised; it had become rigid, as though turned to stone. The eyes were set in the leathery bony face like protruding black glass beads. The hair and beard were like grass-green tree-moss, and the body was starved and haggard, lifeless, rigid and brittle.

Above him was the pale, almost extinguished countenance of his spirit. It did not dwell in the high regions as he thought, but was forged with iron fetters to its tormented body, without knowledge, without longing, without buoyant force, fallen a prey to spiritual death.

Of all these people, none was able to recognise what life is, what love for the Creator and gratitude are. They sat with their small, almost smothered flames in cages that could never again be opened.

Krishna did not utter a word. Only later he said to the Hindu:

"These dead ones can no longer be brought back to life. Let us see to it that the living do not die through them. To the few who understand I will show the way to Life."

"But Master, they are holy men," said the Hindu.

"Open your eyes and follow your alert will, then you will soon see what is holy. I have told you already: they are dead. But as for you, be alive, so that you may become seeing."

Krishna knew that it was necessary to speak to the Hindu in this way. The fact that he did not fully understand his master's words caused the man to occupy himself with them all the more. He was like a child with alert senses, who willingly grasped and eagerly absorbed everything living that was given to him. The traditions of men had never taken possession of his spirit; he had been protected for the sake of his destiny.

THEY CONTINUED THEIR JOURNEY. Gradually the dense forests grew lighter, and the mountains lay behind them. They came to vast meadows with tall grass and rose willows. In part the ground was moist and swampy; further towards the hilly country it became fertile. Magnificent trees with large succulent leaves and white blossoms flourished there, as did others with leathery oval leaves and strong aerial roots. Little streams rippled across the meadows. Blue sky arched above them. The paths were now more level, and better; they even came upon wide roads. Then began pasture land, where tents were pitched for the herdsmen.

Great herds of zebus whirled up much dust on the roads. Black birds with pointed beaks sat on the animals' backs. Eventually the towers of a high-lying city emerged in the distance, then a broad river, and high above it all a gleaming white Palace overlooking the vast land.

Not far from the road they came upon a square surrounded by a wall, with vultures sitting on it. The Hindu whispered only a few words:

"This is the place of execution, Master; you know it, I can tell by your eyes, which look within when they see lost ones."

The Hindu had begun to observe his master. His intuitive perception was very accurate.

As they rode on, they came to a hill marked off with spears.

"A funeral pyre is being prepared there for a cremation," said the Hindu.

When they reached the first houses of the white city, above which the Palace was enthroned like a lustrous pointed crown, a sentry came to meet the travellers. He crossed both hands over his chest and bowed low to the ground. The Hindu addressed the man, explaining to him that his master had come to visit the King.

From their self-assured manner the sentry perceived that their intentions could only be good. And the regal dignity of the quiet, tall man aroused profound respect in his soul. He could not and did not wish to question him further.

Women and children came out of the houses; they looked thoughtfully at the two men. One of them, a woman of about thirty years of age, followed them slowly. The Hindu left his elephant behind at an inn, then they walked on.

Krishna felt a great longing to see the Palace with his own eyes, and

43

he thought in particular of the King, about whom he had already heard. He knew that he would be received by him like a son.

The King of the Jadava was known far and wide, and was renowned for his wealth, his goodness and his noble-mindedness; his beautiful wife enjoyed the same renown.

When they had crossed a bridge over the wide river, the Hindu bowed low before his master, and remained behind without a word. He sensed that Krishna wished to be alone.

Krishna stood still at the great gate. He gazed into a lofty, shimmering hall, with many pillars and golden ornaments, but he saw no human being. Nevertheless the gate opened inwards as if moved by invisible hands, and Krishna entered.

He walked through the hall and lifted a jingling portiere. But in this sombre room, adorned with colourful tapestries and wall-lights, there was no one to be seen. Now, however, something stirred in the corner; Krishna caught sight of a woman wrapped in shawls – a slave perhaps. She raised her beautiful tear-stained face. Her dark eyes were veiled; round her mouth was a deep line of sorrow, and across her knees she held a golden sword.

"You have hidden yourself here in grief, Jaconda, and that is why I was led to you. Rise and go with me. I believe I have come at the right hour."

Krishna heard himself speak the words, and was surprised. Of late he had often experienced this.

The woman obeyed as though in a dream. She took the sword, concealed it in the folds of her clothing, and followed him.

She did not know what was happening to her. The stranger had come to her like a manifestation from higher realms, and he now led her through the Palace as though she were a stranger there. She ought to have questioned him, but she could not. She saw so much radiance and light about him that she thought it was one of the gods who had come to take her to his realm.

Krishna saw the signs of death in this house, and he knew it to be the cause of Jaconda's mourning. But as soon as she realised that Krishna was moving towards the King, she would follow him no longer. Trembling, she stood still.

44

"Come, follow me," said Krishna, "and soon you will suffer no more."

He entered a hall which was draped in black, and stood before a bier shrouded in funeral drapings, and bearing the insignia of a Prince; only the golden sword was missing. The women crouched in a circle, weeping.

But at the head of the bier, illumined by the blazing lights, stood the King, tall and grave, with a long dark beard and kindly eyes; his wife stood by his side.

He looked questioningly at Krishna, who, framed by the golden archway, stood before him like the image of a god. Unable to utter a word, in silent grief and full of dignity he indicated the deceased with his hand.

"Yes, King of the Jadava, I have come at the right hour!" Again Krishna heard himself speak. "For it is the Will of the Most High that you should be comforted in your sorrow. I have been sent to you from Above, because in your realm the enlightenment of human beings is to take place through Krishna.

"This one here, your son, has died, and all the nobility lament his death. But I say to you: do not bind him to yourselves with your lamentations, for you could never make good this wrong. I have come to open your eyes, so that you may recognise the consequences of your actions. Everything on earth is to become new. Make a beginning with that in this hour. Bury with honour the body which he has left. But abandon the old funeral rites; you, O King, take the lead in this!

"Build no funeral pyre; provide no spectacle for the people. Do not burn the women to death; abandon the senseless sacrifices. Realise that with these things you put the spirit in chains that bind it to the World of Matter. Do not do this; it is a sin!"

At that moment loud cries and shouts were heard. Everyone looked round indignantly. Servants burst in and announced that a crowd of people was approaching. Soldiers had gathered round the Palace like a wall that could not be breached, but the people were shouting loudly. A woman called in a clear voice:

"He is a Light-spirit, and has come to save us!"

45

Deeply shaken, the King heard these words as he stood by the bier of his son. He went over to Krishna and offered him his hand.

"Whoever you may be," he said, "abide with us! I will act in accordance with your will, for I wish to serve you."

Krishna rejoiced at the King's trust, and readily took the outstretched hand. Then the King sent for the woman who had called in such a loud voice. She was the one who had followed Krishna from afar.

"Rejoice," said she, "for your Lord has entered! Fetch palm branches, and dance, for he brings peace. Hail Jadava who harbours him! The young King is dead, long live Krishna, the Helper! Two tall lights shine on either side of him, and through him courses a White Flame!"

The woman seemed to be out of her senses; she fell to the ground and had to be carried away.

THE KING KEPT HIS WORD. The mortal remains of his son were buried quietly in a sacred grove. Flowers graced the spot, and a statue created by an artist, depicting his person, was to be placed there. But his wives, his horses and weapons were not consigned to the flames as decreed by law. The King had acted according to Krishna's counsel.

The priests were incensed by this. They tried to find a reason to end Krishna's activities. They seethed with hatred, although they knew him not, knew nothing about him. But they feared him.

The Hindu lived quietly and unobtrusively on the banks of the river. No one ever saw him near Krishna; it was as though he did not know him. But he had his eyes and ears everywhere, and watched over his master.

Krishna lived with the royal couple like a son, for the Queen had said:

"When the gods took our son from us, they gave us a son back."

Calm, peace and blessing had entered since Krishna had set foot in the house. Every action carried out according to his words had manifestly good results. The women too had ceased to lament when they realised that the King paid heed to the wise stranger.

With the King's support, Krishna was soon able to win a small circle of men worthy of his teaching. They listened with rapt attention when, filled with the Power of the White Flame, he told them of the One God. At Krishna's express bidding, the elephant-guide was invited to these meetings.

Krishna also went frequently to visit people, and he would appear unexpectedly where there was suffering. He always had a word of solace, words that were never forgotten. And when he left them, they were strengthened.

THUS HAD KRISHNA ENTERED the realm of men. His work on earthly soil was now to begin. The Will of the White Flame had guided him to a place where he could scatter his spiritual seed.

The woman of the Jadava people had been allowed to recognise what a high spirit was sent to them in Krishna. She spread the tidings in the city, and soon it became known throughout the land.

The people listened attentively; the priests and wise men murmured. The magicians consulted their spirits, and used incantations. Within a· short time a welter of outrageous rumours was woven round the mysterious stranger, into whom the spirit of the young King was said to have entered, that he might continue to rule over the people in his body. Many factions formed, and there were as many opposing views.

The priestly caste demanded adherence to the funeral customs, thereby setting themselves against the King. It was a very powerful group, and thus gave rise to a terrible conflict among the people. But the King stood firm and confident, untouched by the malicious threats and clandestine attacks of his opponents. His Palace became more radiant each day; any regular visitor sensed the blessing and power since Krishna lived there.

The Queen was released from the dark veils of a depression which had not left her since the birth of her deceased son. Her wonderful eyes had assumed the soft radiance that was theirs when, still almost a child, she had been given to the King as his wife.

She had never understood life, which had always seemed to her like a pointless captivity in a dreary place, though abounding in outward splendour. Now all at once it had meaning and purpose. She understood the distress of the women who married far too early, the suffering of the mothers who were much too young, on whose not-yet-matured body and not-yet-awakened inner life too heavy a burden was laid. With a few words Krishna had explained the origin of the oppression that weighed upon her being, and thereby freed her from it.

She made no complaint about spending her life so devoid of understanding until now. She simply began a new life, and was happy that the painful experiences of her youth now brought her a rich harvest. In retrospect she could understand everything. It was as though all her life she had only been awaiting the moment when Krishna appeared among them. Yet it came to her as a surprise, and like a miracle.

Everything now had a meaning: the splendour and wealth of the Palace, which were meant for Krishna, the power of her husband, who ruled over many countries, and the love of the peoples. Matured through longing, her rich heart now opened like a flower in the sunshine, and with all the love of which she was capable she strove towards the Light.

Often the Queen listened for hours while Krishna discussed the conditions among the people with her husband, when he advised the kindly, much-experienced King in all the affairs of government. His wise, simple words, each of which was so meaningful that it could free a soul instantly from a great burden, seemed to her to be inspired from Above.

Often questions that had distressed humanity for centuries were answered and clarified with one brief word, and it seemed to her that man, now liberated, could soar aloft to purer, better worlds.

No longer was she sad, nor did she weep; no longer did she know any sorrow to oppress her soul. She was happy; her spirit had been awakened.

The austere, severe earnestness of the King had also changed. The proud, almost rigid attitude had yielded to a calm self-confidence and majesty, and the dark eyes had taken on a warm, kindly radiance.

For Krishna it was a gift of grace to find in this kindly, wise man both a fatherly friend and the most willing student. Humbly he gave thanks for it to the Supreme One.

48

Everyone in the Palace served the young King devotedly, the women too made an effort to win his approval, indeed his respect. Even the shy Jaconda conquered herself. She followed him in silent reverence, endeavouring to be near him. One day she stood at the door of his apartment with the golden sword in her hands. She bowed low. Then modestly and reverently, she looked towards him, wondering whether he would accept her gift.

"You have now been living in our house for six months as our Master. I needed this much time to overcome the grief at the loss of my husband. For six months I have guarded his golden sword, which you saved from the flames as you saved me.

"Now I have overcome, as you wished. Since the hour of your command my will has no longer called back my husband's spirit to the lowly bonds of the earth, and there has been no further pain; instead, like precious oil, healing comfort flowed from the Sublime Fields on to my aching wounds.

"I myself can no longer belong to any man. What the death by fire would prevent by force of law, the faithfulness of spiritual love will accomplish through free volition. This is what you have taught me. But the sword that I once kept in childish defiance lest another should seize hold of it, this sword I lay at your feet for the battle that will soon begin. It is the greatest treasure of my departed ancestry. It was wielded only in loyalty and purity, therefore it is also worthy of you. May I ask you, Master, to accept it?"

Krishna laid his hand on her ebony hair, saying:

"I was well aware, Jaconda, that you would bring it. Behold, it belongs to me! You have overcome the suffering for my sake, but One Higher than I will repay you a thousandfold for it. Abide in this peace!"

JACONDA WAS RIGHT: he was soon to make use of the sword. The reports brought by scouts from the borders were increasingly alarming. Maro, who wove threads of evil against the spread of the Light on earth, incited a ruler of dark blood who, filled with hate, was equipping a wild, marauding horde.

Suspicion rankled among people of the high castes. Their thrones began to totter; the power of conjurers and magicians in the temples was threatened by the prohibitions of the King.

How could they still be assured of protection from the awakening of the people? This man was dangerous, he was poison, a raging fire to consume tradition, belief and the old order.

The people were beginning to look up to Krishna. It became light around them, for he proved to them by word and deed that they could free themselves from all Darkness. Of course he demanded from them deeds, not words, but deeds arising from the spirit, which logically had to be expressed in earthly activity.

The festival of Durga, lasting several days, was about to be celebrated. This was an opportunity to persuade themselves and the people of the stranger's presumption. The King was feared and hated, because he protected Krishna with his power.

The faithful Hindu had much to do in these days. His vigilance enabled the King to be informed about every one of his enemies' schemes. Krishna did not trouble about these things. He glowed in the sacred fire of a new Power-wave coming from Above. As in times past at home in the luminous realm of the white mountains, he felt the connection with the White Flame. He was filled with joy; and radiantly he conveyed gifts of the spirit in abundance to those around him.

Often his spirit became absorbed; then he would receive powers and tidings of which he never spoke to anyone. He also explored the stars, drawing from them significant conclusions for what was to come.

Menacingly, the red rays of the god of war moved across India. The earth quaked thunderously. People became engulfed in dread and fear, sacrificing more blood than ever. Sweltering sandstorms raged across the land; at times the sky turned red. Rumours of great upheavals in the high mountains, of fiery explosions on the small southern archipelagos, circulated among the people.

Great heat and drought followed a very long rainy season, which had transformed the mighty rivers into sources of peril for the flat land. Swamps and stretches of marshland spread about, producing serious fevers among man and beast.

There were many dead in the huts of the poor, as in the palaces of the rich. Sick people with yellow, terribly disfigured faces and blue lips were carried into the temples, where they imperilled even the healthy.

Placing their last hope of recovery on the putrid, vile-smelling waters, the half-dead encamped on the banks of the yellow rivers, into which white steps led. Things were in a sorry state throughout the great land of India, and people could not free themselves from the heavy burden weighing upon them.

They did not know that in fact it was they themselves who constantly nurtured those agonising conditions. Instead they became increasingly ensnared in the tenacious threads which, formed by their volition, thoughts and deeds, could hardly be disentangled any more. The bloody scenes of sacrifice, by which they sought to wring grace and help from their gods, were a horrible source of this evil. Men were afraid, afraid of everything. They did not bow in gratitude and joyous worship; no, trembling with fear, they crawled about the ground.

Thus the time when the pure will of Krishna sought to approach men in helping love was filled with confused apprehension.

His spirit tried to fathom the deep human misery, and he implored the White Flame for the strength to carry Light into this Darkness. But he now realised how difficult it would be to rouse men from their fever-sleep.

When Krishna became deeply absorbed, the chaos of the earth was remote from him. But when, as his mission now demanded, he mingled with human beings who continued to burrow like blind moles, he was seized by holy wrath. Wrath had never been known to him – the loving one, the servant and helper, the humble one. Now it often blazed from him like a fiery column; his eyes looked menacing, and his voice had a metallic ring. Then his will was unbending, and the Light of the White Flame shone brightly above him.

It was thus, too, that Krishna entered the temple of Durga. The people, who were rolling on the ground, trembling in agonised fear, broke up in terror. They crept away on all fours, peering up from the ground like timid, startled beasts, with little resemblance to human beings any more.

51

On the sacrificial altar stone of Durga the blood ran down; the sweetish smell of human blood mingled with the smoke of the green torches that were smeared with it. The blood dripped from the knives and robes of the priest, whose clenched hands were also blood-red. The garishly bedecked man, disguised with a horrible mask, screamed in ecstasy, and his wild eyes glittered. The people, however, monotonously intoned so-called "sacrificial songs".

Six more beautiful young maidens were kneeling naked before the stone, their arms tied behind them with raffia. A grey pallor covered the brown faces, and the tearless eyes stared in rising madness.

Like an angel of wrath, Krishna strode up to the sacrificial stone, his sword raised. With one blow he struck the mask from the priest's face; it fell away in two parts like a shell. The face of a criminal, torn by hate, fear and evil lust, stared ashen-grey with fright, as though demented, at Krishna, the "desecrator of the temple".

A trembling gesture was meant to signify: "Seize the criminal!" But only a hoarse sound escaped the dry lips agape with terror. No one stirred. Paralysed by fear, with a feeling akin to that of criminals caught unawares, priests, servants and magicians simply stood still, even though it would not have been difficult for them to lay hands on the one man.

What kind of constraint held them? None of them even remotely thought of turning against Krishna. Boundless astonishment kept in check the rage that could erupt at any moment. Krishna looked round. His shining eyes met those of the faithful Hindu, who had followed his master.

"Out with you, the blood-bath is over! If you had eyes you would be blinded by the hideousness of your doings! They will roll back on you a thousandfold, coil round you like snakes, and throttle you to death. Would you then be bound to the earth for ever?

"I say to you, throw off these practices like poisonous snakes, put on white linen, bathe in clear water; cleanse yourselves from the sacrifices, and pray through work and cheerfulness. Then fear will leave you. Only when these creepers have dropped away from you will I be able to show you a Light which will lead you into Life. In the name of the

King I now proclaim: The temples are closed. The death penalty to him who enters them!"

Weapons clanking, soldiers entered the temple and took possession of the whole room. In an instant the priests were surrounded and led away; the people were thrust out through the wide-open gates. Smoking, steaming, smouldering green, the larger than life-sized statue of the goddess stared into the empty room. Before it still lay the dead body of a maiden, but the living victims had been freed and taken into the care of women.

Krishna sheathed his sword, and went out with bowed head. The bright light of his presence had dispelled the vile phantoms and demons. At the stroke of his sword they had fallen away in thousands from the innocent victims who, unsuspecting, were defenceless against them.

Krishna had begun a battle of deliverance, but men neither knew nor understood, for they saw only the outward deeds. To them his measures appeared coercive, an interference in their personal freedom; they regarded them as acts of violence and brutality against the high priests.

Some grumbled apathetically, others clenched their fists in defiance against the King's authority, and some shook their heads thoughtfully, pondering whether the resistance to tradition and priesthood was right.

Some opinions were diffidently expressed; cautious questions were asked, such as: "Do you too have a feeling of relief? Is it possible that the priests have been acting wrongly? Were the sacrifices a sin? Is this man a liberator or a criminal?"

But others were also heard, such as:

"Our beliefs cannot possibly be wrong, therefore *he* must be wrong! He is a threat to law and order; he has confused the King!"

"Yes, but he has healed the Queen; she was half insane before …"

"… and so she is now, only in a different way! She regards him as her son. Maybe he even killed him!"

"Jaconda probably loves him."

"He draws everything to himself: power, gold, love!"

"He is a conjurer of the worst kind. He even wants to become King;

what a good-for-nothing impostor! Nobody knows where he came from. People must be protected from him!"

"But he has never yet done anything evil; all he wants is to help us, he wants to guide us into Life, did you not hear him say so? If he were evil where would the feeling of relief come from?"

It was a twelve-year-old girl who spoke. For that, a man threatened her with a stone.

THE WHEEL HAD BEEN SET ROLLING, and no one gripped the spokes. Krishna rejoiced. The Power of the Spirit flowed through him; the White Flame spoke to him in a loud voice, and led him from temple to temple, from village to village, from province to province.

He travelled with a band of loyal followers, acclaimed by adherents and admired by strangers, feared and hated, loved and celebrated in songs of enthusiasm and ecstasy.

He rode on a white steed amid waving banners, or spoke from the back of the faithful elephant, which was led by the Hindu, and he saw the grey souls of men and their burning pain.

"I should like to remove the dross from your souls by force, so that you might at last become free for my rousing call! Do not sleep yourselves to death, you human beings! Observe but *one* of my commandments with joy during the day, and it will soon grow lighter and brighter in your gloomy house. But make haste, for we have much to do to clear away the rubble. And do not throw stones at your neighbour. Let each one do his work, so that we may be ready when He Who will teach you Love comes. He is higher than I, and He will lead you home."

The masses stood amazed; they were in total suspense, wordless, indeed almost breathless, as Krishna spoke. When he had finished, and raised his hands in a gesture of blessing and salutation, the suppressed feeling of enthusiasm, joy and gratitude burst powerfully forth, like the raging of a storm.

But as soon as the drums resounded and he was leaving the place, the crowd fell back and bowed low, in such awe as they had never known

54

before. A wide lane opened of itself, along which Krishna quietly continued with his companions.

And what did he leave behind? Thousands had listened to him in silence. Shaken to their inmost core they stood musing or praying. But among thousands there was only one here and there who did not relapse into the apathy of his previous ways.

Among thousands one here and there!

The dark forces massed in secret; they were not to be found among the poor and lowly; no, they were among the respected, among the dignitaries, among the leading rich men. Maro called up his army, and mankind made it easy for him.

Indolence, vanity, ambition and conceit about their knowledge, the great desire to rule, the craving for influence, the fear of being ridiculed – all these threw open the doors to temptation, so that ugly, deceptive enticements were able to gain entrance. Maro sowed confusion, and the seed sprang up.

Krishna saw it all. He knew that it was the crisis after his wielding of the sharp knife, and the deep incisions made by it. Around him the pure life of the helping forces grew stronger. He stood in a shining circle of luminous helpers who wove a protective mantle around him.

Krishna looked up. He recognised the effect of the Light-power on earth, and knew himself to be the instrument of a higher Will. His lips formed a Word which he found inscribed in the clouds and stars. But his lips only breathed It, for this Word was holy, and no one on earth was mature for It. Day and night, waking and sleeping, the Word was in him. When he opened himself trustingly to It, life streamed into him, and everything became clear before him.

The Word was: *Imanuel.*

For Krishna everything lay in this Name, and he hardly dared to think It. The Name guided him. It drew his spirit upwards with a shining cord into Its Luminous Realm, and there, within moments, Krishna was accorded recognitions enabling him to grasp many thousands of years of evolution.

He was infinitely grateful for this grace! He was permitted to be a pioneer! He was to tear men from the tangle of their self-created torments, and show them the way to the Light.

He always remained in contact with his earthly home up in the white mountains, but no one, not even the faithful Hindu, knew of it. Often he went to his parental home, and stepped into the circle of his chosen helpers. He then spoke to them of the Will of the White Flame, to enable them to understand his words and deeds. In complete trust they strove to follow him on the most arduous paths, spiritually and in the earthly.

And these paths became increasingly dangerous for the helpers. The fierce hatred of the priests knew no bounds. The sacrificial festivals had been taken from them, and they were compelled to serve under surveillance in accordance with the will of Krishna, if they did not wish to forfeit their office, reputation and wealth. Furtively this hatred was nurtured, engendering ethereal forms which grew to terrible proportions, and burdened those of like mind. Conspiracies were plotted against the royal house.

Thus unrest was threatening, together with invasion at the borders of the realm by an enraged neighbour whose fierce hatred was also directed against the Renewer of Faith.

Human beings suffered. The rainy season and the drought that followed it had brought increased famine and disease. The suffering was intended to rouse men and help them to mature, but there were many who turned away from Krishna and complained. They imagined that the old gods had taken revenge, and were angered by the prohibition of sacrifices; and the priests supported them in this delusion.

But those who had fallen away became the worst enemies. All that Krishna had given them in love they turned into hatred against him. Confused, they fell into despair or apathy, and Maro's helpers hurled themselves fiercely at these forlorn spirits.

Krishna, however, did not delay. Labouring tirelessly, his alert will spared no effort. His spiritual helpers revealed every danger to him; his earthly supporters prepared the weapons. War was inevitable; war against all that opposed the pure Will. His helping, supportive love had become a brilliant flame to scorch everything evil and rotten, and

56

make room for the Blessing. Purification from this plague was his sole aim.

Having first appeared to men as a loving helper who showed them the ways, which indeed they recognised yet did not follow, now at the hour of his fulfilment he became the destroyer of everything that would not yield. For in the relentlessly-turning wheel of development there was neither standstill nor return, but only steady progress in accordance with the Will of the Most High.

Krishna knew that there would not be the slightest change in the Law for the sake of negligent mankind. He too could avert nothing, for like a sounding ray his will was attuned to the Holy Will of the Most High.

And as Krishna thus swung in the Will of the Lord, he was successful in all his undertakings, even the most difficult. But he must not hesitate a moment; always he had to transform his volition strictly and unremittingly into deed. That was difficult at times, for even the best of his helpers often did not understand him. And to carry out something not understood was the hardest of all, especially for the most competent. If they were unassuming, at least they often realised that they themselves had woven the many dense obstructions, which they now had to cut away amid bitter suffering.

Krishna saw how they grappled with themselves, and loved them for it, but frequently he was also deeply saddened because of them. They made the battle against evil harder for him, for always he had to enlighten his helpers first. But since they were ignorant of so much regarding the consequences of deeds and wrong thoughts, of an ill-adjusted volition, he did not hold it against them. He only prayed for them, who were his dearest on earth, whenever he strengthened his spirit in the Light of the White Flame.

And so everything had to be fulfilled without a break, as ordained by the Will of the White Flame. When, roused by Maro's hatred, the old neighbouring king, who clung to the priesthood, violated the borders, and in league with fanatical agitators turned the borderland into an inferno, those in leading positions finally consented to the campaign.

Meanwhile the enemy had gained advantage, and their hordes of troopers took fierce revenge for the offended gods. Impenetrable human walls advanced further and further. But there was no blessing on their undertakings.

Imperturbably, Krishna advised and commanded his faithful people. Not a word of reproach passed his lips. Shamed, they now redoubled their efforts to obey his will.

"It was Krishna who taught us that mistakes made with the best intentions can cause such bitter pain," said the King to his wife. "Never to be able to make good one's omission is the most grievous affliction on earth."

Now, however, a fresh danger emerged: in their excessive zeal his followers made other mistakes. Where at first Krishna had to urge them on, he now had difficulty in restraining them.

But the enemies raged unabated. Murder, blood and fire smouldered across the land, over which the red star of war blazed at night.

Then Krishna prepared to set forth himself, and this brought the turning-point. The war for the inviolability of the dogma became the Holy War of the Light. Krishna's army sped towards the enemy. At first his warriors were outnumbered, but they were full of trust and courage, and the flame of conviction shone forth from the troops. By the time they reached the enemy's vanguard, Krishna's army had already doubled in number, and every day there were more reinforcements.

In silent wonder and grateful awe, his faithful ones experienced the great help. They saw how whatever they undertook in accord with his volition succeeded quickly, and turned out well. They revered Krishna even more, whispering conjectures about his origin to each other.

Krishna lived with them. Just as he shared the rigours of the frequently arduous rides, so he also shared their hours of rest and the short intervals of joy. During the long marches the people thronged round him; they wanted to see him, to ask questions, wanted to be blessed and taught, comforted and encouraged by him. And if they came impelled by the true longing of their spirit, he did not refuse them.

But his servants were often harsh with the petitioners, and did not know how to help them in the right way. Mostly they were biased in judging the people's concerns, seeing them from their own viewpoint. That caused many difficulties between his helpers and the people. The errors of the helpers, however, were blamed on Krishna. Yet he stood like a clear light above it all, untouched.

As his servants witnessed and experienced ever more frequently how they were driven forward with him from battle to battle, from victory to victory, how easily they triumphed when their obedience was un-questioning, and how on the other hand they suffered if they were tempted to yield to weariness, they recognised the Power of the White Flame and revered it. But his enemies, and those who were not his servants, believed Vishnu to have reappeared in him, and proclaimed him a god.

The bloody battles ceased. The armies of the neighbouring people left the country in headlong flight. Krishna's soldiers pursued them, and conquered the neighbouring lands.

KRISHNA'S POWER GREW, and he prayed:

"Lord, Who hast permitted me to go forth in Thy Will, be severe with me lest I stumble!"

To Krishna the adoration of the masses was more dreadful than their hatred. It seemed impossible to eradicate their wrong ideas on all vital questions and the meaning of their existence – to convey to them in-stead the knowledge of the Creation-Laws and their effects.

Everyone believed Krishna to be happy at the height of his power. But he knew that he had assumed full responsibility for these human beings from the Hand of the Most High, and profound earnestness suf-fused his whole being. He had become very quiet. Everywhere he saw men's faults and spiritual confusion, everywhere duty and work for himself. The field of his activity was beset with difficulties.

But just as at first they had gone out of their way to put obstacles in his path, so the people now tormented him with their homage. Heavy at heart he lived among them.

Day and night his activity demanded the strictest attention. He was teacher, leader, statesman and priest, and his helpers developed their

59

talents under his guidance. In the earthly sense, the great realm which he had united under his will was able to flourish, but the people were meant to purify themselves spiritually, and that was the hardest task. He did not want to discipline them, and impose on them a knowledge for which they were not yet sufficiently mature. To his friend the King he said:

"They are still like children, indeed, some of them even less than that. Just as they live, they also see their gods, and hence too they fear their gods. To be able to recognise *God* they must first learn to live aright, to live as human beings with free will. That I can only begin to teach them; it will be completed by One Who will come after me."

"When will that be?" asked the King of the Jadava.

"The time cannot be measured in years and days; these are epochs of development from out of the Law," said Krishna.

The King would have liked to compress his ideas about the great question of evolution into space and time. Krishna tried to give him a wide view; he wanted to protect him from error and the disappointment that would arise from it, because he loved him. But he observed that the King did not understand him either. Then, for the first time, Krishna longed to return to his white mountains, to the Twelve Guardians.

A SHINING RING OF LIGHT swung resoundingly above Krishna. Every day he sought an hour of absorption. It brought him recovery. Alone and in the swinging ray of the White Light he found an answer to every question. At the same time he was approached by pure helping spirits whom he needed.

So Astarte appeared to him again after a long time.

Ringing like delicate crystal, with the bluish shimmer of ice, rays and circles swung down from an approaching heavenly body. It was not of the dense material substance of the stars, which Krishna's spirit had already beheld. This was of a much finer nature. It was formed in lawful volition on a plane set aglow by Astarte.

Enveloped in this form, in her flowing, spiritualised radiation, she inclined towards the spirit in the World of Matter. Her whispering voice rang clear as a bell. Krishna heard it with delight. An atmosphere, cool and bracing as snowy air, pure and lovely as the fragrance of blossoms, surrounded her.

"Yes, I bring you a breath of Paradise," said Astarte. "You have now beheld human suffering, and can understand my sorrow. Do you remember what I told you, that the woman of Subsequent Creation no longer knows me? That is why my tears flow, for much as I would like to work, I can no longer do so. The way to earth-woman is closed to me; her volition has gone to sleep. You, Krishna, can and shall awaken her, for only through her can you guide human beings back to life. She must take the lead, for she has failed. Follow me, so that you may learn what I ask of womanly virtue."

The ringing increased, the rays became finer, more luminous, lighter, and Krishna was ascending swiftly. Blue light enveloped him. Silvery moonlight glinted across blue-grey billows; lovely ripples sparkled with reflected light. Trees swayed to and fro, little streams murmured, clouds scudded across the sky, beautiful landscapes spread below them.

With exquisitely lustrous threads, gracious beings were weaving tapestries and pictures that became steadily more dense and heavy, and glided downwards. Whence came the threads which they spun? Whence the patterns for the wonderful pictures of grace and virtue?

They worked out of the powerful primordial volition that pervaded their sphere.

Astarte was able to ascend and lead Krishna on further. Up there in the melodious Light was a golden gate. Two luminous figures, holding out their hands, came to meet them. They were shown into a garden filled with most beautiful flowers. All the flowers of the world were to be found there; none was missing, and each was of choice beauty. They stretched their great luminous cups towards the Light.

There was humming and singing of bees, of dragon-flies and wonderful birds. White doves flew down from a golden Temple. This Light-sphere was radiant and brilliant; Astarte in her luminous glow was dim and pale in comparison.

"Here in these Heavenly Gardens is the Fountain-head of Purity and Loyalty," she said, "here you will find the virtues that swing in the Law of the Divine Will."

Afloat in a blue lake was an Island of Light, on which white lilies bloomed in luxuriant splendour.

In its centre stood a golden lily, irradiated by the roseate light of a full, star-studded mantle.

"This is the Fountain-head of Purity and Loyalty," whispered Astarte.

And then Krishna saw a queenly Woman, encircled by weaving rays of light, borne downwards by shining Light-steps. Through this wonderful Form passed a ray of White Light, the "White Flame".

In the Crown of the queenly Woman shone seven light-stars, representing the heavenly virtues which he was to recognise as the most important. Her Mantle, shining in a roseate light, flowed far down, and lovely beings wove and worked at its hem.

Flowers bloomed out of it; all that the world calls beautiful was nurtured by the radiance of the connecting forces, through which Divine Light and Divine Power wove and worked on unceasingly. The sovereign undulation of this Mantle, which flashed as though set aglow by stars, was eternal.

The First, the Form-Perfect, the Archetype, the Queen of Womanhood – he was allowed to behold Her countenance, and to recognise how She protected the Garden of Purity, and solicitously enveloped it with the wide folds of Her Mantle.

Krishna was overawed. Trembling, he hid his face in his hands. Exultation and sobbing gripped his soul simultaneously.

When his spirit was back on earth Krishna found himself alone. But the picture of spiritual Purity and Loyalty had impressed itself on his memory, and he never forgot it again.

WHEN KRISHNA HAD BEEN THUS raised On High, he also underwent a great outward transformation. He became even more radiant, and an aura of remoteness and supremacy enveloped his being.

He had beheld the Source of Purity, and with the swiftness of spiritual processes the unforgettable, overwhelming impression had at once possessed him completely. And thus it was meant to be, for Krishna was to blaze the trail again for Purity.

For a long time afterwards he lived in spirit in the Blessed Gardens of Purity. Only through seclusion and prayer could he transform his experiences into calm and clarity within him. Therefore he walked alone through the peaceful gardens which surrounded the spacious Palace, and sat by the golden pool in which the still lotus unfolded its snow-white blossoms at night in the moonlight.

There he reflected upon the Garden in which he had received a concept of Purity. He had to translate this concept in order to make it intelligible for human beings. But filled with its archetype, he was not yet capable of doing so.

Then Astarte appeared again over the waters, more radiant and joyous than ever.

"I will lead you now to the Realm of the Fate-spinning Women," said she, "there you will learn many things."

This time Krishna perceived his path to be not a steep ascent, but rather a gentle rise into a finer, more luminous environment.

He felt that he was in a sphere of vaporous light, only a few steps above the World of Gross Matter. Delicate shapes were in constant motion about him. For some time he walked on a soft mossy floor, so it appeared to him, until he reached a huge tree, whose tall branches towered upward.

In form and kind it resembled an oak. Its trunk was enormous, and its mighty roots spread out around it, thrusting downward into lower spheres, and extending through these as well. Vast gardens encircled this – the World-Tree.

Like newly-lit, waxing flames, three figures emerged from the undulating mists. At the foot of the World-Tree they could be more readily discerned; through them flowed the threads formed by the animistic.

With the animistic forces they wove the threads from the spirit into pictures which, in sinking downward, increased in weight and density.

Like beautiful mirror-images, forms of coming-into-being, of birth and of growth shone before the first and youngest of the women.

Lost in wonder, Krishna beheld this. It seemed to him that he heard soft words from the lips of the weaving women, who diligently, with fine fingers, joined the delicate Light-threads, without however mingling the different kinds in the process. Luminous threads flowed from above, especially to the youngest who sat at the highest point. She held a golden vessel from which she twisted the rolling thread. Radiant life was weaving about her. Sparkling, it dropped downward in many emerging archetypes, received and disseminated by creative and helping beings.

The second of the women appeared to Krishna more mature and grave. Her head was covered by a veil. In her lap she gathered the fine substance of this sphere and joined it with the luminous threads from the hand of her sister. Around her arose the crystal-clear forms of what had come into being. Everything that is created and completed becomes a picture there, condensing as it sinks, and the active forces of the Animistic Realm continue to work upon it.

Within him Krishna heard the word "workshop"; it had a musical sound and a clear brilliance, spreading spiritual purity and beauty around it.

The third and last of the women wove the threads of the future. New development was unfurled there reciprocally from what had come into being. All the threads flowed through her white hands, and her perceptive gaze penetrated the most hidden mysteries of approaching events.

Thus was Krishna initiated into the knowledge of coming-into-being and development, of love and death and of rebirth. The activity of the three extended from the sphere of their being right down to what took place in the World of Matter. Far-sighted was the gaze of the women, and the pictures of the working forces were spread beneath their weaving fingers.

"You are a Forerunner, like many who have already come and are yet to appear. But God, Who enlightens and sustains us, will send a Part out of Himself for the second time. Heavens and human beings will undergo changes. Your people will long since have ascended to their homeland, and your name will remain among men as a divine one. But the great epochs of Divine Activity must needs return, for men will not improve. Floods, wars, horrors destroy them now, and the Fist of Power will smite them harder still. You, Krishna, will return, though not in the flesh, when for the third time the Son of God sets foot in the earthly sphere. Then the third ring of Divine Activity will be closed, and redemption or collapse of all material substance will follow!"

Thus did Krishna hear the wise woman whispering, not in words, but in the living weaving of future time. With it crystal-clear forms emerged in the fine hazy substances, forms which he, Krishna, did not understand either.

The first coming-into-being of form out of the Will of the Primordial Power illuminated his spirit, blinding and utterly confusing him. He stood shaken before the mysteries whose veils had been lifted; yet he could not quite fathom or comprehend them so long as he bore the earthly body.

KRISHNA'S CONCERN was now focussed on how to find the right way to make understandable to human beings that which the Grace of the Most High had permitted him to behold. He knew that only in accord with the White Flame could he be enabled to do so.

For this he was in need of prayer, for with all its might the wild surging of the world claimed his attention. He alone was answerable for everything. His faithful, vigilant servants did their work as best they could. But not only in all spiritual, but also in all worldly matters the ultimate resolution lay in his will, in his decision.

Krishna knew that he would never speak to men about his supreme knowledge, for they were unable to follow him. But the knowledge he had gathered through his experiences about the high spiritual connections, that he must teach them by means of compulsion, guidance and laws. He had examined the causes of their errors and was able to give his instructions accordingly. With keen thinking he traced the effects of his decrees.

Indra, whom Krishna deemed especially exalted among the gods of India, sometimes appeared to him in a glorious circle of rays. He still lived in the belief of a number of the great Indian people, but as nothing more than a beautiful dream which had been effaced by the angry demigods. Originally he was regarded as lord of the airy element, and was associated with all higher and purer swinging.

Indra too was an animistic helper. Only now, through Krishna, he found the connection again with human beings, just as did Astarte.

Krishna was resting by the lotus pond in the quiet of his garden, when he noticed the fresh, pure breath of the airy element, for all around no palm or shrub stirred.

But at the point from which the movement of the air emanated, the water rippled, and above it a gossamer oval layer of mist took shape. It became wider and clearer, assuming opalescent hues with blue and green prevailing, and inclined towards Krishna. The core became ever more translucent, and the outlines of a noble male head appeared.

In a position of rest, with legs drawn up, the animistic being sat upon a large ample cloud-cushion. Above him, whose clear face was dominated by the radiance of deep-blue eyes, a rainbow of colours broke through the fine mist. Out of him flowed the movement of the mists and colourful light-rays which, circling at some distance, revolved about him, creating the impression that he was sitting in a luminous, colourful sun. From it, variegated threads spun upwards in harmoniously beautiful movements. But the threads of rays downwards were slack and feeble, and those intended to lead to human beings were shrivelled and lifeless. Thus did Indra appear to the sage.

How different indeed he was from the pictures that had arisen in the imagination of men! Here too Krishna saw the difference between life itself and the distortions evoked by the human mind.

"The origin of their suffering lies in the over-estimation of their intellect," said Krishna.

Indra nodded his head in agreement and said:

"All beings live in bliss. Only men know suffering. Through their actions and the false direction of their volition the supply-channels for the forces from Above become twisted, and we can no longer help them. So they harm themselves; for they withdraw ever further from their only help. But the power which life bestows upon us is filled with such love that it now sends helps of a stronger kind. Only we are able to sense what love lies in this; men cannot do it.

"Krishna, how blessed you are to be granted such might! Behold, soon you will also be given the power to change the mind of men. All pure beings of higher spheres are approaching you, you who are able to provide the link; all of them hope and work with you in the service of the Light."

Above Krishna arched a blue vault, filled with starlight; it drew him upwards with a wondrous power. So swift was his ascent that he was unable to see anything of the Ethereal Sphere. Ever more light and luminous was each of the subsequent spheres that received him. He seemed to be immersed in the flow of a deep blue gleaming river, whose calm waves moved along eternally. Delicate air-beings frolicked about here. Resplendent dream-cities in silvery white radiance floated like islands in the waters, and the higher he rose the clearer and calmer everything became, the more remote from time and space. But before one gate Indra remained behind. To him it was firmly shut.

Krishna, however, passed through it, and ascended in the ray of flowing Light. To him the gate was open. He rose ever higher, and beneath him shining cities and glorious landscapes, mountains and lakes spread out like wonderful prototypes of all the glories offered by the earth.

They were filled with floating, delicate beings working diligently in order to benefit Creation through their deeds. Gladness and untiring activity prevailed everywhere. Krishna saw not one troubled, tired, or even listless face, not one movement that would have evidenced sorrow or discontent. This plane was without sorrow, for it swung in the Laws of the Light.

But he had no time to tarry; onward, ever higher he rose. Now his path no longer led vertically upwards, but in a circle, horizontally, and he journeyed from sphere to sphere, from one step to the next, and absorbed within him the splendour of Creation. The radiations of the various planes meshed like fine lace-work, and shone like glowing metal.

Unceasingly the flood of Light flowed through this fine lace and animated it, producing the effect of a huge lung whose tissues are suffused with blood and in constant motion. Every sphere was inhabited; each was perfect in beauty and lawfulness.

So Krishna approached that mighty, surging, wonderful sea, above which shone at a great distance the Holy Light. Loneliness, a faint anxiety stole over even his strong spirit; yet remembrance dawned upon him, as though he had traversed all this once before.

Then a shining star-flower ascended from below, or was it a star? Its light was silvery blue, and Krishna recognised that it was Astarte. She looked up at him, and he heard her voice:

"It was here, at this point, that the Light-bringer who issued from out of the Power of the Most High began to fail; here the lust for influence and knowing better stirred in him, and he subsequently tried to enforce his principle in the World of Matter. Here he stood at the threshold, and here he realised for the first time that he could no longer go back up, for he had acted contrary to the Law – he who should have helped human beings to live in the Law. From here his spiritual fall began.

"Krishna, I know that your spirit is mature in its comprehension of the loyalty of all the animistic. Therefore you will also comprehend how terribly we dread Lucifer. How could man listen to him? He will approach you also once more, for this is the threshold. The higher the spirit, the more formidable is his attack. Krishna, be vigilant!"

Effortlessly, he ascended further. A soft mantle enveloped him and bore him aloft. For a long time he was aware of nothing. Then suddenly he perceived that he was in a radiant room, from whose infinite blue-golden domed height Light flowed like a broad river. A golden throne was placed at the topmost end of the hall. The hall was so spacious that a world could have revolved within it, but Krishna was able to grasp this for but an instant, since he himself was beyond space and time. The enhanced bliss, the beatific lightness were present here to an even greater degree. Fragrance, radiance and warmth, not without freshness, wafted to and fro. And now the Sublime Woman with the Crown of Stars appeared again before his dazzled eyes.

"Elizabeth!" He knew not who had told him.

"Behold my Son!" thus spoke her voice.

The Heavens parted, and in flowing abundance the Light bore down a Shining Knight. He wore a crown. His countenance, framed in curling hair of brilliant white, was that of a young man. In His hand He held a Sword with a hilt in the shape of a Cross.

Krishna knelt, his head bowed, his hands crossed over his breast.

"This is He Whom you serve – Parsifal!" spoke Elizabeth.

Krishna saw the White Flame shining from His head, it leapt high upwards; there was a radiation-connection which he was unable to follow.

White flame blazed from Parsifal, dazzling white flowed into Him from Above.

"Where am I?" Krishna whispered.

"In the Holy Grail!"

"Thy Holy Spirit has illumined me, I know Thee, Lord, now I know that Thou comest out of God."

And Parsifal laid the shining point of His Sword upon Krishna's head.

Filled with the flaming Light of the Sword Krishna began the journey back through the spheres.

"Now I know Whom I serve to all Eternity. It will be Parsifal Who vanquishes Lucifer."

THESE SACRED EXPERIENCES, that were Krishna's actual life, claimed the smallest part of his existence, which was filled with work, disquiet and danger, with constant struggle.

He was always surrounded by people who were in need of his help. All of them were dependent on his guidance and his counsel. Many amazing stories circulated about the help that came with surprising speed, wherever unwavering trust and personal co-operation were brought to him.

Disease and anguish of mind were quickly remedied by Krishna's presence. People began to set up altars for him, and to revere him as God.

The power of his presence exerted a particularly strong influence upon the masses. As soon as his faithful ones left the Palace in order to clear the way for him, the crowd gathered, often waiting for hours until he came. When he spoke there was silence in the great squares so that the rustle of the palms could be heard. Spellbound, the people received what he told them.

Meanwhile the old places of worship had become quiet and empty. The darkness of their past clung to them heavily, and Krishna no longer set foot there.

His journeys became infrequent, for the people made pilgrimages to see him. The scorching heat could not restrain them from waiting for him for hours, even for days. Gravely ill persons were brought to him. Always he had to move through misery and malady.

People started to make unreasonable demands when they did not see him. This necessitated the formation of a strong bodyguard, led by the faithful Hindu.

Krishna still rode on Amba. Doves flew around him when he strolled in the gardens. Song-birds gathered near him, and even the shy herons flew in great flocks from the vast marshes to where he was.

A golden light-radiance seemed to hover over the place of his earthly abode. It was the helpful presence of the shining Light-figures that surrounded him. The gardens of the Palace flourished in unusual beauty and abundance.

The help of the Divine Light was always with Krishna.

Ever since the Name of the Lord had been proclaimed to him, and he had recognised Him again in the Figure of Parsifal, ever since the Mother of the Universe had shown him the Source of Purity, the Sage, the Enlightened One, had become a Priest of the Light.

Unforgettable within him was the immense abundance of his experiences, unforgettable the magnitude of everything created. Infinitely wide was the gulf that separated him from human beings spiritually. Their manner of serving him and of approaching him was demanding, impetuous or effusive, at all events always selfish.

What he gave them in his teaching satisfied them for the moment. They also thought they understood him, and would do what he asked of them, that they might attain all, which in spirit and in the flesh, as beautiful fruits of their sowing, he held out in prospect to them.

But how difficult was the path, how little they were prepared to exert themselves, and how pleasant it was to imagine that they were far in advance of other human beings.

Ever again and increasingly the spirits of temptation made themselves felt, inciting ambition, vanity and would-be-knowledge. Again the consequence was arrogance, confusion and downfall.

Out of a great throng of hangers-on and listeners there remained only a small band of the truly reliable.

The people started a cult nurtured by many selfish thoughts of avarice. Little altars, amulets and all kinds of things were produced and sold, and again Lucifer's followers mingled with the people.

Krishna, they maintained, was the cause of these aberrations, he, the Pure One, who lived wholly in the Divine Laws and desired nothing but to open the eyes of mankind, so that they might at last become seeing. Wherever he turned, he felt Lucifer's power rising, Lucifer, of whom Astarte had spoken to him. And in him too there welled up an indescribable abhorrence of the Adversary.

TURBID YELLOW VAPOURS lay over the land; columns of smoke rose from the craters of volcanoes, heat and dryness weighed upon man and beast. Febrile air quivered over the marshes. The atmosphere was saturated with impending danger. Thousands of sick people were encamped by the banks of the great, filthy rivers. Even while dying, they were burned by the sun which could barely penetrate the haze. Decomposed animals lay about, contaminating water and air.

Krishna moved through the streets, bringing comfort; he gave instructions with a view to averting the impending plague. But the crowd, dazed and apathetic, grumbled; in part they seemed to have become brutalised under the pressure of their burden.

Krishna left the large cities one by one, and shook off their dust from his feet; these men filled him with loathing.

71

He walked in the groves of the penitent and the wise, but there too he was soon overcome with the same feeling of emptiness, disgust and futility. Conceit and self-love had taken root there.

A state of fear and dismay overcame him. His spirit drove him more and more into solitude; he withdrew from all those who were usually with him. They remained behind in a quiet grove where they were to wait for him.

Once before, solitude had summoned him on the sacred heights of his pure homeland, and drawn him upwards into ever greater silence. Now Krishna experienced again what he had at that time, when Maro, the "Lord of the Earth," had come to him.

And he beheld the suffering, he saw the death. The firmament became sombre in colour. He saw the earth covered with the shadows of a night filled with horror. The sadness of his heart was almost unbearable.

Then from the deep darkness around him there broke forth a brilliant ray, and out of it rose an exceedingly beautiful angel with luminous wings. The eyes were like gold, the countenance as of alabaster, the voice like the rolling of thunder. A golden shield covered the breast; the robe was as white as snow. In both hands the angel carried a chalice which shone like ruby. And Krishna drank from the radiant chalice.

Again darkness enveloped him; the Luminous Messenger of God had vanished.

Only now did Krishna remember the voice, and because he could not forget it, he reflected on whether he also still knew the words spoken by the angel.

"*I am* the Lord, thy God, thou shalt have no other gods but Me!"

These were the words the angel, the Messenger of the Most High, had spoken to him.

Krishna pondered these words which he perceived intuitively as Law. This was self-evident to him.

And again figures emerged from out of the darkness. He heard the lamenting voice of a woman, issuing from the depths of the earth:

"I bear the spirit-germ to the earth, the germ that was destined for

72

the highest in the World of Matter, and woman on earth has distorted it!"

As if fraught with eternal agony, the plaintive words fell upon Krishna's ear. Another animistic being bringing accusation against the human spirit!

There, what was that? A tremendous power seemed to be approaching Krishna. His heart nearly stood still.

Gigantic, filling the whole of the Universe, a face with ice-blue eyes and a scornful mouth surmounted the terrestrial globe. The horizon was tinged with copper.

"I am the Lord of the World," the voice spoke. "You holy man, walking confidently the road taken by far too many, abandon the delusion that you can grant true life to man. I know him better than you, I give him the object of his desires. I will give you a part of my power if you will follow me."

"How blind you truly are, Fallen One, if you imagine that you can tempt him who longs for the Light! I recognise you now by sight; know this: I am no longer afraid. I will fight you even more relentlessly, for I hear the lamentations raised against you by all life. All that is pure has turned away from you; your nature can no longer maintain connection with it. How could you ever rise again with your broken pinions! You can harm only such as yourself until the Coming of Him Who will disarm you!"

Terrible hues coloured the copper-red firmament. The figure of Lucifer towered monstrously above the earth. Thunder rolled in the depths, the oceans raged, the earth quaked, but the heavens remained still. Radiant blue and golden light came down from Above, while in the dark layer below, the red colours were still massing. Mountains collapsed and trees fell; Lucifer held sway over the earth.

The Light came from the Heights. It was transformed into the figure of a young man in white raiment. At His Father's Command he set out upon a long journey over the face of the earth, and the earth grew bright.

Lucifer had concealed himself before the Radiance emanating from the Divine. But the mind of man was opposed to the Light!

Briars proliferated again, and once more Lucifer rose slowly over the

73

horizon. The shrill, scornful laughter of the Adversary reverberated across the world.

Again Krishna saw nothing but Darkness. And he was very sad, for it appeared that Lucifer would triumph. It was an unbearable ordeal, a suffering such as Krishna had never intuitively perceived before. His heart bled, yet it was not only Krishna's heart, no, all Creation bled. Heavy drops of blood ran down over the Darkness into the depths, and all of them fell on Lucifer's head. Krishna gazed down into his dark realm. He closed his eyes in dread. And he prayed:

"Lord, wilt Thou permit such as this to come over the earth? Is this the end of Thy glorious Creation?"

Then Heaven opened a second time, and again the luminous figure of the angel descended.

"Remember the Sword in the Holy Grail!" said the thunderous Voice of Heaven.

These words were supreme comfort to Krishna, and he knew that he was to see the history of the world from this day until its end.

On a solitary height Krishna had entered a cave and seated himself. All that he had beheld had come to him in a state of spiritual exaltation. The mighty entities that had approached him had shaken him deeply. His body was like an empty shell, motionless and cold. And still the agony was not at an end.

Now he again beheld the earth, and everything that could be seen on it had undergone vast changes. Only that which was guarded by the pure animistic beings had remained beautiful: Nature. Above the world there was enthroned a mighty demon with a golden whip. Under its lashes prodigious works arose that made men proud, rich and arrogant, but not happy.

And again it was the same as long ago, again the earth was full of misery, war and horror, and utterly dark. It was still under the sway of Lucifer.

Then once more Light came into the Darkness. A White Ray descended from Heaven. The earth quaked, and the dark shroud of mist rolled aside like a heavy curtain pressing downward what was of similar substance. But a lucid radiance was received by the earth from the pure Heaven.

Roaring, Lucifer turned his back on the earth, he could not endure the clear Ray of Light. But this time It dogged his steps, even pursuing him so far into the depths that Krishna could no longer follow.

Lucifer was no more to be seen, and a sigh of relief went through Creation. The world was cleansed and fresh, as after a violent thunderstorm. Above it hovered the White, Holy Dove of the Grail in a luminous white ring.

After a long time the White Ray returned from below. Lucifer did not follow It. But out of the Luminous Ray that remained on earth, the Cross formed, bearing the Light-filled features of the Son of Man.

Krishna reflected on this change in the Holy Happening; thereupon his spirit awakened again in the physical body.

"LORD," he prayed, "grant that I may keep Thy Commandments so that I may serve Thee unto eternity."

UNDISTURBED, KRISHNA SPENT three days and three nights in isolation. He knew that his servants were keeping faithful vigil. Tranquillity and blissful seclusion filled his soul. He could not return to men immediately after the overwhelming experience. His body needed rest, his spirit relaxation, for it had stood within a mighty Radiation directly before the Son of God.

As he was aware of the Power of the White Light, and was able to open himself consciously to It, It pervaded him completely. Being close to fully comprehending the magnitude of the Divine Sacrifice of Love, he was bound to be deeply shaken by the experience.

And with his intellect Krishna relived everything that had been bestowed upon him by the Spirit. What he had received he had so to transform into the earthly that the still-undeveloped human beings of his people could understand him. This was Krishna's most difficult task.

To his companions the time of Krishna's absence seemed like an eternity. They waited anxiously for him. There were twelve of them, and the Hindu, his most loyal companion, was their leader. Even the King, who did not wish to leave him during the days of this spiritual struggle, submitted out of love for Krishna to the simple Hindu, the mahout.

For that reason a shining crown far more precious than his immeasurable wealth was bestowed on him in spirit. So great was his wealth that he was able to give exquisite gems and plates of gold for the wars, and ten times as much for the buildings to the glory of the Most High. The extent of his riches was inestimable. Yet the radiant love poured out over him by the Primordial Spiritual Beings, for placing himself at the service of the Servant of God, outweighed all his earthly treasures.

The Hindu was wise in his natural simplicity. He was the most familiar with the world of Nature, and had an unerring knowledge of man. The King was convinced of his loyalty, therefore he obeyed him, and the others followed the example of their King.

Everyone – men, women and youths, looked forward to Krishna's return. The time passed slowly. The heat was terribly oppressive, and there was no work to do. Idleness brought with it the danger of temptation, but the thought of their master kept them on the alert. They did not perceive the mists of gloom that would lull them into stupefying slumber; they fought the fatigue seeking to penetrate their souls like leaden threads.

Preparing the meals was a welcome occupation. The men looked for herbs, the women wove fine baskets and mats from the tall plant-fibres. Nevertheless the morning of the second day crept by like an eternity.

Heavy showers of rain alternated with scorching sun; but they did not forsake the place where Krishna had taken leave of them. With natural loyalty they endured, and the common will united them in harmony. Thus they created eternal values for themselves, values of which they had no idea.

When Krishna returned to them, he found the Hindu pale, with sunken cheeks and burning eyes. Chewing betel, he sat with clasped hands, deep in thought, awaiting his master. The King was praying. He had had a vision: Krishna, the Master, at the foot of a Radiating Cross, and that had kept him awake.

Calmly and kindly, Krishna greeted them all. With a single glance he measured his faithful ones, then he shared their simple meal. It was as though nothing special had happened.

ON THEIR HOMEWARD JOURNEY they visited many settlements and towns. Finally they also came upon the walls of a great palace standing on a huge rock in the midst of the flat land. It was surrounded by a broad river, and gleaming towers soared above the square walls. This building was of indescribable splendour, and the wealth of its ornamentations seemed endless. Only the lavish imagination of India could bring forth this glorification of bizarre idols.

"Behold," said Krishna, as the small procession approached the riverside, "look at this place which is so magnificent, great and rich; not a stone, not one little gold plate will remain of it. And as with this opulence, so will much else also fare in this country. Everything will be dust and ashes before the new age begins."

His companions gazed thoughtfully at the beautiful spectacle.

"Do not believe in your wish, but hear what I say to you, for it will be but a little while before you will no longer have me with you. I know that all this, and much more besides, must perish. I have beheld many things that have not yet come to pass; the threads of fate of earthly mankind are weaving at them. These too will not endure. Only the Will of God, the One, is real and living. Apart from Him, there is nothing that is lasting save His Love and His Justice, Which issue from Him Himself, and they also are in Him eternally. Can you understand me?"

They nodded.

"Therefore do not set your hopes on the works of men, and view also your goal only in the light of the great Divine Happening. Redemption of the world from death and destruction, that alone is the goal. Do not calculate and remonstrate, do not long for earthly happiness. The fruits of your deeds will ripen only when the Holy Dove hovers for the third time above the earth in the Radiating Light of God.

"I see It now only as a Sign, but before long It will dwell on earth as It now dwells in Eternity.

"But woe unto men! They will not heed It, they will die and perish as before in the frenzy of evil. You know Maro. But I know One Who created Maro. Only when a Divine One comes will Maro perish."

"Master, so you are not God, as they are calling you?"

"Oh, you gullible children, can not even you who are always with me distinguish between what is human and what is Divine? Have I not told you again and again that I am created like you?"

They bowed their heads in shame. Though Krishna had told them so, they could not grasp it, for he was indeed so remote from them, so inaccessibly high and exalted.

Meanwhile they had approached the city and were awaited by soldiers and servants. Sariputta, the Prince, had ordered that the illustrious King be received in a worthy manner.

The people surrounded him and his companions. Their entry through the mighty walls, into the magnificent gold-plated avenues of the palatial city, resembled a triumphal procession. In the minds of the small band, however, lingered Krishna's words, and formed a sharp contrast to the rapturous transport of the people.

One gate after another of the gleaming city opened. Beauty, a luxuriant array of flowers, the charm of graceful gardens and rippling springs were revealed to the guests.

Upon the highest steps, before a golden gate, Sariputta, the Prince, stepped forth to receive his exalted visitor. He was richly attired, and a precious stone shone like a scintillating dew-drop on his forehead. His noble face, however, showed the anguish of loneliness. His eyes were brown and radiant, but now and then a slight sadness fell across them.

"Illustrious King," came the words from the lips of Sariputta, "thus do I call you, Krishna, the much extolled. It has long been my desire to approach your lofty seat, but a great anxiety restrained me."

"I know, Prince. The time had not yet come for you."

Earnest and searching, Sariputta raised his eyes to Krishna.

"Master, I ask you to enter my Palace and to regard it as yours. My soul's yearning has triumphed: may I be your pupil?"

"You have given voice to your request, Sariputta, count yourself as one of my own."

That was all Krishna said, but at that moment the Prince experienced remarkable things. It seemed to him that strong arms carried him safely, that invisible beings supported and directed his ways. He felt that his body and spirit were as if released from a heavy burden. He felt happy and young, as if newly born.

Whatever he undertook strove back to him a thousandfold. He was never able to free himself from the heavy burden of his possessions.

His country was rich, the earth teemed with treasures; all that he owned had to be employed to advantage under the compulsion of his own volition. He brought about much happiness, for no one in his land was without work or bread. Nevertheless the wealth, the sheer inexhaustible abundance, had burdened him and did so to this very hour. His riches had seemed to him like a curse hitherto, and he would gladly have rid himself of them. But Krishna's few words had provided his spirit with a home, a goal, and with peace; the oppression departed from him.

"Master, how is it that from the moment I saw you I intuitively perceive the world and myself in a different way?"

"You have listened to your spirit, Sariputta. You have wanted to free yourself from the fetters that oppressed you; your will to live is strong."

"Master, perhaps I do not understand your words, for it seems to me that I have hitherto longed for death."

"You mean the death of your body, but I speak of your ego which can be eternal."

Sariputta thought deeply.

"Master, I can see that one word from you gives me work for days. How am I to find the time to make up for my neglect?"

The men were still standing on the top step of the broad terrace, which afforded a glorious view over the towers and walls of the Palace, over the gardens and the busy life of the prosperous city. Filled with awe, the servants gazed at the Illustrious One; and filled with surprise they looked at their master who was quite oblivious of the duties incumbent on the host, to conduct this most exalted and venerable guest into his house in keeping with the strict rules of tradition.

As though grasping the thoughts of the bystanders, Krishna gestured towards the gate, and said:

"Let us go in!"

"Master, enter into that which is yours!" said Sariputta, and passed through the Palace-gate behind his guest.

In the forehall, beside the golden pool filled with bubbling water, women were awaiting him. They wore costly raiment, and were richly adorned with precious stones, pearls and gold.

Krishna greeted them with a slight movement of his hands. They did not dare to approach him. They raised their faces, and a touching expression of devotion could be read in them.

"These women are like beautiful animals, well kept, and richly adorned, but they do not have within them the life with which God endowed every creature. They have allowed their spirit to become stunted in the enjoyment of earthly possessions. They are surfeited and indolent. That is also why you have no children."

These words of Krishna's grieved the Prince like an accusation. With a movement of his right hand he signalled the women to withdraw. Disappointed, they left.

"Master, what am I to do to repair this mistake?"

"Give them work and joy, give them freedom. Then live according to my teaching, and select new women for yourself."

Sariputta opened himself completely to Krishna's words, leaving none unheeded. Each of them he absorbed like a man starving to death. He longed to rush jubilantly towards everyone, telling them of the inconceivable Grace.

From now on he administered his country with great prudence, and the blessing of work was united with the blessing of possession.

Hence the people were no longer to serve the idols either. The splendour of the temples, the shrines and columned halls seemed empty and cold to Sariputta, for now he had drunk from the Fount of Life flowing from Krishna's teaching. With absolute clarity he perceived intuitively the difference between lifeless property and the living, creative blessing of wealth. Joyously he complied with everything Krishna bade him do, and his beneficent activity spread far and wide across the land.

The people no longer offered sacrifices in fear and trembling to the grotesque gods; instead they prayed and worked. Hence there sprang from this people a pure, noble race which journeyed through thousands of years carrying within them the knowledge of God. A chosen people!

All human beings became more beautiful and better. But as always, wherever Krishna went, the temples became empty and desolate, and here too the priests grumbled about it.

Sariputta annexed his country to that of Krishna. This too enraged the priests and fed their discontent. They sought to stir up enmity, biding their time for the right moment to attack.

Only after many months did Krishna return to his earthly home, to the people of the Jadava. The parting from Sariputta was not easy, but it was the Prince's intention to follow soon after to the land of his friends, once Krishna considered the time for this to have come.

For the present he still had to lay a solid foundation in his own country for all the reforms, which the people could accept only gradually. Sariputta wished to introduce personally all the changes in government, religion and economy. The enemies must first be persuaded through deeds that the new seed would produce good fruit. Sariputta stood confidently at the helm.

FOR KRISHNA and his companions it was high time to return home. Disease, drought and hunger had once more spread misery and affliction in the country. Again the discontented stirred up trouble; again the old customs proliferated in secret.

"How will it be when I turn my back on the world?" Krishna asked his faithful followers. "Keep your eyes open so that you may recognise how weak, how unstable and unpredictable human beings are. They will not retain much from the time of their awakening; they will again become engulfed in their sins. It will be even worse, and evil will spread alarmingly in all countries of the earth. But there are some who will no longer be capable of sleep, for their spirit has awakened, and their journey will lead them upwards. Ever again they will return, here and there, and the longing for the Most High will remain in them.

"They will come every time an Envoy of the Light completes His circle on earth. They will be connected with Him in the Holy Will of the White Flame. In that way they will have a term of apprenticeship extending over thousands of years for the time when they are meant to have reached maturity. That will be when the Divine One binds the Adversary. You will also be among those who return; that is why I tell you.

"Guard this as a sacred mystery, for which I shall one day call you to account before the Lord. You are as dear to me as brothers. My eyes dwell upon you with loving solicitude.

"When I journey through the planes of the departed, I perceive with horror how difficult it is for them to detach themselves from the World of Matter. That is why I say to you: free yourselves in spirit; do not let yourselves be held back by material substance!

"Whenever you discern that human beings are ensnared in this danger, try to warn and to teach them. Not with many words, but rather by example. On the whole, human beings still lack the maturity required for so much knowledge. Therefore the time has not yet come to speak of it to them. But be on your guard, for if you fail, it is more dangerous for you who are knowing than for those who are still ignorant. Keep yourselves pure so that the others may follow your example."

"Master," said the Hindu, "I am so afraid! Often when you now speak, I feel as if you are saying all these things to us in farewell. My soul grows sad. I would like to weep. Will you leave us so soon?"

"I shall not leave you until the Call comes for me, but then in an instant. When the White Flame summons me, my hour will have come, and I shall not allow myself to be detained, not by any bond of Creation. Do you understand? I have beheld a Light, Which bears all Life within It. My longing is directed toward this Light alone!"

Sorrowfully they bowed their heads. They felt so unworthy. Each one was horrified to realise how very deficient he still was.

Since Krishna had been permitted to behold the Light of God, his spirit had been raised far up into other spheres. His earthly helpers carried out his will. He gave voice to it. His spirit, however, rested in the Glory of the Holy Grail.

THERE WAS MUCH TO BE DONE. New battles with words and weapons awaited them. The King had to sit in strict judgment over his servants and his people when it was evident that the laws were still not alive in them. Evil had made further inroads. Tenaciously it continued to return.

Priests were relieved of their duties, temples were demolished or closed. People cast nervous glances about them. Implacable severity prevailed everywhere.

But there was joy among those who lived according to Krishna's teachings. Peace and contentment prevailed in their homes, and they prospered. Justice enlightened the huts of the poor as well as the palaces of the rich; it was plain to see who walked in the Laws of God.

A POWERFUL LONGING seized Krishna's spirit; he placed all his earthly works in the hands of his faithful. Under his direction they tended the seed sown by his will, and the Realm enjoyed peace, wealth and harmony.

In a quiet garden Krishna strolled with his dear ones when they rested from the labours of the day. The King and the Hindu were always near him. He told them many things about the time when he would no longer be with them, and the King shook his head sorrowfully. He could not comprehend that he, the aged man, was to outlive Krishna.

"Your time has not yet come. You must still wait," said Krishna, who answered every thought instantly before it was voiced. "But you," he said, turning to the Hindu, "will go before me."

With that, a bright ray illuminated the spirit of the Hindu.

IN THE WONDERFULLY radiant nights extending across the Indian skies, a great, brilliant star shone just above the horizon. The people whispered about manifold promises, and prayed to Krishna in the temples. Only seldom did he appear in public now. His wisdom and goodness and the power of his support poured out to them through his helpers. Much as people strove at first to be near him, they were humbled when he told them:

"Were you ever so far away from me, and acted in accordance with my will, which is rooted in the Laws of a Higher One, you would be near me. But were you to be ever so close to me day and night, and failed to do that will, which is mine, then I would be far from you and would remain so. Therefore, do my will at all times and you will be happy."

Krishna saw the time of his departure drawing nigh. The animistic beings whispered to him the Laws governing their rays, and he calculated the course of his stars accordingly. And behold, in a celestial picture the imminent Call from the Light was shown. Krishna was prepared.

Henceforth he spoke no more of it to anyone. He was joyful with his dear ones, delighted in the gardens, his animals and the glorious music which always made him happy. When he walked through the forests and the flowering gardens, all the entities that enabled him to recognise the Love of the Creator were around him. Stronger, ever firmer, grew the connection with the eternal forces raising him up On High.

At Krishna's request the King organised a splendid festival; it was to be celebrated within a small circle. Nevertheless several hundred men and women participated. People from all castes were present, according to their spiritual maturity.

Colourful lamps illuminated the gardens, gondolas rocked on the water, and festive song rang out across the waves.

A strange wistfulness filled every soul. The Queen sat beside Krishna; she did not dare to look at him, for the far-away expression in his eyes made her uneasy. Her hands trembled.

Silently they partook of the meal which Krishna himself gave them, and drank from the shining chalice of jasper, which was filled with blood-red wine. As Krishna raised it up and passed it to the King, it took on a glowing, wondrous light.

"Did you see," said the Queen to the Hindu, "how the wine began to glow?"

Silence, quiet joy, and a deep, sacred solemnity lay over everything. They felt united as never before.

Suddenly a tremendous roaring was heard, coming from outside, from above. It marked the onset of a storm; all the hanging lamps dropped to the floor and went out. Here and there, flames leapt up, but they were instantly extinguished. Soldiers who were in the hall gave protection and help, and the necessary defence against incursions from outside.

The storm raged terribly in the city, if only for a short time. Nevertheless it caused the people to be completely preoccupied with themselves to the exclusion of all else.

The faithful Hindu stood with raised arms, looking upwards. He had a vision. High above in the cupola of the hall a brilliant White Flame, tall and slender as a column, and dazzling as a flash of lightning, had appeared simultaneously with the arrival of the storm.

"The sign, Master, I go on ahead!"

Those were his last words. Then the great, heavy body dropped on to the golden tiles of the hall. Everyone wished to attend to the deceased. They were overcome with dismay, anxiety and grief; only the faithful Jaconda raised her eyes to seek out Krishna. But she could not find him. He had disappeared.

Deeply troubled, they searched for him. They were consumed with pain and fear. But Jaconda said:

"Do not worry any longer; I know, he has gone home!"

And they believed her. –

The Hindu was buried with the highest honours.

"KRISHNA HAS GONE HOME"; those words of Jaconda's haunted them as more and more hours rolled by slowly and heavily after this great event. Ever more painfully did the memory tremble within them, ever more vividly did it come to life. A disconsolate feeling of loss crept into their souls, a grievous emptiness made itself felt. Wherever they were, whatever they undertook – they felt lonely, forsaken, full of woe, miserable.

They were abandoned. He who had inspired their lives with meaning, who was the pulse-beat of their entire existence, the flame that had

85

nurtured, warmed and illumined them, had left them; he had left – without farewell, without a single last word, without a clasping of hands. How human was their pain even though they controlled it!

They felt empty, scattered like a string of pearls that had broken, and yet they supported each other; each drew from the strength, loyalty and silent suffering of the other. In their sorrow they strongly perceived the mutual love; the desire to help united them as with a spiritual bond. All drawn towards the Light of their longing, all equal in the one goal, they were like *one* spirit in many bodies.

"It is like this that we should always have been, so at one, so united! This too we had first to be taught by pain," the King said to them. But the words of Jaconda: "He has gone home," allowed him no peace day and night.

And it came to pass that his ardent longing so united him with his Master that he beheld his luminous path in a vision:

Three tall figures in white garments mounted on splendid steeds were leading a snow-white horse by the reins. Never before had he seen so magnificent an animal, with such a long white tail and waving mane. Its gait was prancing. The pink nostrils were distended, the eyes glowed, the ears were pricked up, and twitched gently. Pawing the ground, it waited impatiently before the gates to the Palace of the King of the Jadava.

The raging storm whirled up dense clouds of dust, so that it was hardly possible to open one's eyes. The houses shuddered, and the people were rushing about, powerless in their struggle against the violent storm.

Then quietly the massive gate opened, and Krishna emerged. Without a word he mounted his horse and saluted the riders. Without a word they rode away through the dense dust and vanished, as if swallowed up by the storm.

Dust, nothing but swirling storm and dust all around, and the dreadful fear of losing the trail of his Master.

But then the dense veils cleared, the gale abated, the dust slowly settled to the ground, and the King was able to discern a luminous cloud-formation, which his yearning spirit followed.

The luminous cloud, gleaming ever more clearly through the dust, moved swiftly on.

Like a faithful dog that has found the scent of its master, and is determined to pursue it, so he clung to this luminosity with his whole volition. And the thought intervened: what strength the human spirit derives from pain and longing!

Reproach, and shame that his volition had not always bestirred itself so faithfully, now pulsated through the King's soul.

"Thou Eternal One, Thou Lord of our Master, help Thy servant!"

His ardent entreaty rose up to God.

And he saw how the vast plain became marshland and brush, how rivers were crossed, lakes were bypassed or swum over, how the landscape changed into jungle and gradually rose. He saw how the day drew to a close, how the stars faded again, retreating before the new day, how the gleam of Light enveloping the beloved Master ascended higher and higher into the wilderness, right up into the gigantic mountains, on which hardly any human being had ever set foot.

They disappeared into a narrow gorge, where the King was no longer able to follow. The thought of this route never again left his memory. The picture had been imprinted, firm and clear.

SLOWLY AND DREARILY day after day rolled by for Krishna's faithful ones. Above all they now had to comfort the questioning, lamenting people, to support them in the spirit that Krishna had demanded of them, and there was more work than ever to be done.

The people celebrated holy festivals in honour of Vishnu, who in their opinion had sojourned on earth as Krishna, and now had left it, some day to return.

The temple housing the precious golden shrine, upon which pictures of Krishna's deeds were depicted, they surrounded with sacred symbols and a wealth of decoration; the fragrances of rare herbs and burning scents rose up to the sky in honour of Krishna, the departed one.

Only the initiated knew that Krishna still sojourned on earth, but they kept this knowledge to themselves. No one person discussed it with another. Yet the wish to discover Krishna's whereabouts grew ever more powerful in them.

Then Sariputta made his entry into Jadava with a hundred faithful followers. A messenger had announced to him:

"Krishna, the Master, has returned home. But you are to enter upon your duties on earth. Go into the country of the Jadava where sorrow reigns, and where all his servants are assembled. There take over his office from the aged King. United under your rule, the Realm will blossom; you will be the shepherd of the people, acting in accord with Krishna's wishes. Everything will come to pass as ordained!"

Sariputta followed the messenger. Unseen by any of the Prince's companions, he led him part of the way, then took his leave, and rode off toward the mountains.

Sariputta told his friends everything. The King of the Jadava, however, nodded silently; then he rose to his feet and indicated to Sariputta that he should follow him.

And Sariputta became King of the country. The old King, however, sought out the route he had seen in spirit, and followed Krishna. His faithful wife accompanied him.

THE GATES OF THE CASTLE in the mountains had opened, and Krishna had returned home. Thunderously the singing tones of light poured from the silver mirror, which still revolved rhythmically with the sun's orbit. Their surging rays flowed over the shining leafy crowns and the emerald lawns, over the seven sacred streams from the pure heights, and over the fine mist of the fountains. Scintillating in countless colours, birds flew from branch to branch and sang their songs of jubilation.

And once more, as at the Festival of his Consecration, the women, beautifully adorned, moved through the gardens. All the castes, dressed in the most costly robes with the insignia of their rank, came to meet him. It was a festival no less imposing than that of the Initiation.

The cupolas of the Castle towered into the deep-blue shining sky, reflecting the white light received by the silver mirror in the Sanctuary.

Even Krishna, who through the gloom of the lowlands had become disaccustomed to the radiating brilliance, even he had to shade his eyes from this splendour.

In radiant light the twelve Knights stood beneath the opened gate. Their robes shone white; white also was the fullness of their long locks and beards. But their faces shone as in times past with beauty, purity and youthful vigour. Krishna was received into their midst, and led by them into the house of his forefathers.

In the golden hall of the vestibule the Wise Knight stepped from the circle of his Brothers, and greeted his son. In silent contemplation, he beheld the course of his son's life hitherto, his maturity, his greatness, and the power of his fulfilment shining out of him. And something happened which had never occurred since the Wise Knight lived in the Castle, since his ancestors ruled there: the Circle of the Twelve bowed low to the ground before one of their own.

In the background the throng of young initiates waited with shining eyes and cheeks aglow for the summons that would bring them before Krishna. With heartfelt, holy awe they beheld him who had filled their minds and their spirits with reverence since childhood. Full of love they gazed up at him as though at a long-missing father who had returned home. Spiritually they divined the wonderful experiences to come through the Master of whom they had already heard so many glorious things.

Krishna's radiant eyes gazed at them with loving kindness. To one of them he said:

"I know that you will lead this Realm one day. Your mother has given you beauty and intelligence, take the loyalty to the White Flame as your father's heritage. I love you because of your destiny and will be a teacher to you and your brothers."

Then he greeted all of them with a kind look and raised hand.

As Krishna had promised, he introduced the young people wisely to the higher recognitions of his teaching, and greatly benefited the youth Subhaddo in particular. In these open, swinging souls, in the unspoilt spirits, he rejoiced to find that understanding which he had so sorely missed on his earthly journey. The seed of his words sprang up immediately.

89

Again Krishna lived in the rooms at the foot of the tower, beside which the glorious terraces rose up, fragrant with lovely flower-gardens. Again he spent the nights on the tower and talked with the pure animistic beings who found their way to him.

Like a web, fine threads spread out above him, bright, pure and strong, reaching up and bordering the luminous path on which his spirit could rise into the Realm of Light. And on this pure pathway of rays the White Flame sent messengers to him.

He was granted a sacred preparation, so that his spirit would be able in full consciousness to experience the gentle, rapid severance. Quietly he prepared the luminous path for himself.

Krishna gathered his students round him during the day, and discussed many things with the gifted Subhaddo, who had absorbed the wisdom of the forefathers as well as Krishna's Word within himself.

But the twelve Guardians also sat reverently in the shining circle around him, and listened to the wisdom of his words. While he was not of the same age, yet he far excelled them in clarity, and he introduced them to the secret knowledge of the stupendous Creation of the All-One, and of its coming-into-being and rotation. Blissfully they listened, and their purified spirits ascended with him on the paths of wisdom.

ONE MORNING Krishna told them about the Luminous Home of the spirit, whence they had all come, and of their return there. He spoke to them also of the grace they had found before the Most High, by holding fast to the longing for His pure, eternal Realm.

He said that this was not generally true on earth and told them of his encounters with human beings. He told of how the pure spirits and the animistic creatures had complained of having to witness the decline of the World of Matter, powerless to help because the impure forces proliferated and suffocated everything sown by the Love of God. And he described the struggle on earth with the spirit of denial.

While he thus spoke, he began to glow in the Light of the spirit, and what he said no longer emanated from himself, but from the Light, and his voice sounded from afar like the pealing of mighty bells. All of them listened, deeply moved.

Krishna had found them sufficiently mature to hear of the raptures of the Kingdom and its Glory, and of the One Who had created them.

They would have liked to go on listening forever, for days and nights, when Krishna spoke to them, but they were stopped abruptly.

Krishna's radiant countenance changed; it assumed an expression of earthly alertness as he said:

"I am setting out on the homeward journey. A person from the realm of sleepers is at this very moment on the way up to this place with his companion; he will be illumined by his loyalty, so that he may experience my release from here. Admit him into your midst, for he is mature in having found his way here. He is rich in years of earthly life, rich in spiritual experiencing, and rich in loyalty to the Light!"

At that moment the curtain of pearls at the entrance to the golden hall parted. A servant came quietly and whispered a message to the Wise Knight.

"My son, the pilgrims whom you have announced are waiting, dust-covered and with bleeding feet and torn clothes, before the first gate. Blessed are they who attain to it!"

"Loyalty has led them, Father, loyalty to the Light!"

It was as though the circle of the illumined ones was sending strength to the pilgrims. Gate after gate opened; effortlessly they climbed the many steps, dazzled by the resplendence of the Palace.

Covered with dust they approached the last gate, and were received by a servant. He led them to the golden pool in which they could wash away the dust of the journey; he exchanged their clothes for white robes. He refreshed their parched lips from a chalice that seemed to contain living fire, for strength and vigour penetrated the two ageing people. Nonetheless they bowed their heads in humility and went on bare feet through the golden hall when the Guardian summoned them.

Softly they stepped through the jingling curtain into the Golden Hall of the Twelve. Guided by the spirit, they had found the arduous path. Sparing no effort, they had followed it, supporting one another in loyalty. Now they had attained their goal.

91

"Master, now I would die peacefully or, if it be your will, would return to men, since I have beheld you once more near the Glory of the Most High."

"You, my helper, once King of the Jadava on earth, have come home. Await the call from the Light here among the Illumined in the service of the White Flame!" said Krishna.

"The hour has come when HE to Whom I belong calls me!"

He rose to his feet, and walked with the Twelve, followed by the two pilgrims, into the Holy Room.

The light of the sun sang wondrously, its golden rays refracted by the spirit-given work wrought by human hands, the silver mirror. On the shining White Stone the little flame formed, which became a fiery column.

And the voice of the Wise Knight called:

"Krishna, I call you, you have fulfilled!"

In a few minutes the spirit of the Illumined One had released itself from its body. Luminous and light, it had ascended, fully conscious of the past, of the fulfilment and of the awakening, and he found himself again in the flood of Light as the Servant of God in the *Holy Grail*.

The terrestrial globe revolves, and in its movement drives forward everything it contains and bears. In its swinging Egypt appears.

NAHOME

A GREAT HAPPENING approached the terrestrial globe and descended upon Egypt, blessing the tranquil Grove of Isis.

Around the lavish gardens, which were in full bloom, rushed the waters of the Nile. Golden sunlight filtered through the branches.

Flocks of ibises flew to the place and gathered by the reed-nests, as though they wished to be present at the hour of the great happening. The acacias, with their cascades of flowers, rustled. Tall as pillars they towered above the gleaming, pale yellow Sanctuary of Isis.

Rocking gently, a magnificent skiff lay at anchor by the stone steps leading to the terraces of the Temple. Coolness wafted from the spacious, seemingly dark halls, right down to the sunny warm air beside the river.

Nubian attendants were sitting in the skiff with that calm, imperturbable dreaminess characteristic only of the women of hot countries. They always have time, for there is not much for them to do. Plenteous Mother Nature feeds and cares for them. But because of this they are forever in danger of falling asleep spiritually as well. Now too they had forgotten that they were to keep watch here before the Temple. Their thoughts were of earthly pleasures, for these alone could still stir their blood; they dreamed of finery and trinkets, of the triumph of their beauty over the heart of some insignificant man. No vestige of spiritual life stirred within them.

When they were given the signal to depart by a young white-clad priest who stood between the pillars of the Temple, they lowered their golden oars into the water and rowed up the Nile.

Slowly the boat of the Princess, adorned at the edges on either side with precious silk tapestries, moved away; a golden image of Isis shone at the prow.

Over the flower-clusters of the peacefully-dreaming island the setting sun cast roseate lights.

A WOMAN OF MEDIUM HEIGHT, in rich and exquisite garb, stood deep in thought under the pillars of the entrance hall.

She was enveloped by the cool of the halls and the dusky blue light from the interior of the Temple.

Priests in white robes approached her. In reverence they bowed their heads, remained standing and waited.

Aloe, the young Princess, appeared to be listening within. She trembled slightly in bliss, hope, and awe of something sublime, unknown. Then her slender form straightened, and she walked gracefully towards the gate of the Temple-hall.

There, a grave-looking priest of Isis came towards her. With his white hair and long white beard he was distinguished in appearance.

Benevolently, like a father, he looked at the Princess, who spoke a few words to him in a low voice. Her awe of the holy place restrained her from speaking aloud.

Kindly, Amon-Asro took her hand, and silently led her into the Sanctuary.

Deeply solemn, soul-stirring music poured from the halls. Again and again the pillars seemed to reflect the mighty chords until they quietly died away.

The Princess bowed in humility and placed a large flower at the foot of a statue which stood like a sentinel in the first hall. Twilight enveloped her. The music had ended, but the sounds still seemed to be surging through the great halls.

At the threshold of the inner room gentle hands placed a long white mantle over the woman's shoulders. Here and there lights shone out, pale blue and flickering. At the end of the Temple, however, there was a bright gleam like the brilliance of a sun. There the glorious image of Isis stood resplendent with the golden solar disk upon her head.

Priestesses robed in white were serving here. Solemnity, sublime reverent beauty, worship and purity dominated the room. Seven white steps led to a table of offering upon which stood a bowl filled with grain and surrounded by a wreath of white flowers.

Again the High Priest approached the Princess. She bowed low and knelt down on the top step. Then Amon-Asro solemnly offered her one grain from the bowl of Isis.

With that it was as if something wondrous suddenly happened to her! Everything about her was forgotten. A rushing of song and of wings sounded from Above and re-echoed from the walls and pillars. Light of indescribable clarity pervaded the Temple. The ceiling appeared to open, clearing the way right up into Heaven. A snow-white Dove appeared in a brilliant ray.

Aloe was fully alert. Wide open to the Heavenly Radiance, she heard and beheld a lovely figure, beautiful as an angel and majestic as a queen, with deep-blue radiant eyes. Upon her head she wore a crown of lilies. She was bathed in roseate light, and the scent of lilies was in the air around her.

The Luminous One inclined towards the Princess and entered her pure earthly covering.

"I am Irmingard. Call me Nahome!" Love and joy resounded in the voice like a wonderful promise.

At the same hour the child in her womb stirred, and she called it by its name: *Nahome!*

THE DAYS FOLLOWING the incarnation slipped by for the earthly mother like a wonderful dream. She lived well protected as a guest amid the women who served Isis. Among them were wise, mature persons. Each had a duty in the varied activities of the great household. All classes were represented. But the priestesses belonged to the most noble class and were specially educated.

Much knowledge was gathered here; much beautiful, noble art was cultivated. The choirs of the priests and the singing school of the women constituted the most perfect of their time. All of them endeavoured to lead a peaceful, pure life. A pure spiritual current was clearly perceptible on the isle, and this was what the expectant mother had been seeking.

From the moment she knew that her longing would be fulfilled, Aloe lived solely for the thought of her child. Even the sorrow over her husband, whom Pharaoh had sent forth, had receded into the background.

She had been leading a quiet life and had kept away from the false glitter of the court. Aloe hated the web of lies and the morass of immorality that was ever more apparent there.

In a small palace on the Nile she had awaited the return of her husband.

Only seldom had she received visitors, for she was alien to all. As the daughter of a Greek woman, she was unable to accept the cold, calculating Egyptian manner; in turn the Egyptians could not find the bridge to her quiet yet warm nature. Her soul had to starve among them. For that reason she had gradually withdrawn from everyone.

But now the great felicity had entered her life: the child! Out of gratitude Aloe had become devout. She longed to carry her grateful joy upwards to the gods, but her ardent feeling of bliss found no echo in the temples. When she would give thanks, the ceremonies of the priests remained cold and lifeless to her, and their cult struck her as being a great well-constructed intellectual edifice.

So she again felt lonely. Then guided by a high power, of which she herself, however, was still completely unconscious, she had finally been led in her quest to the Temple of Isis.

Since she had set foot in that Temple, since Amon-Asro had taken her under his care like a father, since he had spoken to her of the will of the goddess that she was to await her child in this pure and tranquil atmosphere, from that hour the Princess had come to life again.

She was permitted to experience and learn many things through the wise guidance of the priest. Her spirit opened wide. With a view to her child's well-being, Aloe changed everything concerning her personal life. In this too she was guided.

The days were filled with the radiant splendour of the sun. All the melancholy and pressure that had usually weighed upon her being had departed since the Luminous Spirit was dwelling near her.

100

A wonderful life arose in her soul. She viewed the world with its people and their destinies in a new light, and acquired knowledge of matters which she had never thought of before.

Amon-Asro and Nanna, one of the nursing attendants, had the task of assisting her in this. Both felt especially drawn to the Princess.

ELSEWHERE IN EGYPT things were not so calm and peaceful as on this sacred island. The iron fist of Pharaoh held sway over the land. Cheerful human beings who trusted in God were not to be seen. Severe suffering prevailed under the spiritual pressure of sin.

Great buildings, splendid monuments and colossal pyramids were to be constructed. The enforced labour weighed ever more heavily upon the people of the Jews. And many believed that soon the time would come for the fulfilment of the promise:

"A Light shall rise over Egypt, and terrible plagues shall purify it."

In her seclusion Aloe was informed about everything by the priests.

She had a strict spiritual guidance. Her close confidants left her alone, for they perceived that she was protected by unusually lofty powers.

Nanna was the first to speak about it to Amon-Asro.

"All I can do is to assist her. Her will is quite clear and sure. She will never burden herself with anything that might harm her body or soul. It is as if helpful spirits were advising her."

Amon-Asro nodded.

"I have been able to establish the same with regard to spiritual questions and worldly matters. I have cast her horoscope. It clearly confirms your observations.

"It promises her a spiritual revival for the sake of the child. But before earthly ascent is possible she will first have to undergo grievous suffering here on earth. She must give up her self for the sake of this child. This she now does completely; that is why she is so happy.

"In her constellation I see confirmed those mysterious auguries for Egypt which have long occupied me. They presage the coming of One Who will destroy Pharaoh. He stands in the Divine Sign.

"I am happy that this woman is dwelling here. She can become my teacher in the wisdom of that which is to come."

Nanna listened, amazed. Never before had Amon-Asro, the silent one, spoken so much all at once. And Nanna wanted to know still more, but not out of curiosity. Rather a great feeling of sympathy and the desire to serve prompted her. Hence she said:

"In the evening hours, after the songs and prayers, when everyone has retired and all is quiet, we often stroll through the halls. She always visits the Temple of Isis, where she becomes absorbed for a few minutes. I do not know what happens to me at that time. It is as though we were journeying across worlds. I see nothing, I hear nothing, yet a great sensation of power always pervades me when we go home afterwards. But it seems to me that at those times she experiences even more."

"I shall observe these hours in the orbit of the stars. Perhaps we will find enlightenment there. She never speaks to me about her inner experiences. Her lips appear to be sealed, although she is usually quite communicative when subjects arise that captivate her, such as the theory regarding the structure of the skull and hands, or the correlation between colour, sound and number. She cannot hear enough about these, and longs to develop her knowledge further."

"But sometimes," Amon-Asro continued almost haltingly after a short pause, "I feel as though I cannot give voice to certain recognitions, as though a hand were held over my lips."

"You should not burden her with knowledge. I feel urged to tell you this. She must remain free."

Intuitively Nanna had grasped this correctly. Amon-Asro looked searchingly at her. He nodded thoughtfully. Then, after a while he said:

"You have observant eyes, Nanna, and a clear understanding. I believe that we teachers have all become learners."

"Only he who is so wise that he has become humble can speak in this way. You are right, Amon-Asro."

Nanna had lifted her face to the Priest. She was small and delicate, the longish oval of her face was bronze in colour. She was not beautiful, but her intelligent, lively eyes and expressive mouth inspired confidence, and her face shone with helping love.

"I wish that you may be proved right in everything and that we may find Him Whom the stars of the Princess proclaim to you. My soul is full of longing, and I know that I will serve her because of this longing. Is it not as though threads were being woven between this woman and us?

"Often I ask myself why I alone, among the many who are better than I, feel this. My comfort is that you too, the High Priest of Isis, intuitively perceive this wondrous bond, and I thank you for sharing your knowledge with me."

She bowed, raised her arms and stepped backwards.

"Not that way, Nanna," said the Priest, and offered her his hand, "we both serve Isis."

Nanna hurried away as if embarrassed by this distinction.

"Where have you been so long, Nanna? I feel so strange today. I sense a dreadful fear coming upon me, oppressing me even before its arrival – or as if a storm were soon to rise, or the earth about to quake. I have never been afraid since coming here to this sacred island. What can be the cause of it?"

Nanna was unaccustomed to being expected or even missed by Aloe. Nor was she prepared for such impetuous questioning. Therefore she only shook her head slightly and said:

"I will give you an infusion of flower petals which should soothe you. You had too little movement today and have been poring over Amon-Asro's writings for too long. Let us go into the gardens and breathe the cool air of the river. First assimilate what you have read before asking for more.

"Princess, I perceive a luminous wave of power around you! Listen to it, it will touch a similar chord in your being, and you will draw benefit from it for body and spirit. Think too of such work as will provide you with physical movement."

With these words the two women left the tall, airy room that served as Aloe's apartment. Its open hall, which could be curtained off with close-woven veils, led into the garden of Isis.

The golden blossoms of the trees trembled in the light wind of evening; groups of palms towered upwards. The rigid forms of the luxuriantly flowering cacti gleamed pitch black and silvery green.

An elaborately-wrought lattice-gate closed off the garden. Nanna opened it. They walked on a wide well-tended pathway under tall palms down to the very tip of the island where there was a small tumbledown temple of grey, brittle rock. At its centre a colonnade surrounded a small square courtyard. In the walls were niches with sculptures from times gone by. An aura of mystery lay over the tranquillity of this deserted place.

From the steps of the temple, on whose pillars the figure of a female deity with three doves was depicted in simple stone-work, the viewer could behold the wide, merging surface of the river. Warm, rose-coloured sunlight lay over the greenish-grey waves; the sandy edge of the bank was as if bordered by a red glow.

"Soon the time will come when the waters will rise and these buildings will scarcely be visible. Then the front part of our temple will be partly submerged, and we will only be able to reach this little hall in a boat."

Aloe did not reply. She gazed pensively into the distance, towards the immeasurably vast heavens, into which the Nile, in the light of the setting sun, seemed to be flowing. At the same time her lips uttered wondrous words:

"I will give unto you of the river of the Water of Life freely."

Starting up, she looked about her wide-eyed and struggled to regain her composure:

"Nanna, who was it that spoke just then?"

"It was you, Princess. You yourself!"

"Indeed, I formed the words with my lips, but the sound, Nanna, the voice, surely it was not my own?"

"I heard only your voice, perhaps you heard a Higher one."

"Nanna, look, does it not appear to you that in the depth of heaven a shining Cross is standing in the light of the last reflections of the sun? And behold how bright points rise from the river and over the trees as if countless radiant gleams from the hot sunny day were striving to return to the currents of light from which they came.

"Now I am no longer afraid; the holy power of Nature has opened a gate within me. Thanks be to Isis!"

But hardly had she said this than she paused, trembling a little, and continued hesitantly:

"No, Nature is kind indeed, and I love her. But ... I must think of a higher being when I would give thanks!

"I have neither name nor form for it. But this radiant sign there on the horizon, the rising Cross which so strongly brings to mind my child, this sign I would like to worship!"

Nanna was deeply moved, almost helpless, but she did not show it, although she too had perceived the heavenly phenomenon.

FOR ALOE ONE EXPERIENCE now followed another in rapid succession and mounting intensity. Spiritually as well as in the earthly she learned of things that previously had never approached her.

A kindly but purposeful hand seemed to have taken the helm of her life's ship, guiding her through unknown waters with such power and speed as was not her own nature.

At the same time she felt better each day, and became happier and freer, more confident and clear ... only now had she become a human being. Moreover her work, and whatever she undertook, succeeded.

She also learned to play a stringed instrument, and occupied herself with artistic embroideries; everything succeeded quickly, surely and without effort. Often she clasped her hands in gratitude, but found no words. Then there stood before her inner eye the luminous sign of the Cross in the golden sky of evening. She could not forget it.

THE PRIESTS OF ISIS were preparing for a festival. It was one of those solemn occasions to which only the initiated were admitted.

The days preceding it were filled with brisk activity. But twenty-four hours before the festive day everything had to come to a standstill.

Amon-Asro had gone to visit Aloe. He stood with her in the portico outside her apartment, and looked down at the garden in which the golden leaves were falling softly and steadily to the ground.

"This is the time of ripeness, Aloe! Glorious fruits ripen for the Festival of Isis. May yours also bring you happiness!"

Aloe nodded.

"I feel as though it could not be otherwise; if it were, the fault would be mine alone."

"You have opened your soul in the days of your maternity, and I know that supreme bliss is to come to you. I can but wish you blessing and happiness. But you are right, much depends on you, for the gods do not incline towards man without demanding much of him."

"Amon-Asro, tell me, do you know the wondrous entities that descend at night from Heaven to those on earth?

"Do you know the one who dispenses sunlight? She wears a winged cap and the starry cow-horn. Do you know the light-suffused bodies around her? Do you know the one who spins golden threads, and that female being who bestows strength and fertility, love and loyalty, as well as purity, in support of womanhood?

"She is more luminous and purer still; for she has not connected herself with material substance as has Isis with the sun. She is to be found in that realm in which everything appears to be still only a concept.

"I discover steps upon steps, and it is always women from these spheres who approach me. Your priestesses are beautiful and pure in their service. But compared to these beings they are like mere shadows.

"They appear before me, so distinct and clear that I imagine all of you must perceive them. They are beautiful and kind. Do they always come at the time of your festivals?"

"Aloe, I believe new helps are now inclining mercifully towards this earth, for I have never before experienced such things.

"You have guides wiser than I, old Priest that I am. Listen to them. I can give you but fragmentary knowledge, for what man can conceive of and enquire into is only piecework. If what he has gained in this way is assembled, many gaps remain which can never be filled.

"Learn to be patient and silent; enjoy and make use of the moment, then everything will be given to you of itself. Grasp the meaning of the ripeness in Nature in that way, experience that too completely, and you will learn much. If you desire to attend the Festival of Isis, you may do so, for I can number you among the initiated."

Aloe thanked the Priest. She knew that this was the greatest thing that could befall a human being in the opinion of the faithful servants of Isis. All of them rejoiced with her.

ON THE WHITE STEPS before the pedestal on which stood the golden statue of Mother Isis lay flowers of exquisite beauty in form and colour, of a brilliance and fragrance such as appear only in blessed gardens through the care of devoted gardeners. The fresh yet sweet fragrance which seemed to alternate between lily and orange blossoms, between the pungent scent of the carnation and the delicate waft of the lime-tree, mingled with that of incense from the opalescent bowls. These stood upon golden columns in a circle round the statue of Isis, which today, with the rich adornment of the Temple and the fabulous robes, shone like a jewel. But to Aloe, the flowers seemed the most beautiful and purest of all.

The wind-players, led by the first Temple-servant, strode in through the central gate of the Temple; their trombones were decorated with broad golden ribbons on which colourful hieroglyphic embroidery glistened. With measured steps the players moved through the middle of the Temple; then, dividing into two files, they mounted to the top of the concealed gallery, one from the right and the other from the left.

The wind-players were followed by the singers, who carried small golden harps; these were earnest men dressed in white with white bands round their foreheads. They wore their hair and beards long. They too mounted to the gallery. There was a flourish of fanfares. Now white-robed women entered; they were in charge of the earthly service. Holding flower-garlands they arranged themselves in precise order around the altar and on either side.

Aloe, garbed in white and heavily veiled, entered from the side, accompanied by some elders.

Nanna remained at her side – a task assigned to her by Amon-Asro,

107

although she normally performed the duties of priestess. They took their seats in the centre, before the statue of Isis.

Usually this festival was attended only by priests and priestesses. All gates were closed. Over the vast Temple-building lay silence that began to vibrate like a tone. This sacred, expectant silence was part of the preparation for the actual festal hour.

Luminous circles began to revolve vibrantly round the statue of Isis. From the top of the roof trembled a sunbeam, indicating that the sun had almost reached its zenith. The light-particles glittered; they descended gradually, almost touching the winged crest of Mother Isis with its crown of symbols.

Thunderously the music began. A choir, whose well-trained voices were joined gradually by the resonant strings, sang a hymn to fertility. Then the jubilation of gratitude rose up in blaring tones from the golden wind-instruments, and filled the room with trembling. A hymn of radiant power to the sun!

To its resounding, vibrating music the priests entered the Temple. They came from its inmost room, accessible to no other mortal. Dressed in gold, boys stood motionless as statues at the small doors.

Then the central gate swung open for Amon-Asro, followed by six priests and then the priestesses of Isis. All of them were attired in white and bore wreaths of lotus flowers.

The women were veiled. In two rows, with arms and faces raised, they descended slowly and rhythmically, forming a semi-circle. At the foot of Isis they received the luminous bowls with aromatic herbs smouldering in a delicate haze. The light-bowls in their hands looked like iridescent flower-bells.

They met at the centre before the altar and moved past one another. The movement of the air intensified the brilliance and luminosity of the colours of the light-bowls and smouldering herbs. Quivering, the colourful currents intertwined in the ascending smoke, producing a strange picture in the light of the rising sun. At the crown of Mother Isis glowed the huge diamond from the treasures of an ancient royal family; its powerful radiation was refracted a thousandfold in the light of the sun.

108

As though spellbound, the delicate figures suddenly stood motionless. The High Priest raised his staff, and with a rustle, countless white doves fluttered upwards out of the pedestal of the Isis-statue. They flew round the statue in circles, while the priestesses held aloft their bowls and chanted a solemn hymn.

Priestesses of the sacrificial service entered from the side and offered the bowls with herbs, fruit and grain. A fiery column rose high up to the opening of the Temple-roof.

Then the Priest washed his hands in the golden basin offered him by the two youngest kneeling maidens, while two others poured water over his hands from golden pitchers.

The second part of the Festival began. The songs of praise were followed by the mysteries. Amon-Asro raised his hands. The host of priests followed his example, at the same time solemnly singing the word "Isis".

A gentle breath of air filled the room, and the doves rose heavenwards. The people in the Temple bowed low to the ground.

The rushing sound intensified. But only Aloe saw an unearthly radiance filling the hall.

The faces of the priests reflected eager expectation, changing to disappointment, for they did not see the radiance of the unearthly Light. The magic charm of their artificial experiments, however, failed this time, and the connection with the plane of fine gross matter, which they were usually able to reach, did not materialise.

Amon-Asro stood in worship and trust, but pale and waiting to see if Isis would incline to human beings. Instead he perceived above the head of the Princess a halo ever increasing in size.

The priestess, usually able to establish the connection with the world beyond, who described extra-terrestrial happenings and conveyed instructions to the High Priest from the mouth of Isis, was silent.

Aloe's countenance, however, shone with joy, for she beheld the picture of an angelic woman with a crown! From her emanated rays of roseate golden light, thrusting aside the base spectres conjured up by the priests; they allowed no other rays to enter the room save the pure ones from the Highest Height.

Deeply stirred with bliss, many bowed unconsciously before the Holy Power, pulsating into them in blessing insofar as they were able to open themselves to it. But they perceived none of the mysteries which usually enthralled them. They experienced the purity, simplicity and clarity of the Festival, which culminated in the upliftment of their opened souls and in the reception of a high Power-wave which they did not understand.

Aloe knew that all this was not mediated by Isis, but by the manifestation from Heavenly Heights. It came from those sacred Realms which were the Home of her child. Her understanding spirit bowed in gratitude.

The last songs had died away. The fragrances of the flame-bowls drifted gently through the wide-open Temple-gates. All the devout, including the singers, had left the Temple. Only the serving priestesses moved with calm dignity through the halls. No loud, unseemly talk disturbed the lingering impression of the solemn hours. The task of clearing up and putting things in order was as much Divine service as was that during the hours of the Festival itself.

Soon the decorations and splendid attire were removed from the statue of Isis, and in its simplicity, solely as a work of art, it stood upon the white altar, more lovely and uplifting than before.

Amon-Asro had withdrawn from the circle of the whispering priests. They were discussing the unusual course of the Festival. He did not wish to hear the many false conjectures and idle talk about the occult.

He was in a solemn mood. With reverence he considered this Festival, which had nothing whatever in common with the other festivals. It uniquely outshone the previous ones, which had resembled an exhibition of conjuring tricks rather than a religious celebration.

He contemplated henceforth planning the festivals in this new spirit. Of course, he knew that this would meet with opposition. He thought of certain priests who had achieved great success in the art of attracting radiation-forces and of carrying out experiments of a hypnotic and telekinetic nature. They were devoted to these sciences with fanatical determination and deemed themselves great. Actually they were indeed feared, and Pharaoh supported them, because they could keep the people under control with their hocus-pocus.

To take a stand against these men or to restrict their activities was almost impossible; indeed, it was for him, the highest and no doubt most important Priest of Isis, equivalent to attempted suicide.

He realised that all who shared his opinion would keep silent out of prudence and caution. Thus he was once again alone with his will to voice the power of his conviction and to act accordingly.

He gave his attention to the calculation of his stars to obtain enlightenment, instruction and advice about the baffling phenomenon. Only then would he weigh the matter.

He unfurled sheet after sheet of closely-written papyrus; he wrote, calculated and drew. For some time he then gazed pensively into space. Ever more recognitions were given to him. He took his own horoscope and that of Pharaoh in order to compare the signs. A sinister fate lay over the ruling dynasty, which was threatened by powerful enemies.

As for himself, the aspects showed a similar position. If he were able to transform them into knowledge he could attain to great spiritual power.

He had so clearly recognised the effects of the stellar radiations that with the aid of many ancient principles originating in those times when the forefathers still worshipped the Light, he was able to explain wonderful correlations. Thus far, however, he had lacked a great deal of the knowledge required to enable him to do this. Now it was as if a mysterious bandage were suddenly removed from before his eyes, as if a chamber were opening within him that had hitherto been closed and dark.

All at once there was bright daylight in his spirit! As yet he did not divine the full connection and the central point of all these happenings, but he felt imbued with a fervent desire to investigate. To him it seemed that his science had now become a Divine service.

So the Eternal Ones built up a pure circle of Light for the reception of the little human flower who was soon to be born.

And again the Priest of Isis caught himself hastening in thought to her who had not yet been born. The Light which he saw clearly above

111

the young mother was fresh proof to him that something great was in preparation here.

And he opened the book "Aloe" to study her signs.

In them he beheld the fall of the dynasty and the rise of a spirit through the power of a new Light. The Light-manifestation at the arrival of Aloe in the Temple formed the starting-point of a calculation which told him that at that time Aloe's signs were the same as at the hour of today's Festival: a Ray of Powers from Heavenly Heights in the house of children.

He realised that here the influence came from a star which he did not yet know because he could not see it with his physical eyes. This star must be sending high spiritual vibrations to the earth; to this star must be entrusted the well-being of the coming child.

Amon-Asro recognised that he, Aloe and Nanna were the only ones who had been helped, uplifted and guided to recognition through the stellar radiations at the moment of the sun's zenith during this Festival hour. By all the other leading priests they must have been felt to be an obstruction, and therefore they could not understand them. But the words of Isis which were meant to be proclaimed by the priestess in that fateful hour were eclipsed.

Thus from the rays of the stars the wise Priest, Amon-Asro, was permitted to divine the coming of a great turning-point.

NANNA ATTENDED WITH MUCH SOLICITUDE to the Princess. Deeply moved by the strong experience of the Isis-Festival, Aloe needed rest and attention.

She became increasingly clairaudient and clairvoyant with regard to coming events on this earth. Whatever was revealed to her in words or pictures she conveyed to the Priest, who compared it with his stellar charts. And behold, these conveyed with ever greater clarity a picture of an important spiritual and earthly happening in Egypt.

IT WAS THE TIME when the waters of the Nile had risen in mighty flood-tides.* Grey, gurgling eddies surged about the sacred isle. The light of the sunbeams, veiled by clouds, lay soft and warm upon the waters. Sultry, fine mists floated above the tree-tops as if the eager fingers of animistic beings sought to weave delicate grey webs, to isolate from the gaze of the world the quiet purity of that which was coming into being.

Then the flood waters rose so high that they closely surrounded the halls. Only half of the beautiful pillars and porches still towered above the water.

In the sacred halls, in the long corridors of the women's building, soft steps hurried purposefully to and fro, while in the Temple a quiet hour of prayer was held before the golden statue of the holy mother. Peace lay over the Temple of Isis.

In the trees, birds sang softly; their sweet voices were heard in the open halls, even reaching the woman who lay in pain, anxious and yet joyful. Loyal servants, women to help her, and an able physician were in attendance.

The working of the Holy Love of God and of His Will was made manifest. It was perceptible to all beings, who rejoiced, for to the world was born a Pure Flower Who was to bring blessing to all women and to anchor Purity and Faithfulness from out of the Light. Then womanhood might again thrive on earth in a God-willed manner. A petition that had been made in Eternity would be fulfilled.

Nature opened out. Isis, the holy mother, was preparing the soil for Astarte to descend again.

All the helping powers of the Light were now able to re-establish connection with the earth since Purity was incarnated in an earthly body. Jubilant song resounded through the spheres.

THE PRIEST AMON-ASRO approached the bedside of Princess Aloe. He was the first to lay his hand upon the little head covered with thick,

* Early September according to our present chronology.

silken hair, that was barely visible among the white, dainty cloths. The mother cradled the child in her arms with fervent joy.

"I will not dedicate her to Isis, Princess!" said Amon-Asro. "She belongs to a higher Power, which I first wish to recognise. Let us comply with the requisite rules to satisfy the priests, for a festival in the Temple cannot be avoided, but it may take place quietly and at some later time."

To Nanna he said softly:

"The health of mother and child are now our foremost concern. Remain constantly near the Princess, also at night."

Aloe was so weary that she was unable to lift her head. With a silent smile she thanked the wise Priest for his fatherly kindness. Once he had left the room she closed her eyes. A deep, invigorating sleep enveloped mother and child.

THE FLOOD-WATERS of the Nile had reached their highest level. Greyish yellow in colour, the raging waters rolled along, bearing with them the most lively traffic. They formed the main trade route leading from south to north into the sea.

From below the sound of song could be heard in the quiet halls where women of the Isis-Temple tended the little Nahome and her mother with loving care. Beautiful ships sailed past in the strong current of the river.

The bodies of huge animals that had perished in the flood: elephant, buffalo and rhinoceros, rolled about like monsters in the grey, foaming waters. Fishermen stood on the shores, retrieving much precious booty that had been snatched from its owners. Troop-transports and many ships with prisoners sailed past as well.

With the tides of the Nile the rhythm of daily life began gradually to penetrate to the blessed souls again.

Before long, the Light-child Nahome was to awaken to earthly suffering, and soon thereafter happiness in fabulous abundance would lift this delicate human child from a small princely court into the radiant sun of a Heavenly Kingdom!

Day and night, with burning eyes, Amon-Asro sat poring over the papyrus, for he had been seized by a tremendous power to fathom the child's destiny. He felt that a great task had been entrusted to him.

So completely did he yield to his inexplicable inner urge that he was no longer capable of considering any critical intellectual question.

In spite of this, as the High Priest of Isis he neglected none of his duties. He was strict and just, kind and pleasant to all his subordinates. A true father, counsellor and friend, but also one of the most experienced and discerning in questions of politics, religion and science. Amon-Asro had no time to pass the night in sleeping. It was precisely in the quiet of the night that he occupied himself with the work that brought him the great results during the day.

Now, however, he was about to investigate a life which had begun in Heights inaccessible to his comprehension. How humble the wise man became as he entered the signs of the stars recognisable to him into the square that was covered with fine lines, while he drew circles and calculated the aspects.

At the top, in the centre of the heavens, stood a mighty sun which he entered in blue with golden rays. Signs became visible to him, which his pen captured on the spur of the moment, although their meaning was altogether unintelligible to him. Yet they resembled the Chaldean forms for the sun, moon and stars, whose character and radiation they expressed in geometric form. Totally engrossed in the swinging of these radiation-laws, he recognised a great deal suggesting new ways to him.

On the path of these unshakeable logical explanations revealed in the horoscope of a child a few days old, he found the One God. He found God, and knelt before Him in a fervent prayer of gratitude!

But there was one who did not take a favourable view of the High Priest's deeply-serious work. That was the second priest, Jech-tu, who regarded life with the eyes of earthly ambition.

He was reputed to be one of the greatest magicians in Egypt, and he believed that his powers gave him the right to be sole ruler over religion and the realm. He hated Pharaoh; he really hated everybody who had power apart from himself. And as he himself had only a limited sphere of activity in the quiet of his temple, he was filled with restlessness. He wanted to work, to attain to renown, power and influence at all costs, wherever it might be. Therefore, the moment the opportunity arose, he insinuated himself into all the circles of Egypt, fearing nothing.

He was faced with but one enemy who was dangerous and nearly as powerful as he himself, and yet elusive. He was a friend of Pharaoh: Eb-ra-nit.

Since the Isis-Festival Jech-tu also sat in his study far into the night. Brooding, he unrolled one papyrus after another and sought in all his subtly-combined works explanations for the total failure of experiments in which he had usually succeeded effortlessly.

The sharp furrow in his forehead had become deeper still, and the expression around his thin, wry mouth reflected growing bitterness. His piercing black eyes, otherwise at least aglow with enthusiasm regarding his own ability, looked up bleakly from beneath his brows, and the narrow, high, clean-shaven head with longish, slightly pointed ears, ducked as though under an invisible heavy pressure.

Toilsome and difficult were the intellectual struggles over an issue that could be grasped solely with higher wisdom. Of what use to him was all his imagined ability, all his knowledge? Sheer obstinacy would never win for him the key to the secret of this Isis-Festival, nor could it be granted him, since he closed himself to the Divine Power.

That Jech-tu did not know. He groped in the dark, entangling himself in fantastic conjectures. In the end he was close to despair. He knew only one person who could enlighten him: Amon-Asro. But obstinacy, pride and conceit prevented him from asking the High Priest of Isis.

Like a beast of prey, he prowled around the apartment of the Princess. She was a thorn in his side. He had already fiercely resisted her admittance to the Isis-Festival. Now he sought to blame "the disturbance at the festival" on her. He became obsessed with suspecting Aloe, and it was a blessing for the women that he was not in authority, and furthermore that at this time the priests were prohibited from leaving the Island of Isis, for they were subject to strict laws in the Temple.

Nanna, whose watchful eye was everywhere, also saw this ominous cloud gathering, and warned the High Priest of Isis.

"I know, Nanna, but I cannot help him. He would never understand. Were I to initiate him into the higher knowledge of the spirit and the

Fountain-head of all life, by which he is constantly sustained without making use of it, he would merely exploit such knowledge, turning it into a weapon against us, for he grows ever darker. I shall guide him with kindness; perhaps I can at least save him from a deep, headlong fall."

Amon-Asro's voice was grave. Distressed, Nanna looked up at him.

"I am only concerned for the Princess and the child, should he explain his fantastic ideas to the other priests."

"I fear nothing in that respect, Nanna. A few are themselves too conceited to give credence to his words. The others, however, are too pure and will abide by my interpretation. Be patient, Nanna, do not make the mistake of seeking to arrest developments yourself out of solicitude.

"Behold, this great transformation of all problems, revealed to me through our stellar aspects, brings conflicts and also resolves them. They are heralds and will constantly increase. Those who tread the path of the Coming One must walk through blood and suffering, through danger and death."

Nanna knew that Amon-Asro numbered her too among these. With gratitude she accepted his warning and reproof, locking them in her heart.

SLOWLY THE CONTINUOUS rain and sudden violent storms ceased. The waters subsided, at first imperceptibly, but then ever more rapidly. The sacred fires burned with joyous thanksgiving along the banks of the river, and hymns of praise rose to the heavens and to the holy Father Nile, who had bestowed his fertile silt on the land.

A sweetish smell of fish hung over the gardens. A fresh northerly wind arose, driving the lingering vapours before it. The trees re-emerged from the waters with mud-covered trunks, and the bushes slowly raised their bent branches. The showers that still pelted down from time to time cleansed them of the heavy mud. On the island man and beast rejoiced at their greater freedom of movement.

Aloe spent the days with her child in the beautiful quiet garden, accompanied by Nanna, her faithful companion and friend.

117

Nahome grew noticeably. At first her eyes had the radiant expression of a knowledge about which a child's lips can never speak, since with the ability to speak the memory of its spirit's origin also begins to fade. While these shining eyes retained their mysterious radiance, they also assumed the expression of maturity with surprising swiftness.

The little body, which was not wrapped up like a mummy in the customary manner, but warmly and loosely swathed in light-weight fine materials, breathed contentedly. The child's exceedingly delicate but healthy limbs were in constant motion, and it sometimes appeared that the radiant golden eyes beheld something quite special and wondrous.

It might well have been that at that time Nahome still saw the luminous entities which filled the house and garden in the early days after her birth and constantly surrounded child and mother – friends whom the Love of the Lord had bestowed to keep her company on the dreary earth.

The days passed by uneventfully in peace and beauty. The young mother's attention was devoted solely to the child; she could not take her eyes from her.

Just as she had previously served the coming-into-being of the body, so she now began to look after the development of the little human child. The first part of her task was fulfilled, and she could apply herself with renewed effort to spiritual interests.

Amon-Asro did not yet speak to her of his observations. He saw that the time for it had not yet come. Let her enjoy her maternal bliss. He would show her the responsibility only when it became necessary. And yet he believed she would be safest if she were left without his influence. It had become clear to him that Nahome had taken upon herself a great, self-chosen fate.

In his astrological signs the visit of a spirit still dwelling in its physical body had been made known to him. Now Amon-Asro awaited what would come. Then the picture of a man who called himself Isma-el appeared to him in an iridescent light-sphere.

Thus did the Priest's mature soul experience miracle upon miracle.

BUT ALREADY DARK webs were approaching the radiant happiness on the island. The magician Jech-tu called on the High Priest to speak with him.

Through Amon-Asro's calm reserve he lost himself in lengthy preliminaries, quite inconsistent with his usual manner.

Amon-Asro waited deliberately, giving the priest time to ask the first question, for he knew how difficult it was for him.

This caused the sceptical, superior composure of the hypocrite to dwindle still further. Amon-Asro handled his questions with growing calm, forbearance and courtesy. But quite suddenly, after Jech-tu had already resolved to ask no more questions today, Amon-Asro said:

"Let us come to the point, Jech-tu! Our conversation has gone on long enough now. You wished to ask me about matters other than the weather and the law."

Again an embarrassed silence, and then the hoarse words erupted:

"High Priest of Isis, may I take the liberty of asking: since when has the Temple of Isis become a nursery? Is it fitting to keep the guest here any longer?"

"I knew very well that you would ask this question, but I am unaware of the reason for your concern. Always I have safeguarded the authority of Isis; always I have protected Temple and house as is the duty of the High Priest. There is no flaw in my performance, that you know very well! Nor are you unaware of who the Princess is, and that Pharaoh himself has entrusted her to my care."

"Yes, indeed, but I believe that this was meant in a different way."

"To understand how it was meant remains the concern of him to whom the charge was given. Since when do my priests cavil over my decisions? The Halls of Isis are a refuge and stronghold of Purity and Innocence according to the Law; therefore Purity and Innocence may abide here also. But falsehood and insidious poison cannot endure within these walls! This in itself tells you that the Princess is protected by Isis, otherwise she would no longer be here."

"Why then did the goddess deny the mysteries in the presence of the Princess?"

119

The magician posed the question cunningly.

A head taller than the man, the High Priest stood calmly before him, measuring him with a steady, penetrating gaze.

"Your explanations on this point are already circulating among the priests. Why then do you still ask? But I tell you: what you think is wrong. It is not the mysteries that are desecrated and soiled. Purity Itself invalidated impure measures. That is the solution to the puzzle!"

Silently, with pursed lips, Jech-tu bowed. Evil thoughts gathered within him.

"But if you believe, Jech-tu," Amon-Asro went on, "that you must act the part of judge of tradition, and defend magic against the pure worship of God at this Festival, just go ahead. I will certainly accept the challenge!"

Leaving behind him the priest with his dark thoughts, he turned towards the house.

AFTER A FEW MONTHS Pharaoh recalled Princess Aloe to her palace. A courteous letter announced the imminent return of the troops which had repelled the invaders of the country.

Fervent joy welled up in Aloe, for her husband was one of the generals. So she would soon be reunited with him! But then anxious thoughts arose in her: now she must leave the sacred island, must bring her beloved child into the environment of Pharaoh's residence, must expose her to the dangers of furtive daggers and poisons, must bring her into those rooms, into those magnificent gardens and halls which had always appeared sinister and oppressive to her, which indeed had even aroused dread!

For a long time she had not known the true cause of her fear. But now under Amon-Asro's guidance she had gained deep insights and learned much about the relationships of all happenings in this realm. But come what may, let the whirlpools of life draw her and her child into the fate destined for them ... they would mature through it; she now realised that it must lead to a high goal.

It was difficult for her to part from the quiet island and from her friends. Faint of heart she awaited the hour when she could speak with the High Priest.

But he made it easy for her.

"Princess, I have been looking for you. The stars proclaim an imminent change for you and the child. Fear nothing! The radiations are favourable, and you will experience that there too the protection of the Sublime Spirit surrounds you both.

"But never forget that you now belong to another sphere. Wherever Nahome may be, there also is life and peace for you in eternity. Thus is it written in the laws of the wise, immovable numbers and stars. Turn and twist as he may, man cannot depart from them.

"Keep what you have and do not let yourself be confused by the wickedness of the world. Whoever has gained the power of loyalty at the gates of Isis and cultivates Purity and Love cannot perish."

"But when must we part, Amon-Asro?"

"Three days before the moon is full."

"It shall be as you say," Aloe's eyes were filled with tears. "But may we visit you from time to time?"

"The Temple and the House of Isis are meant to be a homestead for Nahome. See to it that her young, awakening spirit never forgets these gardens until it has found its true home. You will rejoice in the child, whose radiant vitality will sweep you along with it. See to it that you never stand in the way of her joy, be it even in deep sorrow, for joy is the breath of life for Nahome on this dark earth.

"In joy and in activity she will develop. Whatever life may have in store, she will overcome victoriously!"

THE HOUSE WAS festively adorned for the reception of its mistress.

Joyfully the faithful servants awaited her and the little girl.

How different the gloomy house and the silent park with its huge palms now appeared to Aloe.

Mother and child often sat by the river. There too Nahome made her first attempts to walk. When Prince Abheb came home with rich booty and many slaves, his child, whom he had not yet seen, could already run to meet him.

Time passed quickly. The child, who had first seemed to live more in Heaven than on earth, became a lively little girl.

Nahome liked to sit in the warm river-sand and play with the iridescent lizards. She also dug deep holes in the sand, which were filled by the water of the river; upon it she floated large blossoms.

Soon a pronounced self-will arose in the happy child. Ever cheerful and friendly, but determined, she did only what she liked. Nahome was never given to tears or moodiness. If she was forbidden to do something, she knew how to pass over it obediently and lightly, only to return soon afterwards to her wish with even greater persistence and compelling friendliness. But it was indeed unusual for the little one to make a request that had to be denied.

Old Thonny, her personal slave, had a wonderful way of dealing with her. She often looked after her for days when Nahome's parents had to be present at the inevitable court-festivities of Pharaoh. Their reunion was then all the happier.

Aloe wanted to find playmates for Nahome, since the lively child longed for company. She asked Amon-Asro the Priest about it during a visit to the Temple of Isis. But he shook his head.

"You will find no one suited to her. You would soon feel the great gulf that lies between her and other children. Give her joy, then she will always be happy and willing to be without human beings.

"For the present there are no human beings in her life who could approach her except you and we here on the island. Only with the time of earthly maturity will those come who understand her."

IN THE TEMPLE OF ISIS too a few things had changed. New priests had come and Jech-tu was no longer there.

He had been summoned to Pharaoh in order to serve the ruler with his artifices. In the great temple he zealously performed his duties, and found his boundless lust for power gratified.

Amon-Asro was well aware that from there Jech-tu was trying to gain authority over the priests of Isis, but he did not succeed so long as Amon-Asro lived, whose spirit and body up to old age were filled with the blessing of the hours in which he had been permitted to open the gate to earth-life for Nahome. Wisdom and knowledge had matured in him to full blossom, and he enjoyed the fruits of his activities. He had trained new pupils, new priests. Under his dominion the abode of Isis had become the centre of religious power. Art had blossomed into beauty and from here spread over the land.

The Island of Isis had become a strong counterpole to the rest of Egypt, which was steadily heading for ruin. But the people knew nothing of this yet.

AMON-ASRO was right. The years passed in blissful harmony and quiet joy for Aloe and her child.

Nahome was already beginning to take a lively interest in conversations between her mother and Nanna. She would play quietly with flowers while the two women sat in the garden and discussed serious questions. They hardly noticed that Nahome was following their conversation, for it seemed inconceivable that so young a child could do so.

Although she devoted her attention to playing, Nahome always grasped the conversation of the women. It concerned spiritual matters, the approach of an active Will, the Power of the Divine Light which, like a storm, would sweep from the earth everything dark and ugly, and triumphantly spread Justice and Love. It concerned the stars and the writings of Amon-Asro, and from that hour there lived in the child the thought:

"The glorious Light must come, the evil must perish. I want to read the books; I want Amon-Asro to teach me how to read."

This wish welled up fervently in Nahome, nurtured by the first ray of remembering her destiny. Unconsciously the longing within her had become volition, and what Nahome wanted, she attained.

So she besieged her mother to let Amon-Asro teach her.

But Aloe shook her head.

"Child, it is still too early. But I will ask him, perhaps we can start something together in preparation."

But that was not what Nahome had in mind.

"Either properly or not at all!"

That was her answer. Aloe consulted with the Priest.

"She will be able to do it," he said, "in a way different from what is the usual practice, for within her resides a knowledge that will awaken when she sees the means that men use. All we need do is to begin with a script that was received in purity from the spirit, the Chaldean script, for example.

"Let me direct Nahome, only a few hours will be required, then she herself can learn what she needs. Only thus will she have joy, only thus will she benefit."

Aloe thanked him and was happy. Never had she departed from Amon-Asro empty-handed and without help.

So they stayed again as guests on the Island of Isis. Everyone was happy, especially Nanna and Nahome, who were close friends.

And soon Nahome was sitting with glowing cheeks and shining eyes at the feet of the old Priest. In her little hands she held a small wax tablet and a stylus, with which she painstakingly drew the characters that Amon-Asro had written in the sand for her.

But the doves fluttering in dazzling flocks about the pillars of the temple gave her special pleasure. She stood with a bowl, scattering grains for them, and soon they were such good friends that they no longer took wing when Nahome approached them.

The forays and border skirmishes of Pharaoh had accomplished little. The soldiers, brutalised by fighting and plundering, would not desist. There was always strife and disagreement among them. From the desert, motley bands of wily individuals drifted in, bent upon scavenging the battle-grounds.

The palaces had to be fortified in the direction of the desert, the towns needed special protection. There was much construction work in Egypt, and in the great brickyards countless human beings were forced to toil like animals.

Nahome had never become acquainted with the dark aspect of her homeland. She believed that everyone must live in magnificent palaces, with the wealth of flowers and fruits, the love of parents and friends dropping into their laps.

Of course, she was still a little girl. And yet! The delicate mouth often began to quiver in distress, and the eyes took on a deep colour. Such emotions stole upon her like a dark shadow. Quietly warning, Nahome's destiny announced itself in her intuitive perception. At times she perceived a faint anxiety within, of which however she was barely conscious. With redoubled fervour, she would then lay hold of the moment.

She experienced every beautiful minute with her pure child's soul, and her presence became a gift for all who were permitted to be near her.

PRINCE ABHEB WAS OFTEN away, for his duties called him to the fortifications of the capital. Nonetheless Aloe was unwilling to exchange the small secluded castle for the palace of Pharaoh. Amon-Asro too advised her against it.

"In your charts I see the difficulties gathering momentum for Nahome. A cataclysmic development will come to pass – spiritually inevitable, predestined and willed. While the effect may be deeply upsetting – for Nahome it signifies bliss!

"But you, Aloe, summon all your strength and think of the child's path lest your anguish cause you to stumble. You must be harder, unconditionally harder and more severe with yourself, otherwise you will suffer too much. Be mindful of this at every hour when woe besets you. Arm yourself!"

The admonishing words gripped Aloe's soul. Never before had Amon-Asro spoken so earnestly to her. She was deeply disturbed. But at the same time he placed the staff in her hand:

"Think of your child's path!"

She would never relinquish this staff.

Again they returned home. Amon-Asro stood down at the shore of the river and bade them farewell. A few of the women, among them Nanna, had accompanied him.

A faint shudder seemed to course through the tall frame of the High Priest, and Nanna said:

"If only I could go with them, Amon-Asro! I feel as though it were my duty."

He gazed clearly and demandingly at her as if expecting her to venture the great step. Then he turned and said:

"Let us go up."

IT WAS AS IF Nahome had matured by years during the short stay on the Island of Isis, which coincided with her seventh birthday.

When Aloe remembered the first week of their stay, and saw Nahome sitting at play in the garden, and then followed the course of the succeeding weeks, during which the child had listened to the words of Amon-Asro, their stay on the island appeared to her long and fraught with meaning, every minute filled with beautiful, precious experiencing.

It seemed to her that her child understood and matured much faster than other children of the same age. Yet Nahome retained that childlike pure nature which made her so uniquely attractive.

Upon their return Nahome saw everything around her with new eyes. It all appeared to her smaller, darker, denser and heavier. Nevertheless she had an eye for earthly beauty, and a sense for colour and form. She moved through the rooms of her father's house with alert interest, no longer lost in a child's dreams alternating between heaven and earth.

It appeared that also the Luminous Helpers solicitously guiding her had become different, more serious. She no longer perceived them. She had become conscious in the earthly. With the vigorous zest for life characteristic of her she now abandoned herself to these impressions.

126

The beautiful days on the island were not forgotten, but past. New things awaited her in the present.

With her mother it was different. Again the voices and sounds of her homeland, the roar of the great river, the scents and noises that came floating upon the warm humid air settled over her. Many sad, many beautiful memories were associated with them. Thoughts of persons long deceased hung in the rooms. Aloe's blood seemed to flow more sluggishly again, something weighed oppressively upon her.

"Think of the child's path ...," she heard Amon-Asro's voice, and pulled herself together. She forced herself to appear cheerful, and attend to Nahome's childlike chatter so that she might answer all her questions.

They were standing together by the small window of a living-room. At the gate below them, lions carved of stone lay like sentries in the blazing sun. The sultriness was stifling, and only the muted footsteps of the Nubians could be heard.

The most beautiful time here was in the evenings when the red cup-shaped flowers exuded their heavy scent from the gardens, and misty figures seemed to rise up from the dusky Nile. Forgotten, then, were the lurking crocodiles with their horrible green eyes and bared teeth, which emerged now and then from the water.

Early in the morning, when the light of the moon had vanished and daytime noises had returned, the cool breezes from the river found their way to this room, offering refreshment in readiness for the hot hours of the day.

The gleaming white walls were adorned with gold and covered with dainty russet drawings. The pillars of the room were shaped like tall slender lotus stalks, with the wide capital adorned in the form of large lotus leaves. Blue, red and gold, colours mixed from the earth, predominated here.

But a unique ornament of the room was a golden, delicately-painted frieze inlaid with gold plating. It depicted an unbroken line of birds in flight, the holy ibises, their outspread wings touching.

Nahome pushed a pearl-curtain aside and looked upon a circular colonnade enclosing a spacious courtyard.

127

The meandering paths in the golden sand were paved with small colourful stones, and resembled a carpet made of jewels. Here too, gold was predominant. According to legend an immense hoard of gold lay buried beneath this old courtyard. The patterns on the floor showed pictures of flowers and fruits, and portrayed scenes from the life of the builders of this palace.

On ground level was the temple-passage, graced with golden statues and stone sculptures of the kings.

Like guests, mother and child roamed together through the rooms. The cool treasures on every side meant nothing to them. Nahome took her mother's hand and drew her questioningly from one sculpture to another. She wanted to know everything, but suddenly she said abruptly with trembling lips:

"Were they always so dead? Each has but one expression; one is wicked, another clever, the third lazy, the fourth treacherous, the fifth lurking, and all of them are so rigid, so cold.

"Those are supposed to be our ancestors? They are supposed to have lived? Oh, how they make me shudder!"

But they were at once forgotten; with a slight shrug of her shoulders she turned her attention to something else.

A wide exit led into the great hall where banquets and receptions had been held in the past. There stood mighty pillars with rich, almost gigantic stone carvings of a natural simple beauty. Running lengthwise along the hall, the lofty pedestals bearing the pillars were encircled by golden latticework resembling spider-webs.

The hall was empty. The clattering of their sandals had a sinister sound on the stone floor. It was smooth and shiny like the surface of a mirror, and Nahome saw in it her strangely shortened reflection.

"Look, it is just like the ponds, only no fish are peeping out here," she laughed and at the same time was frightened by the shrill echo of her laughter from the pillars.

It almost looked as if the ornamental elephants were laughing as well. But their rigidity suddenly frightened Nahome again.

"Come, let us go."

And again they walked through a gate into fragrant, restful gardens.

Near the Nile a long row of Nubian sentries stood on the large terraces. The motley, garish colours of their turbans and weapons startled the eye.

These gigantic black figures looked like demons. But Nahome knew them well and was not afraid of them, for they were all happy when she passed by. But intuitively her mother perceived ever more clearly:

"These people will bring no good to the land of Egypt. They will not rest until they rule over it."

Again gloomy forebodings assailed her, but Nahome's cheerful voice dispelled them.

A SULTRY, leaden evening descended. Aloe walked about restlessly on the terrace of the room adjacent to her bedroom and that of Nahome. She was awaiting her husband, who could only return late from his rigorous duties.

A mild wind blew from the desert, carrying with it much fine, hot dust. There was an eerie rustling of palms in the garden, and the wind whistled and moaned through the colonnades. The sky in its evening blue looked pale, for the sun had gone down behind dark grey clouds. The yellow-white palace appeared empty, deserted, frightening in the leaden twilight of this evening.

Aloe was driven from room to room; tired as she was, she could find no peace.

"Be vigilant, be vigilant!" a voice whispered warningly within her. She believed it to be that of Amon-Asro.

Seeking the cause of her restlessness, she attributed it to the approaching storm, the sultriness, but deep within her she had to admit that it must be something else. She found it increasingly difficult to breathe. She thought of Nahome. Perhaps the child needed her. All the servants had gone to rest. Quietly she went to her bedside and seated herself on a low cushion.

Nahome was sleeping peacefully.

A clear radiance lay above her, illuminating the eyes of the Princess so that she saw it distinctly. A power emanated from that Light which almost overwhelmed her. Weary, overcome with sleep, she leaned her head back against the pillows.

She seemed to be sitting with Nahome in a small boat that carried them across a vast sea. The water was slightly turbulent. A white swan came towards them.

Heavenly gardens lay in a clear golden light; in them blossomed flowers on tall stems, similar to the flame-coloured lilies in their gardens, but these were white, as though bathed in moonlight. Hands lifted her child out of the boat and laid her in the midst of this flower-glade.

Nahome had grown tall and more mature and looked at her dispassionately, aloof. The expanse of blue water widened increasingly between them until Aloe no longer saw the golden gardens ... she was alone.

When she opened her eyes she saw Nahome sleeping peacefully.

Then she suddenly started back, pale with fright! What noise was that? People were screaming and shouting. Below, weapons or axes were striking against a garden gate. Could it be Abheb?

The glare of fire blazed above the trees. The sentry blew a warning from the main gate:

"Enemies!"

"Horror, oh horror! Nahome, wake up!"

The child was awake instantly. Pale, trembling, with huge frightened eyes, she sprang up.

Hurriedly the women brought clothes, but in the confusion the servants were useless. Aloe had to see to everything herself. Meanwhile the noise constantly increased.

"Abheb, Abheb!" whispered her pale lips.

Then, like a flaming torch in the midst of the nerve-racking terror of the raid came the thought: "Be strict with yourself, think of the child's path – –!"

"Amon-Asro, thank you! You faithful one, you remind me of my duty!"

And she managed. Gathering up what was possible, she devoted herself solely to the child.

She sent for the guard.

130

"What is it?" she asked him hoarsely.

"It is a raid, Mistress, from the desert! Soldiers, renegades, some even from Pharaoh's army. Brigands!"

A dreadful blow!

"They are hurling stones! Help, ye gods, they are taking us by assault!" And he rushed out.

"Abheb, where are you? Protect our house, our child!" Her cry rang out shrilly across the garden. Nahome wept and hid in her mother's clothes.

Terrible roars and coarse laughter rose up from the garden below. Already they had reached the garden! It was as well that the gates of the palace still offered resistance. The sentry's voice overpowered the din:

"The Master is here!"

Mother and child ran out into the hall. Now he must be coming up the steps.

"Father, Father!" The sound of Nahome's imploring voice was like a plaintive flute. Never before had that quality been present in it. The tone vibrated through the halls and was submerged in the clash of arms. The women stood on the upper level while below the wild bands scuffled with Prince Abheb and his small troop, who assailed them from the rear.

The tense minutes extended to an infinity.

"Thou Light-Bringer, Thou, Whose Name I do not know – help!"

Then Nahome uttered a piercing cry. She had seen her father fall. White, as though dead, she lay in the arms of the Princess, who in holding the child could not heed her own pain and terror. She carried her back into the room.

The brigands rushed headlong over the dead Prince into the upper colonnade. One side of the palace was already burning. The walls turned black, the huge pillars with the elephant-ornaments swayed under the impact of the battering rams. What did they really want? Were they out of their minds?

"They are looking for the treasure!"

Thonny, the faithful old woman, had heard it. They would do nothing to her, who was but a slave.

131

Already the light was becoming pale and grey. The enemies entered the hall of the women. The Egyptian with the sneering, beastly face, who introduced himself as the leader, was hideous.

Obviously he had already sampled the wine in the cellar. Horrible, bestial, he kept his eyes fixed upon Nahome. Impulsively Aloe shielded the child with her own body. An icy calm came over her.

"That would be unthinkable for her child! Rather death, but together! Take us together, Luminous Queen! Take us away, do not leave Nahome alone on this earth, Elizabeth!"

Like a prayer, the name was suddenly wrenched from her lips.

And the scoundrel turned. He gave orders to bind the women and to drag them downstairs.

So they were forced to leave their smoking, collapsing home, which had buried father and husband beneath its ruins. The brigands dragged them outside and lifted them on to horses and camels. A mounted troop carried them into the desert, towards an uncertain fate.

THE JOURNEY ACROSS the desert was agonising. In the slate-blue morning sky stood a great star shining with a cold light. The desert foxes howled in the distance and skittered away from the approaching caravan. This morning ride across the desert was as bleak and unpredictable as their future destiny.

After many hours they saw in the distance a small oasis, towards which the caravan proceeded.

The captive women were in danger of falling from their saddles, so exhausted were they from thirst, fear and the horrors of the night. They were insolently treated. But when the men realised that their brutality was of no avail, the captives were placed in a kind of litter and carried between two pack-animals.

Slowly the light of the sun rose over the vault of heaven. Violet and rosy lights, flickering rays shot across the endless expanse of undulating sand. The orb of the sun shone golden. A gentle wind arose, driving sand eddies before it.

The warmth quickly increased to heat. The rays became sharp and scorching when the wind subsided. The ground began to reflect the burning heat. The air quivered above the oasis which was still far in the distance.

But fortunately they reached it before midday. Tents were not pitched, for the leader of the band was in a hurry to get away from this region. They would only wait for the hottest period to pass. That in itself was a blessing.

They also found a small pool of grey water, but did not drink much from it. The water-skins of the camels were still full, and the water in the pool did not look good.

Apathy and desolation weighed heavily upon everyone. The crowd of depraved men aroused disgust. Aloe stared vacantly ahead of her. Nahome hid her face in the folds of her mother's dress. They were barely able to stand when they were told to alight from the carrying-basket. Silently they collapsed beside a boulder.

The captives were not allowed to come together or to speak. No one could give the Princess and her child any assistance; no one had a word or a kind look for them. But this was of no concern to Aloe and Nahome, who were only too glad when they did not see the ringleader, for he was the most terrible of them all.

After a long hot rest, the journey finally resumed. They were travelling quite systematically in a definite direction, even though no path was discernible. But far away on the horizon there appeared to be a luminous, radiant flame. Was it only an illusion or a mirage?

Aloe saw it clearly. But soon apathy descended upon her again. When she perceived the despondent silence of the little one beside her, she felt as if a dagger were piercing her heart. Her happy child – what else would she still experience today? But as though in a dream she heard within her the voice of Amon-Asro:

"While it may be deeply upsetting, for *her* it signifies bliss!"

Gently, hope entered her heart, and she dared to send out a silent entreaty for help. It seemed to her that fine waves traversed the desert; they picked up this cry for help and bore it to where it was heard. In her anguish she suddenly perceived intuitively that in truth they were not forsaken. From that hour Aloe and her child fared better.

The monotonous movement of the animals lulled them to sleep. The sun no longer seemed pitiless.

When evening came they halted. Tents were pitched and fires lit to ward off any beasts of prey. Aloe and Nahome had to sleep in the chieftain's tent. What a dreadful thought! Again Aloe felt as though her blood ran cold. Fortunately, the child sensed no danger.

The hours of the night became frightful and endless. Aloe did not dare to close her eyes. Nahome, however, was able to sleep. She had laid her head on her mother's knee, and forgot all the terrible suffering while she slept.

But in Aloe the horrors that had raged over her awakened anew. As if in a fever she experienced once more the last twenty-four hours. Would this night never end?

At last morning dawned. But they were not allowed to leave the tents.

Suddenly it felt as if the earth were gently quaking, as if many horses' hooves were thundering towards them. Nahome put her ear to the ground and confirmed her mother's observation by nodding her head. They were so frightened that they only feared fresh danger. Again they shivered as if in a fever.

The camp grew restless. The sentries ran to and fro. All of them spoke excitedly of approaching enemies. Was there to be another battle as there had been during the night when a few of the prisoners had tried to escape?

They heard shouts from the distance. Riders with peaceful intent seemed to be approaching. A vibrant voice resounded across the desert. They could not understand the words, but they seemed to be commands.

The stamping of the horses was soon heard on all sides as if the camp had been encircled. Suddenly furious curses burst forth. Then it was quiet.

Again the comforting voice, which had such a reassuring effect on Aloe and her child, rang out from afar. Nahome straightened:

"I seem to know this voice!"

In spite of her overpowering fear, a feeling of bliss was springing up within her. Aloe too grew calmer. Strange, it was as though the world were holding its breath, as though time were standing still.

After a few minutes the tent opened. In the brilliant sunlight that flooded the gloomy, stifling interior stood a white figure of medium height, richly adorned with a sword and a golden chain.

But more luminous to the two within than the sunlight and the white garb appeared the eyes of this man. It seemed to them that a wave of Love and Power came with this stranger, and their fear vanished. They could only gaze. Their eyes opened wide, still reflecting all their misery and yet already manifesting hope. Unspeakable comfort filled them on hearing the words: "You will surrender this woman and her child and all the captives to me."

They trembled at the Egyptian's cry of rage and the ensuing struggle. But the terrible hand-to-hand fight was of short duration.

Swiftly and as if to comfort, the unknown Prince turned to them. Seeking protection, Nahome pressed against him.

"What is your name?" he asked gently and full of goodness.

"Nahome!"

"Will you come with me, Nahome, and will your mother also accompany me to my Realm? You shall live in my Palace."

It was not the prospect of living in a palace that brought tears of joy into their eyes. It was the words: "Will you come with me, and will your mother also accompany me to my Realm?" which struck their spirits like a call from Eternity.

"Come and follow me!"

THE NEARER THEY CAME to the Realm of Abd-ru-shin, the more mother and daughter were filled with strength and animated vitality.

On the Prince's steed Nahome felt safe as never before in her life. An ardent, jubilant feeling of gratitude surged through her pure childlike soul, and she felt herself to be arriving from the gloomy earth onto a new, purer star. Deep in her spirit she perceived intuitively the bliss of having found her way home.

Where the desert merged with lovely hills, they soon discerned the outlines of a gleaming city. The radiance emanated from the domes towering above it. They were the work of a highly inspired architect who, in learning and drawing from the Will of Abd-ru-shin, had been enabled to design them.

Radiantly the domes greeted Nahome, the child, who was soon to be Mistress of the Realm.

There was a ringing in the air; everything breathed joy and peace. The central building, a temple, rose like a crown, surrounded by a number of smaller domes. Beside it, separated by gardens, stood a second mighty edifice with a colonnade. On the highest dome shone a golden Cross.

A luminous cloud seemed to lie above the city, attracting everything pure and providing a continuous connection with the Light.

As they approached the city, a refreshing and animating light seemed to penetrate their souls. Nahome was very quiet; she let the blissful feeling of being safe take effect within her.

The gates opened to admit the home-coming cavalcade. On either side of the road stood the inhabitants of the city, bowing before their Lord. Their faces mirrored unsurpassed calm and goodness, free of any indulgence. These human beings lived within themselves, and therefore also with one another, in perfect harmony. They belonged to the highest caste in Abd-ru-shin's Realm; they were the Ismanites, who with Him had established the Realm and who like a solid rampart stood around their Lord.

Aloe was as though dazed by the deep impressions of their sudden wonderful liberation. What she had perceived intuitively during the ride here was a divining that the Light, for which her soul had always longed, would shine for her in the proximity of this Prince. A silent prayer filled her being.

Helping hands reached out to them. The serving women garbed in white were happy when their Lord summoned them and gave the two guests over to their care. They took the Princess into their midst and conducted her into the rooms assigned to her. But Nahome did not let go of Abd-ru-shin's hand.

"Will you not go with your mother?"

"No, Lord, I shall stay with you!"

And so she walked with the Prince through His magnificent palace and was full of joy.

Her great sense of beauty and the inborn dignity of her being gave the child an indescribable charm. Her grace and the alertness of her spirit, which was apparent in all things, delighted Abd-ru-shin.

Never before had such clear, cheerful laughter rung out in these spacious halls.

Even the quiet Ismanites smiled happily when they heard Nahome's chatter. Soon she was known everywhere and had settled in completely; it was as if it had never been otherwise.

IN THE REALM of Abd-ru-shin, and especially in His immediate proximity, each spirit was an individual flame quite apart, which had to strive towards Him on its own. If that were not the case, the spirit could not be attracted nor could it remain near Him, but had to lose itself again, had even to go astray.

The effect in daily life was clearly discernible. The Chosen Ones and the servants came together, swinging in circles, and strove to give their best to the pure service, which to them was the focal point and zenith of life.

There were no base desires, vanity or place-hunting; for through the natural interplay of their work these could not arise.

The Ismanites, those closest to the Prince, were an example to all. Even their outward appearance, the structure of their skulls, their hands, their figures bore witness to the high degree of their spiritual perfection.

And on earth, wherever human beings dwelt who bore a living spark of longing for the Light within them, they awakened, grew strong and were attracted.

To a certain extent they changed outwardly as well, visible to all. The higher they developed, the more they adapted to the example of the Ismanites.

A VISIT WAS ANNOUNCED. Pharaoh was to come. He brought with him a great retinue, among them also his daughter. Aloe, who was in dread of her country's ruler as never before, kept away altogether. She warned Nahome. Sensitive to all false currents, the woman felt the difference in the pure environment more keenly than ever. But she also perceived that evil was as though fettered and powerless here. During these days she saw the sparkling Stone on Abd-ru-shin's breast shine with unusual intensity; the Ring round His arm flashed.

So great was the Power of the Radiation that even the Chosen Ones who were close to Abd-ru-shin could endure it only when they worked unceasingly in His Will.

An inflexible Law was manifested here; it furthered the purification and development of all.

The guests were struck by the great intellectual alertness of the Ismanites, and by the harmony and joy with which all of them worked. But what each individual did, the strangers could not discover, for in the vast palace they lived quite to themselves and were connected with the main house, in which dwelt the Prince with those nearest to Him, only through the guest-rooms and banqueting halls.

Glorious clumps of trees embellished the extensive gardens. Flowers blossomed in rich profusion. Among them were species unknown in Egypt.

Juri-cheo, the quiet, sad daughter of Pharaoh, liked to stroll through these gardens with Nahome. She felt at ease in the pure atmosphere, especially so in the presence of the royal child.

Nahome's sunny nature, bubbling with purest charm and mirth, swept her along, permitting her happily to enjoy the beauty of the moment. But when Abd-ru-shin joined them and spoke kindly with her, she was incapable of uttering a word, and would have preferred to fall on her knees. She suffered, for she knew that her father hated the Prince. For that reason every demonstration of His hospitality put her to shame.

But slowly the rigidity that had constrained Juri-cheo dissolved, and she opened herself to the beneficent stream of Abd-ru-shin's words.

Nahome was glad when she saw that the guest became more lively and joyous day by day. When she was alone, a dark cloud occasionally stole across her brow. She would only feel free and happy when Pharaoh returned to his homeland.

The latter saw the splendours of the palace with amazement. In thought he compared his power and the wealth of his treasures with those of Abd-ru-shin.

With envy he observed that here love, purity and faith created everlasting values, that everything earthly was also imbued with spirit, and therefore radiated life.

He could not define it, but recognised clearly that the golden vessels which equalled the Egyptian showpieces in splendour and weight eclipsed every work of art created by his talented goldsmith with regard to their beauty, their lustre, and the invisible something radiating from them. And what was it that endowed the stone on Abd-ru-shin's breast with such radiance?

Brooding and sullen, he withdrew into himself.

Wherever he looked he came to the same conclusion; everywhere he encountered that flowering, joyful abundance, that perfection, whose origin he could not grasp. The man must have a secret, and he determined to get to the root of this secret in order to make use of it for himself.

Nahome's keen eyes observed Pharaoh. She kept watch day and night and found no peace of mind.

EVERYONE BREATHED FREELY as though relieved of a heavy burden when Pharaoh spoke of his departure. No one suspected that a cowardly, malicious plan of his had been thwarted by Nahome's vigilance. He went back to Egypt, restless and full of malice.

His daughter accompanied him, in the hope of being permitted to return. She had been the only one among the visitors who had recognised the Light.

But during the days of anxiety Nahome's spirit had developed to an undreamed-of height. Full of love, the Primordial Queen inclined towards her, and enveloped her in Her luminous mantle.

ALOE OFTEN THOUGHT of Amon-Asro with gratitude for his wise schooling. How well she understood Nahome's quick readjustment, for she knew about the child's pure spirit. The wise Priest had indicated her luminous pathway with only a few words, but he had given her mother a great help thereby. She grasped that, for Nahome, her earlier existence had been merely a transition and that it was only here that her true life was beginning.

She also remembered that spiritual picture on the fateful night before the raid. Since then the broad, blue waters had stood between her and her child. Nahome had found her way home. But she, Aloe, had to remain behind at the border.

Aloe had become an Egyptian; she was no longer young, and had been dealt a severe blow by fate. She had to set many things aside, delve deep until she could feel free again as she did at the time when she was expecting Nahome. It seemed to her that her life was completed, that she had lived solely for the sake of this child.

Her earthly suffering had left her deeply shaken. She had to make a completely new beginning, and she felt alone. Such was the state of her soul.

She lived a quiet, withdrawn life. But with alert eyes she observed the development of everything.

She was still reserved and full of pain, shy and proud. In her pride lay the inbred dignity of the Egyptian; her shyness reflected her pure reverence for the greatness that she encountered here.

Nahome was constantly near the Prince, following Him like His shadow. Increasingly she avoided her pensive and often taciturn mother.

As a result Aloe intuitively perceived a great emptiness. She could no longer be anything to her child, but she understood the child's nature and was grateful for Nahome's exalted happiness.

Her clairaudience and clairvoyance had virtually ceased since the severe shocks had overtaken her. They had only been given to her by the Light to guide her for the sake of Nahome, and Nahome had now reached her goal.

But slowly, in the peace and care bestowed upon her, Aloe grew strong, and her spiritual alertness returned. In spirit she saw the figure of a man, who began to guide and advise her, explaining whatever she did not understand.

Thus she was being prepared, without herself realising it at the time.

TIME PASSED QUICKLY. Nahome blossomed forth, and her spirit developed to great power. All women revered in her the prototype of true womanly virtue, and her love, her helpfulness filled everyone with gratitude.

Nahome's crystal-clear love for the Lord had found its way back to its Origin. In purest volition she had journeyed all the way into the World of Matter at her own request.

In accordance with the Law of Attraction of Homogeneous Species, which her Lord and Master had explained to His subjects, Love, Purity and the Most Sublime Womanly Virtue streamed to her abundantly from the Light. Then, in turn, these proceeded from her, strengthening all of pure will, with the blessed Light of the Queen of Heaven.

And there were women on earth in whom the Light could be anchored for the salvation and guidance of the human race.

The women of the tribe of Is-Ra were pure vessels, able to propagate a new, God-willed race on earth.

ABD-RU-SHIN WENT ON long rides through the country with Nahome and a small chosen band. On their way the hearts of the people went out to them in jubilation and gratitude.

They also rode out over the steppes and observed the animals going to their watering-places, but they did not hunt. Abd-ru-shin, who loved and protected all creatures, delighted in their existence. Only in self-defence was killing permissible.

On one occasion they rode across the desert towards the range of hills where Abd-ru-shin had not taken Nahome before. Serene as always when they were alone together in nature, she rode at His side. But her cheerful talk ceased when they came to a path on which she discovered the tracks of many people and wagons.

141

They were approaching a place over which lay what seemed like sacred silence. The light of the sun shone golden on the nearby white mountain-ranges. The desert stretched far into the distance, while the domes of the Light-city could still be seen shimmering like a mirage.

Abd-ru-shin conducted Nahome to a higher elevation and let her look down upon the shining, silent splendour. Nahome had lifted the veil from her face, and her expressive eyes reflected admiration, suspense, and then a question, for at their feet extended a large structure in the shape of a huge square leading far down into the earth. These were the beginnings of a strange edifice built of stone and the most exquisite materials.

Nahome's eyes suddenly took on a deep earnestness as though she perceived grievous experiences in the distant future. In an anxious voice she enquired softly:

"Lord, what is this structure that fills me with such sadness despite its great beauty?"

"This is the place where our earthly bodies will lie one day when we return home to the Light. Calm yourself, that is still many years away!" Abd-ru-shin added comfortingly when He observed her alarm.

"By then you will have come so far, Nahome, that you can rejoice when the Lord summons me to return."

"Only if you take me with you will I rejoice. Do not leave me here alone."

They said no more about it.

Abd-ru-shin showed her the artistic layout of the structure, in which the treasury vaults formed the foundation. Viewed from above, the cross-section revealed the form of a perfect crystal.

"Upon this foundation a pyramid will arise."

The tranquillity of the place where this work awaited completion was impressive.

In the azure sky a large bird, moving towards the east, was describing wide circles.

Nahome hardly breathed; she had withdrawn completely into her-

142

self and had lowered the white veil again. In silence she rode home at the side of her Lord.

CYCLE UPON CYCLE of spiritual happenings was closing, and Abd-ru-shin's Radiation filled ever wider spheres with His Power.

"There is a white brilliance around you, Lord," said Nahome, "when you are near at hand. But when you stand further away, the rays emanate from you in the form of the Cross. Aloe too is able to see it, and many of the women intuitively perceive the intensified rays.

"But the Ismanites know. Actually the Ismanites know everything. They know of your sublime nature and of your Mission, and they also know about what is to come. But they keep silence. They know everything with the spirit."

Abd-ru-shin liked to hear Nahome give voice to her observations, but He rarely said anything in reply. Only when she asked a direct question did He give, in a few words, such simple explanations that she was surprised not to have thought of it herself.

Everything that Abd-ru-shin explained from out of the Law was so natural. It appeared simple as soon as He had voiced it. Whatever He said was fulfilled on and in human beings, depending on their nature, either quickly or slowly, all the more quickly the more mature they were. The more they strove to live in accordance with His Word, the easier their paths became.

As Amon-Asro had said, people who could be Nahome's friends were now being guided to her. But she did not need them. She lived solely for her Lord.

She did not know how this caused the swinging of the radiant rings to grow ever stronger, how they flooded upwards luminously to the Origin, and how she herself thus drew ever nearer to her sublime Goal.

There was only one who knew. There was one who assimilated her strong experiencing of God, her longing for the Light, deep within, who accompanied her child's path and was granted sublime help from the Light for the purpose: Aloe! And yet she kept silent. She did not overcome her shyness and her pride when Abd-ru-shin asked her:

143

"We are riding to Egypt, to the court of Pharaoh! Won't you come with us?"

"Lord, I will joyfully await the hour of your return, and will keep faithful watch here."

Oh, had she but gone with her child on her last journey!

THUS THE HOUR CAME when all preparations had been made, and Abd-ru-shin departed. The finest steeds, the most beautiful jewellery, the most elect troop of His servants of the Arab race – thus they set forth.

The Ismanites were to remain in the Realm. The Power of Abd-ru-shin's Light-Radiation became so intense that the Ismanites, who were most open to it, could hardly endure it.

Abd-ru-shin was determined to unleash necessary happenings. Moses needed Him. Egypt was ripe for the great turning-point. There was terrible ferment everywhere. Into this murky, stifling morass Abd-ru-shin wished to ride, and Nahome did not leave Him; she remained by His side.

The sun shone golden as they left the gleaming white gates. For a long time the eyes of the faithful Ismanites followed them, for a long time Aloe gazed after them from the high tower, until nothing but a light-pervaded dust cloud was visible in the endless desert.

There rode her child at the side of the Divine Envoy, Whom she served in loyalty. At first it was still joyful pride in her child that filled Aloe, but an uneasy feeling announced itself quietly in her soul.

She had awaited and recognised Abd-ru-shin's Mission, and He had graven on her forehead the Sign of His Father with an indelible Seal.

But she had not gone with Him. She was leaving her child in the care of strangers, trustworthy servants though they might be. Amon-Asro had said:

"Summon all your strength and remember the child's path!"

Fate had turned. Like a shining star Nahome pursued her fate, her destiny. At first she was to protect and smooth the child's path. That she had fulfilled. Now the child went before her; she should have followed her now!

Why was it only now that the scales fell from her eyes, now that the dust of the desert had long since taken them out of sight, now that no further call could reach them, and her physical eyes could no more glimpse the light-green banner with the shining Cross, fluttering in the wind?

Now they were riding into the grey of the Egyptian mire in order to bear Light into it, and she who was aware of everything, who knew His Power, who would give her life in loyalty, she had been restrained by one cowardly thought: she would no longer set foot in Egypt, the land of her sorrows, and on that account she let what was most sacred and precious to her, journey alone. Her self-reproaches were terrible.

At the same time she heard within her an urgent voice unceasingly speaking:

"Listen, listen! Ne-so-met no longer hears me! You must listen!"

It startled her; she looked about her nervously. It was broad daylight. Dazzling rays from the crystal dome of the Temple fell across the Palace and the emerald-green, shining gardens. A gentle wind sang, and Nahome's bright songbirds, shimmering like mother-of-pearl, fluttered in the sunlight.

The playing of harps and the rippling of water rose up to her from the sacred groves. The fragrances from the colourful bowls of the Temple merged with the scent from the Persian rose-beds at her feet.

White peacocks and doves approached her. Aloe wished to take care of the animals; it gave her a connection with her child.

But again there was the reproach and the admonishing voice:

"Listen! It concerns the Armlet! Do you not know about Abd-ru-shin's Armlet from the treasure of the Ismanites? Then listen:

"In the hour of Consecration of our Temple it was placed upon the White Stone in the first Ray of Divine Light. Three topazes shone golden in the Armlet.

"'Wait for Him, Whom I have chosen, to bring you help! Guard the Armlet, until the Redeemer dwells in your midst!'

"Thus spoke the voice from Above. The most sublime Power was vested in the Armlet which was created by the hands of animistic guardians with the willing support of a Called smith.

"The years passed. I, Is-ma-el, brought up Abd-ru-shin. When I let the youth depart, I gave Him the Armlet. Now the Armlet is in danger, and He with it!"

The words resounded in Aloe's soul like a lament: The Armlet in danger and He with it!

Hastily she recorded everything. Then she looked for her most reliable servant, who was also the best of riders. Under his fluttering white burnous he carried the roll with the papyrus for Nahome.

And again Aloe stood and gazed across the dazzling land. A fervent prayer welled up in her soul:

"Lord, grant me atonement for my failing! Permit me still to redress what I have neglected!"

Bitter tears of repentance coursed down her cheeks.

ABD-RU-SHIN, who was normally fully occupied, found rest and recuperation in the desert-camp. They experienced glorious days here.

Abd-ru-shin was very solemn, and yet serene. Nahome was the only human being who could remain at His side and be invigorated as Holy Power drew to the completion of Its cycle in the swinging of the Light-Happening.

Abd-ru-shin's face shone. His eyes and the timbre of His voice were radiant. Nahome chatted happily, and He entered into her cheerful tone.

From Egypt many messengers were sent by Eb-ra-nit, who was Abd-ru-shin's close friend, although he was the acknowledged adviser of Pharaoh. They told of Moses and of the horrors which were multiplying in Egypt. In his pure attitude towards God, Moses opened himself trustingly to all the powers bestowed upon him.

Abd-ru-shin told Nahome that the end of His Mission was now drawing near. He said it with joy. Nahome, ready to understand and be guided by Him in all things, opened her ears and her spirit. Within her was the firm resolve, inscribed as with a luminous stylus: "I will follow!"

A PEACEFUL, HAPPY atmosphere prevailed in the camp. At times Abd-ru-shin was as though transported.

In the deep blue of the sky a golden pillar of Light had appeared; in it shimmered the Light of the Spirit of God. Peace lay over the camp, in which the people from the tribe of Is-Ra were resting.

The sentries paced quietly. The night was clear as day, so that the shadows of the tents were particularly dark.

A soft cry rang out from the tent of the Prince, a faint clinking sound ... a darting shadow, then a steed galloping away. Spectral, swift, uncanny – the evil deed of the Darkness flitted across the camp.

The silence of a few seconds was more terrible than the desperate cry, brief and painful, that followed it. Sentries who discovered the dead body of their Prince rushed from the tent:

"Call Nahome!"

Nahome came. She sensed what she would find, and entered the tent. Then deep silence reigned again.

AND NOT LONG AFTERWARDS a white, solemn procession journeyed slowly across the desert towards the City of Light.

The earthly cloak of the White Prince lay as though sleeping upon the bier, and beside it, inseparable as in life, the lovely cloak of the delicate Nahome. Voluntarily she had followed her Lord to be with Him.

Nine hours after the murder Aloe's messenger on horseback met the funeral procession.

AFTER THE BODY OF THE Divine Envoy had received the fatal blow at the hands of the assassin, His Luminous Unsubstantiality, still enveloped by the spiritual and ethereal cloaks, severed itself at once.

Upon this first step of His severance from the material substance needed to anchor Him on earth, many awakening spirits were graciously attracted by His Light-Power. Thus it was granted them to find the way to recognition.

But at that world-overturning moment which affected simultaneously all the spheres of Creation and the entire cosmos, even lofty spirits still dwelling in earthly bodies were so loosened and awakened that they beheld Abd-ru-shin's Light-figure. Indeed, they received tidings and instructions through Him.

But those who had already come into contact with Him on earth, and had been inspired and glowingly permeated by the Holy Spark of God, in that It fanned their faint little spirit-sparks into flame again, those beheld and experienced the hour of separation in one way or another.

Thus Moses received the last charge directly from his Lord. Filled with the Power absorbed by his spirit at that hour through Abd-ru-shin, he set out on his journey through the Red Sea and into the desert. He recognised the Help of God.

Aloe too had perceived the death of Abd-ru-shin. Pale and luminous, He stood before her with the bleeding wound, robbed of His Armlet. And almost at the same moment her spirit experienced the painful separation from her child.

It was a supreme spiritual happening, devoid of any emotion. At the same time there remained the distinct intuitive perception that ties were being severed that had been granted for the sole purpose of providing a natural anchorage for the spirit of Irmingard in the earthly body.

Irmingard's Light-figure also severed itself from the earthly body of Nahome, and seeking support, united firmly with the shining Ray which was still on earth out of Abd-ru-shin. Higher, ever higher, she followed Him, hastening through all the spheres with the speed of purest Light.

Once more, as at the moment of incarnation, Aloe beheld Irmingard's Light-form surrounded by roseate beams, by floating flowers, radiant like a star.

But then she withdrew from her, leaving her, Aloe, behind on earth, with an earnest, conscious longing.

All these things came to pass at the hour of Abd-ru-shin's death.

DEEP SILENCE lay over the Realm of Is-Ra.

Aloe sought out the Ismanites and gave them tidings of what she had seen.

The Ismanites and all the faithful servants of Abd-ru-shin awaited the messenger whom Aloe had dispatched. They were hoping against hope; they perceived intuitively that Aloe's vision was the truth.

A condition had come over them that cannot be described with earthly words. They had forgotten their individual selves and now felt simply as one. As a shining ring they mounted upwards in prayer, following their Lord, and He drew them along with Him and gave them strength.

The sun went down and rose again in the sky the next day, glaring and scorching. The servants of Abd-ru-shin were still keeping watch on the white terraces, so as not to miss the appearance of the procession in the distance. Neither the great heat of day nor the cold of night could drive them from their vigil. Garbed in white, Aloe stood at the highest point, and with keen eyes gazed steadfastly into the blinding glare of noon, as into the dark of night, towards the far horizon.

Finally, after two days and a half, they saw the vanguard formed by the Arab horsemen. The wild but loyal Arabs were solicitously and slowly escorting the two earthly cloaks home.

All the necessary arrangements were made by the Ismanites. Peace and solemnity descended everywhere.

Blazing fires rose heavenwards from huge socles. The rooms, the courtyard and the hall leading to the Temple were draped in white. The tall clusters of palms contrasted beautifully with the white background.

No grief was expressed during the work. Only an indescribable, solemn atmosphere lay over the human beings.

From the Temple, in which the two deceased were to rest until the massive slabs of the death-chambers closed over them, sounded music such as had not been heard on earth since the time of the Isman people. It was a rendering of songs of blessed spirits, which only those human beings could discern whose spiritual ears were allowed to hear it.

To the sounds of these sacred songs the Ismanites carried the earthly cloaks of their Prince and Nahome into the Temple. Once more they all gathered in prayer around their Lord. Then the curtains and the gates were closed to those who did not belong to the Elect.

149

After this Hour of Devotion the bodies were embalmed according to custom.

Aloe went about as though withdrawn from her surroundings; yet in all earthly matters she acted with absolute clarity and was ever ready to help.

Work on the Pyramid continued feverishly. Most of Abd-ru-shin's wealth was carried into the treasure-chambers there. He Himself and the lovely Nahome looked like precious vessels adorned with gemstones, after loving hands had prepared them for the interment.

The Ismanites and the Elect accompanied the biers; they were followed by the women, with Aloe among them. She was permitted as the last to approach Nahome's shrine once more; then it was closed. At that, with a faint sound, like a sigh, she collapsed, no longer to awaken in her earthly body, and was soon laid to rest.

THE RADIATION of the Envoy of God drew the Power of Purity directly upwards.

Divine Power had been anchored on earth through the establishment of the Realm of Is-Ra, whence it now flowed out over the earth, releasing or strengthening what had been begun through the presence of Abd-ru-shin there.

The spiritual guidance of the earthly helpers set in with great intensity immediately after Abd-ru-shin's passing. Each of them stood at the post personally ordained for him by Abd-ru-shin, and from there they worked. Everything they recognised and resolved came out of His Will.

Moses was the first in whom this powerful effect was manifested instantly.

In the ethereal realms, however, a strong movement arose; thoughts condensed with immense force and speed, and all wishes, all deeds, took effect at once. Naturally, in Abd-ru-shin's City and among his helpers, only good things could develop. But in Egypt, where the Darkness held sway, terrible things were unleashed.

Many in the beyond were awakened by this movement, and thus recognised the Light. In ardent longing their spirits were able to rise.

But disturbing scenes and experiences occurred in the lower planes where many spirits had bound themselves through error.

Over Egypt lay a grey, moving haze of fine gross matter which was set into a swirling, ever more accelerating motion. Forms of fear and hatred rose heavenwards like dense poisonous clouds; they attached themselves to the human spirits who had been loosened by fear, affliction and misery, and who, totally lacking in will-power, were at the mercy of all these thought-forms.

The animals too felt the pressure from these lower planes; they became timid, listless, and refused to obey their masters. The sacred bulls fell ill. Flights of large birds flew screeching over the cities. The smell of decay was everywhere; the filth was overpowering. Under the pressure, whose cause was incomprehensible to them, people no longer attended to the most fundamental cleanliness.

Furthermore, diseases came forth from the swamp and were spread by insects.

The Hand of the Lord had sent down heavy blows upon Egypt.

Full of fear, the survivors on earth saw the frightful effects upon their people, but they did not understand that it was the lawful consequence of their own deeds. To them the God of the Jews appeared as an avenger, as a cruel, merciless God. They were afraid, but they failed to recognise what they were meant to learn from this terrible experience.

At first they were as if stunned. Apathetically they waited for fresh blows yet to come. All the first-born had been annihilated already; disease and affliction lay over the land. The army had sunk beneath the waves of the sea; the country was without a ruler.

News of the death of the Light-Prince had been a heavy blow to Juricheo. But the shock had freed her spirit. She saw the futility of the things she still considered of importance. Moses had gone; she had been left alone. Nothing remained to keep her on earth.

A violent fever struck her suddenly and put an end to her earthly life.

"Nahome," whispered her lips as she departed.

Her great longing had guided her spirit aright. Swiftly discarding its cloaks, it followed the Light of the Cross which she had recognised during her mortal existence.

151

ONE OF THE FEW wise Priests of that time, Amon-Asro, had also completed his life on earth. He knew his task to have been faithfully accomplished and wanted to pass on the wealth of his recognitions to mankind, but he was mercifully removed from the earth before floods and hail devastated the sacred island as well.

Nanna was sorely grieved when the cloak of Amon-Asro was buried. She felt that nothing more bound her to the island, neither duty nor the oath of allegiance to Isis. Thus she stood on the banks of the Nile while night was gently falling, and a boat was approaching. The boatmen saw the white shimmer of her clothing, they perceived the beckoning of her veil and came to the bank.

Nanna boarded the vessel, and now she did what she had already longed to do many years before, but had been unable to accomplish: she followed the call of her inner voice. It had never been quite silent since Aloe and the child had left her. Now she would seek the place where Amon-Asro had already seen them in spirit: the Shining City in the desert!

It was a hazardous undertaking for the solitary woman so to journey out into the world, and to heed nothing save the call of a voice that grew ever more demanding, ever clearer, within her.

During the journey her eyes beheld sad things, much frightful suffering and terrible devastations, buildings in ruins, cities destroyed, gardens desolated. A stranger, she walked through all this which the Hand of the Lord had touched. It seemed to her that she was in another world. She was clearly aware of only one thing: she was seeking Nahome!

She was happy once the desolate and grey places of death and horror were behind her, and she was able to join a merchant caravan travelling into the desert. A clear intuitive perception told the solitary woman that this was the direction of her journey. She followed without hesitation, at the same time always keeping her distance from the strangers, for she did not want any connection with human beings.

The light of the moon was soft as they travelled across the silvery-grey sand-dunes at night; the air was balmy and calm. She spent the hot days in the shade of a resting animal or of a tent.

The people soon realised that this was a harmless woman on a solitary journey; they admired her great will-power. They offered her safe-conduct and help inasmuch as she required them, but otherwise they left her alone. A donkey carried her on its back for hours at a time. Thus it went for about three days.

Then suddenly Nanna felt that she must take another route. With gratitude she took leave of her fellow-travellers, and kept the small bag of fruit which they gave her. Shaking their heads, they let her go after she calmly and pleasantly refused to heed all their warnings and advice.

Nanna walked on alone, always following the clear Ray of Light that fell upon the glaringly-yellow sand from the dazzling blue sky.

Far off on the horizon there suddenly appeared riders, approaching at lightning speed.

The sun was going down, red lights were already flitting over the hills of the desert, the shadows became blue. The evening stillness was broken only by the vibration of the earth, occasioned by horsemen approaching. Now Nanna's heart did tremble a little. Almost exhausted from fatigue and thirst, she wondered about the intentions of the riders coming towards her.

Her nerves were strained to the utmost. Already she had decided that the foaming horses would gallop past, when the riders came to an abrupt halt and surrounded her. So she was their captive.

But the brown faces looked at her kindly. Calm and dignified, the men dismounted.

Nanna rejoiced when she learned from them that she was near the Realm of the Is-Ra. A feeling of security came over her.

"Whom do you seek?" the men asked gently.

"Nahome!" came the soft answer.

The name had the effect of a password. The Arabs bowed low before her, but covered their faces silently.

Without a word they lifted Nanna on to one of the horses and rode with her towards their luminous home.

IN THE LIGHT-CITY of the Is-Ra only a few Ismanites had remained behind. After they had buried the mortal cloak of their Lord, and faithfully discharged all the duties demanded of them by the ensuing festivals, they returned to the posts assigned to them in the Realm by their Lord.

But three who had most perfectly grasped the Mission of Abd-ru-shin soon followed Him and were buried in the Pyramid.

The building rose rapidly, being brought to completion with consummate artistic skill. And just as the master-builder continued the work founded and entrusted to him by Abd-ru-shin, so likewise did all the other servants act fully within the Will of their Lord. They worked at the stupendous structure of state in loyalty and with diligence, and simultaneously their strength grew from day to day.

The spiritual leadership was assumed out of the Power of Abd-ru-shin by one of the oldest of the Ismanites. After Is-ma-el's death Abd-ru-shin had given him the name Is-ma-il. His right hand was Nam-chan, who translated Is-ma-il's will into deed. All the talents which Abd-ru-shin had recognised in Nam-chan and developed through His guidance now took effect. Thus he grew into his office as leader, and became the executor of the Divine Will.

The White City shone richly and beautifully in the Light of Divine Grace. Life pulsated powerfully within it, and the guardians of Wisdom and of the Laws ensured that these were preserved in all their vitality as willed by the Lord. Many human spirits still found their way across the desert to the Holy City of Wisdom and Purity, and remained there, for everyone who reached it had followed the Call of the Most High, and had found his goal and his destiny within its white walls. Nanna was one of the first to be permitted to reach the Light-City, where she was received like a long-awaited guest. Her alert, intelligent eyes recognised in the radiance and grace of the women the heavenly stream of Power that had once also transfigured the Temple of Isis when Nahome sojourned there.

Upon crossing the threshold of the Palace, she knew at once that she would no longer find Nahome on earth.

The women tended her lovingly. Among them was Ere-si, the Egyptian temple-dancer, who in particular had matured to goodness

154

and poise. To her Nanna confided her life's story. Already Ere-si knew from Nahome's own lips about Nanna, the guardian and friend of her childhood, as well as about Amon-Asro the Priest.

For a long time the women sat in the white, light-pervaded halls overlooking the gardens, discussing their fate and the wise guidance. With her ardent soul Nanna experienced all that Ere-si told her.

She was introduced to the Laws of God, first by the women, then by the teachers and priests of the Light. In this way she entered the circle of servants of the Lord. She was allowed to hear the hymns sung by the Ismanites; she saw the wonderful festival dances devoted to the Lord by Ere-si.

Nanna, who had come from the place where beauty had been developed to artistic heights, was amazed at the vitality of these festival-customs. All the servants, who performed their sacred service in purest worship, seemed to her endowed with Divine Grace. And for the first time she experienced again the blissful connection with the Power of the Light that she had once known when Nahome entered the Temple of Isis.

And a great Blessing was bestowed upon Nanna. She became clairvoyant! Surging with Light, the Chalice upon the white Altar emitted a vibrating tone. Out of the flood of golden-white Light spreading over the circle of Ismanites and servants, far into the shimmering arches of the Temple-hall, a Face appeared to her.

It was the Countenance of the Divine Mediator. His shining golden Eye radiated in Love and Wisdom. At His left she saw a floating figure in a long white robe with a Crown of Lilies. But at His right stood a regal Woman Whose Countenance shone full of Love. Roseate light undulated around Her like delicate clouds, and She too wore a Crown of Light. A radiant Black Mantle enveloped the shining, almost transparent figure. To Nanna it seemed that only this dark mantle enabled the Luminous Woman to assume form.

Astonished, she enquired in spirit who this Woman was, and heard the name: *Maria*.

Wondrous things befell Nanna at the sound of this name. Overwhelmed, she sank to her knees.

In her spirit vibrated the words:

"Thee do I serve!"

So great was Nanna's experience that she would speak of it to no one, except to Ere-si.

She was given a strong spiritual connection with the two Luminous Women Whom she had seen at either side of the Lord. But she did not yet know who they were. She did not yet recognise the Countenance of the Pure Lily. For this she had first to be prepared slowly.

THE PURE LILY had returned into the Light of Her Home. The surging tones of the Divine Sphere flowed about Her. The pinions of angels rustled; drawing from the Fountain-head of Life, they inclined their vessels to nurture the Sacred Gardens of the Lily.

The Will of God had entered the Fountain-head of Unsubstantiate Power, and sojourned there for a time. But His Will nevertheless worked unceasingly through the Spirit, and in the womb of the great, Eternal Wisdom a new swinging for the start of a new cycle was being prepared.

Rays of Light pervaded Creation; they had been anchored in a few human spirits by the Will of God descending all the way into the World of Matter.

These continued to work in His Will; at His Behest they traversed the earth, forming islands of Light there.

When this was done, and God had scattered His Light like seed-grains, the Ismanites were gradually lifted up into the Luminous Realm of the Spirit.

The Realm of Is-Ra was still maintained in its original beauty on earth, as was ordained. But the number of human beings who were to bear continuous fresh life into it grew steadily smaller.

The time came when all those who had served Abd-ru-shin on earth left it. With that the Realm also approached its end.

It was to sink into a long sleep until the time of its awakening.

And the terrestrial globe rolls on until a point on it begins to glow anew, announcing a great Light-happening:

CASSANDRA

LONG AFTER Parsifal and Irmingard had been on earth as Abd-ru-shin and Nahome, the Radiations of Light and Purity remained anchored in many human souls through this happening. Wherever they found suitable soil they spread. These places glowed in the World of Matter like little points of Light, whereas the higher realms and planes were like fine filters, which transmitted the streams of Power in full force.

Like all higher spirituality, so too all the animistic was set aglow, and the animistic helpers worked joyfully in the World of Gross Matter, wherever human beings recognised them and co-operated with them. Erroneously they described the animistic beings as gods, because they differed from them, vibrating more purely in the Divine Will and therefore appearing to them omnipotent.

Like the other planets, the terrestrial globe revolved in uniform, rhythmic circles around its light-source, the radiant sun. The globe was still young in its development, although to human thinking it had already hastened through aeons of time and unfathomable events in its evolution.

FINE MISTY FORMS, shimmering like opal, whirled and undulated around the earth. They flashed in clear, luminous tones, indicating to the animistic beings places on earth where the Holy Power of the Light was anchored in pure human spirits.

To such places the shimmering Light-streams of Purity were drawn as by strong magnets. The animistic helpers received them and passed them on into the World of Matter, thereby creating a connection for the Light.

But wherever the opalescent circle shimmered in dark colours, there human beings made sacrifices to the intellect; orgies supplanted sacred

Divine Festivals; evil deeds exuded darkness. In such places the Light found no connection.

It was thus over Babylon, over Egypt, over many islands along the coast of Asia Minor, where the times of pure human volition were already sinking away. There the once vigorous development of mature peoples was declining.

But the surging, drifting web of finer gross matter, pervaded by pure animistic forces, gleamed brightly above the blue expanse of the sea. The sun glittered in the waves whose unending thunderous roar resounded to the glory of God like a distant low-pitched organ-recital.

Jubilant nereids hastened through this turbulent world; they plunged their hands into the luminous webs and extended them to the airy beings. Bright, jagged stretches of land, islands and bays gleamed far away in the sunlight.

Pure and simple in its natural pristine state, the coast of Greece also shone across the sea. The broad crest of Olympus towered into the deep blue sky, with the rugged beauty of the country spread around it.

An unusual movement became apparent above the land of the Greeks, above the sea and the opposite coast of Asia Minor. Silver-clear, translucent Light seemed uniquely to transfigure this part of the earth.

Great temples and fortifications rose along the shores of the sea. Mighty cities shone in the sunlight, and their edifices spoke in strict and powerful terms of faith, discipline and order, of diligence and reverence for the eternal gods.

There was as yet no trace of the reckless and pomp-loving frenzy which later shattered the best strength of this people. But already the dogged, heroic obstinacy had appeared which was about to turn these happy, god-fearing heroes into violent, defiant adventurers who subjugated the weaker, not for the sake of progress, but for the sake of power.

Slowly, as if searching this earth, the quickening, silver-radiant Light of Divine Love moved along the coasts. But It did not yet tarry, nor descend, although the luminous animistic helpers were jubilantly ready to form the bridge for the Light of God in the World of Matter.

162

The silver radiance floated through the clouds over the shorelines and the sea, and for a time it hovered above the coast of Troy.

Thus were the country, the people and the house being prepared, into which a Spark from the Light of God was to descend. Unsuspecting, people on earth lived their life of work, struggle and pleasure. They lived from the gifts of God, and saw the power of their gods at work in the forces of Nature.

This land of shepherds, farmers and soldiers was pure and simple, rugged and clear. Through their natural life and activity their spirits developed and matured unconsciously; especially the women opened themselves to receive the pure forces above them. They strove upwards, and this longing for purity ennobled them also in the earthly. Through their natural grace they gained in power and became guardians of the home and the temples built by the men under their influence.

The virtues of Purity and Loyalty worked powerfully through the high animistic beings who formed the bridge to women on earth. The Greeks called these beings Hera and Hestia.

Hestia often appeared to the women in the flames of the sacred hearth that had its place in every house in the centre of the large living-room.

TROY WAS MATURING towards a great Light-happening on earth, and was being prepared for the reception of a Divine Mystery that had already come to pass in the Holy Castle of the Light. For again Creation was to experience the fulfilment of a great Blessing in the Love of God: What Parsifal as Abd-ru-shin had begun, Maria as Cassandra was to complete on earth.

LOST IN TOUGHT, Hecuba, the wife of Priam and mother of the country's most handsome heroes, the Mistress of Troy, sat in the circle of women and maidservants of the stately house. They were spinning fine wool for their loose-fitting garments.

The hearth-fire flared up, and in the newly-risen flame there sud-

163

denly appeared to her a face. Calm and beautiful, full of kindness and purity, it gazed into the eyes of the Queen, helpful, encouraging.

Hecuba rose to her feet with difficulty. Wearily her imposing figure moved towards the hearth and bent over it without a word. The face in the flames had attracted her. She knew that the goddess was about to say something to her.

The women paid no attention. Hecuba often behaved strangely when she was blessed with child. At those times she was more remote from human beings, connected with the invisible forces of Nature, deeply devout and quiet within. This time, however, a very special charm lay over her austere, stern being, and a tranquil radiance upon her countenance.

Hecuba lived in discipline and order. She filled the entire house, the mighty court with her firmness, helpfulness and loyalty, but never with warmth. Everyone obeyed her, everyone respected her greatly, but no one loved her.

And in the crackling of the fire Hestia whispered words of counsel and hope to her; she directed the activities of the woman, and gave her a strength which was felt by many, but whose source was unknown to them. Luminous threads flowed from Hestia through Hecuba, who intuitively perceived them as a gift.

"You have the maturity to receive a pure, sublime Light!" Thus sounded the whispering from out of the fire. Although Hecuba heard the words, she was unaware that they referred to the child she was expecting.

From that hour, things were astir in the house. Light-figures went in and out, filling the rooms with their radiance.

Hecuba prayed to the gods. Every day she adorned the statue of Hestia that stood upon a stone base in a small vestibule with flowers and garlands of leaves.

She herself walked out of the city-gates, over the hills and meadows in order to gather the little white flowers she needed.

Great herds of fat sheep and nimble goats were there with their shepherds. These human creatures were as austere as their Mistress. The tone of their flutes sounded like the sighing of the gentle breeze, and

164

called to mind the silent melancholy of the vast range of hills in the east. It was the expression of the singular quality of their souls. Hecuba was especially fond of the sound of these flutes.

One of the shepherds in particular was happy when he saw the Mistress mounting the hills. Of late he had felt strongly drawn to the high lady, who seemed to him to be filled with unusual Light. He was one of those open human beings who experience God's Love weaving vitally within them. With great love and ever-alert eyes he watched the soil of his homeland flourish and bear fruit.

He was familiar with every stirring of his animals, and he was able to sense the dangers threatening them from enemies of all kinds. Often he also beheld beings of the earth, the air and the water, and he found herbs and stones which he used for healing purposes.

His handsome, tanned face was surrounded by thick curly hair. The coarse-grained clothing he wore covered the tall broad body to his knees. His muscular, wiry arms and legs were bare. Leaning on his crook, he gazed down upon Troy, across the hills and the wide river-valley.

His eyes were so keen that even before the alert animals scented the eagle he discerned it high in the sky as it menaced his flock. Filled with longing, he gazed into the shining light of the firmament as if to drink it in.

He was especially blessed, and spoke naturally of things only whispered diffidently and hardly grasped by others. His life was closely interwoven with animals, plants and the elements. He spoke with them as though they were of his kind; he perceived them intuitively as companions and friends, and loved them more than himself. His endeavour was directed at understanding the language of these mysterious beings and absorbing it within him. But everything that he was told by human beings he classified, comparing the nature of their speech and their expression with natural phenomena.

For everything he had comparisons from Nature, and his judgment was apt and just. He knew more than others, and often went down into the settlements of men to help them. If they were concerned about an animal or had some sickness in the house, he was there, always having with him when he came what they required. They shook their heads over this, but accepted his help gratefully. Sometimes they felt a little uneasy about it; they were afraid of him.

Only Hecuba never avoided him. Also this time she walked towards him with a firm step and a greeting.

But he did something which he had never done before. He went down on his knees. As he did so he did not speak, but only silently offered her the leaves of a plant. Steadfastly and enquiringly he looked into her eyes.

Hecuba's foot halted. She stood still, and then moved to help him up.

"What are you giving me? What am I to do with it, Pericles?"

"You will need it, Mistress, in the hour when you are lying in pain. Do not forget it! It will strengthen you and guide higher thoughts to you, that will fill you with blessing. You must keep your soul like a house that is open to the sunlight. You must tend your body like a precious vessel that shelters the most exquisite Treasure of the earth. You must become altogether different within so that you may discover what Blessing has come into this world, and not pass it by. You yourself are permitted to receive this Treasure because you are pure!"

Hecuba's eyes became glazed. Although she heard the words she did not understand them. They continued to sound within her like a calm soothing stream as she walked downhill.

The shepherd always uttered such mysterious words. He spoke in a language that human beings did not comprehend. He was certainly destined to help many more people, but the majority did not understand him.

Anxiously, Pericles gazed after the Mistress as she was leaving. His spirit divined what was coming.

EVENING WAS ALREADY falling over Troy; the pastures grew quiet. The sheep and goats were gathering. They breathed softly, as though listening. Here and there flutes were heard – a night-greeting from the shepherds. Already the first clear stars glowed in the evening sky. The soul of Pericles became still and solemn.

166

It seemed to him that from the distant east luminous hosts were coming nearer and nearer across mountains, rivers and forests, that he heard jubilant singing of voices he had never heard before.

Then suddenly he felt a gentle touch; he looked up. But dazzled, he had to close his eyes. Only after anxious moments did he clearly recognise that there stood before him a handsome youth in radiant Light, who was addressing him. The voice was so powerful that in its rushing he could hardly absorb the meaning of what was said.

"I am a Messenger of God!" said the Luminous One. "I bring you tidings of great joy. Go forth, Pericles, and tell all who will believe: a Light is rising over Troy! If you recognise this Light, It will give you life in abundance. But if you fail to recognise It you will be doomed to death!"

Under the tremendous pressure of the Light Pericles had sunk to his knees as they gave way beneath him. He was trembling. The power of the proclaiming Angel was too great for him.

Nevertheless a question was wrung from his lips:

"But how are we to find the Light?"

"You will behold It in the hour of Its coming. A Luminous Dove will be seen above the house!"

GREAT MOVEMENT CAME into the World. Pericles, who was closely linked with Nature, felt the revival of plant and animal. It seemed to him that every being stretched, straightened and strove upwards in a new radiance. The whispering in the air intensified, the rushing sound in the rivers and springs increased.

A brilliance descended from Heaven right down to the earth like a clear, delicate path of Light.

This stream of Light affected his soul in a strangely mysterious way.

He spoke of it to the shepherds, yet they could perceive nothing. But they said trustingly:

"It will no doubt be as Pericles sees it."

He prepared them for the Coming of the great Light on earth.

The shepherds believed him, but they did not reflect upon it. Nor did they intuitively perceive that intense joy which is given solely to the spirit who is alert and prepared for God's Love. They awaited what would come to pass. A beast of prey that fell upon the herd, or a sick sheep was more likely to attract their undivided attention.

Pericles knew. It did not surprise him, and he kept silent. But all the more clearly did he perceive the sublime forces of the beyond approaching him.

He looked down on the city which lay in the evening mist. Here and there blazing torches shone at houses and gates. In the east the deep blue had already given way to a colourless dark, but in the west the sky was still light, and a red streak bordered the sea. All nature-beings had disappeared.

Suddenly he saw a clear Radiance. He looked round, for he thought that a shepherd must have come with a lantern. But he was alone.

He cast himself on his knees and prayed, his heart was filled to overflowing. The inner composure did him good; he had become aware that he was awaiting something, something great that would grip his spirit powerfully. Again he remembered the Messenger of God.

What had he said? "I am the Messenger of God!" Of which god had he been speaking?

As he reflected upon it, relaxed, full of trust and humility, a voice, distinct and clear, penetrated to him:

"There is but *One* God! We all serve Him, we are only manifestations of His Will."

It resounded out of the air from Above.

"We weave in His Law; but that Light which is now coming to you, It is from out of Him."

His brain was reeling, for all this was so new to him.

Meanwhile the sky had donned its nocturnal garb; the stars glowed as in wet nights after a warm wind has blown the sky clear. A mild heaviness lay upon the damp fragrant earth.

Then, it was as if a shining river of flame came from Heaven! The whole region was bathed in White Light for but a second. Pericles wanted to close his eyes, but they remained wide open as if under some spell.

168

And he beheld above him a dazzling White Dove, bearing in Its beak a Golden Rose. It descended upon the castle of Priam and disappeared.

The shepherd leapt to his feet, left his flock behind, and hurried down into the city to tell the King.

A jubilation like the pealing of bells rang in his soul:

"There is but *One* God, but *the* Light, Which is *now* descending, That is from out of *Him!*"

AND SO IT CAME TO PASS that the shepherd stood before Priam, telling of his wondrous experience.

Priam listened. In his clear kind manner he let the man finish. But he himself was too much a man of practical earthly life to appreciate the full depth of that experience.

He knew the shepherds to be a peculiar people, a singular lot. He was willing to believe them, and of Pericles' wisdom in particular he had already heard much. But unassuming, simple-hearted and preoccupied with the cares of earthly existence, he was little concerned with those delicate contemplative processes of the soul.

"Pericles, the message you bring comes at the hour when a daughter has been born to me. The child may well stand under the special protection of the gods. Nothing else makes sense to me. Let us faithfully do what is right, then we shall also be serving the gods. Things eternal can wait until after death."

At that the shepherd flared up:

"Beware, Priam! Bethink you, heed every one of my words; for they are momentous. Not I have uttered them, but the Messenger of God, and he does not come for the sake of everyday trivialities. Do not think only of the Divine protection for the child, but remember also the threatening words that accompanied his tidings: "A Light is rising over Troy! If you recognise this Light, It will give you life in abundance. But if you fail to recognise It, you will be doomed to death!"

Menace rang in the voice of the shepherd.

169

IN THESE HOURS a tremendous destiny for mankind began to swing along its course; but human beings perceived nothing of it.

Pericles found no peace. He wandered through the city and to the shepherds, to the farmers; he left his flock in order to proclaim the words of the Angel. He went to the fishermen, that they might carry the tidings across the sea to the islands. He searched out the merchants who landed on Troy's shores, for they should take the tidings of the Angel to their homelands.

But Hecuba the Queen, the mother of the little girl, would not countenance this. First a command came from her to keep silence lest the people be aroused, then a warning to Pericles; ultimately, however, he was exiled from the country.

Distressed, Pericles wandered through Troy and shook its dust from his feet. He even left behind on the shore the hides that had covered them.

"Tell Hecuba: the fate of Troy will not prove the Angel's tidings to be untrue, rather the words will be fulfilled: 'But if you fail to recognise this Light, you will be doomed to death!'"

These words he entrusted to one of his people.

And an ominous, gloomy cloud settled heavily over Troy, while the only human being who had recognised the Truth was leaving the country.

YEARS HAD PASSED.

Blue light shone over the sea. The wet craggy cliffs of Troy's coast glistened in the receding tide. Little white crests adorned the waves; bubbling and murmuring, they moved toward the shore. Red and yellow sails appeared on the water.

Small jagged rocks were scattered along the sandy beach, while rocky tracts, sparsely overgrown with low grass, extended into the interior of the land. A deeply rutted road led from Troy to the sea.

From the city wall, on which older and newer parts were discernible, low trees growing along the ground spread towards the slightly elevated pasture-land.

Troy had been a pastoral village, built of dark, unhewn stones from the surrounding region. The houses had flat roofs on which grasses grew. Small dark window-openings gaped into the sunlight. The walls enclosing small farmsteads were rough.

The newer part abutted directly on the old. It displayed the influence of the highly-developed Greek architectural style, though plainer and more austere than were the buildings of ancient Hellas. Everything was simple and somewhat crude.

The mighty gate of the castle creaked as it opened. Square towers stood on either side of it. These were adjoined by a high wall, sufficiently wide to permit a person's walking on it. Behind it was a wide, deep moat, lined with smooth stones. Opposite the gate was a broad wooden bridge that was drawn up with the aid of an unwieldy folding mechanism.

Behind the moat was a square paved with large stones. To its right stood a tall pillared building, straight ahead rose a second wall with a gate, and to the left, adjoining it, was a lofty hall with an inner and an outer passage.

The inner passage led into what appeared to be cellar-rooms in which stood huge clay vessels. Then followed large storerooms filled with food supplies.

A second courtyard was full of wagons and farming implements. It was surrounded by stables housing many beautiful animals, especially cows, bulls and calves. The horses were quartered separately, together with some ass-like animals. A huge dog with shaggy, yellowish-grey fur guarded the stalls.

To the left a gate led into a sombre, quiet laurel-grove. Sand-paths, all connected, ran through it, forming a square. Along them at intervals stood stone benches. In the centre was a stone basin with water and fish.

Between closely-trimmed pollards, a path led to a dark wall in the old part of the castle. The King's throne stood in a huge anteroom supported by wooden pillars. From here a steep, wide staircase led into the upper rooms. The beams were dark brown and sombre looking; the walls and pillars bristled with weapons of all kinds.

On the other side of the room were tall windows, opening on to a bright courtyard. There were trees and a few flowering hedges framed by pillared halls on whose flat roofs gardens had been laid out. Their luxuriant vines hung far down over the walls.

Above the great hall of the old castle were many rooms. The outermost of these was a corner-room offering a clear view over courtyards and a part of the older suburb, right down to the sea. From the other side the lively activity in the farmyard could be observed.

Colourful drawings adorned the walls of this beautiful, large room; in it stood golden and earthenware vessels.

A bronze couch with furs and a head-roll was in one corner. Chests of clothing lined the walls. The floor was made of colourful tiles.

It was the Queen's room. Beside it there was a second room with martial weapons, trophies and implements. A low, broad table covered with pictures and drawings indicated that this was the King's workroom. It was Priam's favourite place.

The rooms of the women were adjacent to the Queen's apartment, while those of the men adjoined that of the King.

A special part of the castle which could only be reached through the courtyard or the women's apartments accommodated the utility-rooms. Maids of all ages worked here.

Adjacent to the old castle was the new edifice, which resembled a temple, and contained the banqueting halls. It was surrounded by magnificent gardens within a high-walled enclosure.

Brisk activity filled the rooms of the castle. The people were of noble form, approaching the prototype of animistic gods.

In the Queen's apartment stood a tall, vigorous man in the panoply of a warrior, armed with cuirass and a Greek helmet decorated with horsehair. His earnest face was framed by a short, curly beard which at one time may have been dark brown, but now it was mostly grey. The mouth was well-formed, with beautiful teeth. The narrow, finely-shaped nose gave his face an unusual expression, and the furrows on either side of it bespoke will-power and battles won. The grey-blue eyes shone and gazed with the kindly sincerity of the mature human being. They could express courage, even anger, and then again radiate

172

love like the eyes of a happy child. The deeply-furrowed high forehead was shaded by the heavy helmet. The broad hands looked as if they were capable of hard work, as if they might guide a plough as easily as a charger; as if they might indeed wield the sword well, but were equally able to lead the community, the court and the army wisely. Priam's whole being expressed disciplined superiority. Everyone looked up to him with complete confidence.

He was joined by Hector, also in warrior's array, who was taller and leaner than Priam. His supple movements showed that he too was master in the use of weapons. His face was bronzed; tanned by the southern sun. Dark brown hair fell in short curls over his forehead and temples.

His large dark eyes sparkled with cheerfulness and vitality. In his demeanour there was harmony between body and soul, simplicity and clarity.

Hector too was wearing a silver helmet. Around his shoulders he wore a white cape which concealed the chain-mail. Impetuously he took the shield in his hand and rushed from the room with an exultant cry; he was hoping for a new victory in the martial exercises with his brothers.

Now the heavy portiere of the adjoining room opened, and a slender maiden stood in the doorway. Her Greek garment left arms and shoulders bare; the dark, wavy, abundant hair fell over her shoulders, and was held together with a broad white ribbon above the forehead. The narrow face with the delicate nose resembled Hecuba's, except for wider cheek-bones and a higher, more rounded forehead. Her vivid slate-blue eyes shone, large and earnest.

She extended her small, strong hands towards her father who was about to embark on a distant military expedition; her face expressed love and timid veneration.

This hour in which Priam told her of his intention became for Cassandra the first step into her destiny.

Until then she had been well protected and cared for – loyally waited upon by maidservants, loved by her brothers and sisters, carefully guarded by her mother's watchful eye.

Like a bud that has not yet reached the moment of maturity and is shaded and protected by the leaves and flowers surrounding it, so this pure, chosen blossom was maturing.

A Light had arisen over the walls of Troy, the Light to illumine coming generations! Before the great Greek people could sow the seed of depravity within the walls of Troy, this Light was sent by the Highest Will.

For Cassandra a cloak and the soil were to be provided in the earthly form of a healthy royal scion, enabling her to prosper and develop to become the Light of the World and the salvation of woman, to strengthen and guide the spirit, to maintain life and restore the peoples to health!

As yet no one in the halls of Troy knew what Treasure had been entrusted to them. This shepherd-people was gifted with a natural unspoiled appreciation of all that is essential to earthly life, and so were their princes. Their city could become a centre for commerce and shipping, for all the branches of art and science that were beginning to flourish, and at the same time a bridge to the remote realms of the East.

For these reasons Troy was watched furtively from across the sea; it was envied, even openly attacked. Hence the peace-loving shepherds and farmers had no choice but to grow into strong warriors. This was possible, for the people were innately healthy and natural, open to all purity and clarity, and they were guided by high Power.

Just as they grew strong, unassuming and faithful in the conduct of their earthly lives, so too they served the gods like pure, trusting children.

And from the highest Heights, whose existence was still unsuspected by them, this people had been granted in Cassandra a Helper for their further ascent.

WHEN SHE was fifteen years old, Cassandra's soul was seized by a wild impetuous yearning. She sought to flee the constant activity in the house, and whenever she could do so unnoticed went into the gardens

174

which, with their secluded dark grassy coves, invited her to muse and dream. She longed for solitude.

Otherwise she was cheerful and active in the circle of her brothers and sisters and with domestic duties. She liked being with the maids, for she always wanted to have something to do. Her alert mind also strove to survey everything that happened in house and home so that she could faithfully relate it all to her mother.

She felt particularly drawn to the animals; quietly and with great attentiveness she supervised their care. This endeared her very much to the farm-hands, who were happy when they heard her clear, ringing voice in the courtyard. Then a gentle smile would flit across the face of even the most peevish of the old men. All looked up from their work, greeted her and exchanged a few cheerful words whenever she passed.

To diseased or weak animals she devoted special care. The chief stable-hand even insisted that the large black bull would have died had it not been for Cassandra, who dug her little hand into the curls of its head just in time.

And yet, all at once that noticeable gravity had come upon her, driving her into the gardens on her own. She sought out the statues of the gods which, white and silent, gazed down upon her from inside the dark niches of trees. The shade of the laurel had a special attraction for her, and she imagined hearing lovely tones in the grotto of Apollo whenever she walked softly past it. But she neither dared to go inside nor to remain standing outside. Shy as a deer, she sprang past it, and hid nearby.

One midday when everyone in the castle sought shelter from the burning sun, the cool of the grove and its deep shadows again attracted her. She felt an intense pressing pain, like a ring of iron around her head, and the palms of her hands and soles of her feet were burning. Her eyes glistened with suppressed tears; a painful pressure weighed on her heart, which was beating fitfully as if seeking to escape the crushing fist of a giant.

Cassandra no longer understood herself. She did not know where she belonged; nothing tied her to her brothers and sisters, nothing to her parents, nor to the court and the house at this hour. She did not

175

think of her far distant beloved father, nor of her brother, Paris, of whom confused, disquieting news had come from across the sea.

Again she arrived at Apollo's grotto, in whose cupola the sunbeams were reflected, bathing the white figure of Apollo in the brilliance of his star. A spring was bubbling softly; its fine mist refracted the sunlight as well.

In an anxious intuitive perceiving of pain and nostalgia for something unknown, Cassandra yielded completely to the magic of this hour.

Breathing deeply, she closed her eyes. It seemed to her that they had drawn into her soul the drifting clouds and the shining blue sky, and that, like a bird, she was flying in this radiant space. She felt so light.

From an immense distance a great brilliant Light was approaching her. It was surrounded by many rings of colour that gave forth rushing chords. With her soul wide-open, Cassandra listened.

A beautiful, luminous head, surrounded by flowing curly hair, inclined towards her, breathing upon her and thus awakening within her the gift of wisdom and prophecy, which had been bestowed by a higher Power for her earthly path.

While on earth she was enveloped by the protection of the highest animistic helpers. Apollo had visibly approached her and removed a bandage from her eyes. Now she was permitted to look into the Animistic Realm, which she regarded as her home.

The sun was already setting when Cassandra recovered her senses. Her head was clear and her body vigorous. The sadness had vanished, and her eyes shone like two brilliant suns. For the first time she found that the words of a prayer evoked a clear resonance within her soul; this made her happy.

From that day Cassandra changed noticeably. The impetuous child became a quiet, thoughtful maiden with radiant eyes. A luminosity emanated from her, the glow of purity and of freshness that are part of a childlike nature, and a clear light shone upon her forehead.

Everyone looked at her wonder-struck when she appeared unexpectedly among the maidservants or in the circle of women, and people began to whisper furtively about her.

176

"Is it not as though one of the eternal ones had consecrated her for service?" asked Andromache, the quiet, sad one, who day in, day out, waited anxiously for her far-away husband.

Time passed swiftly. Those were happy days for Cassandra, who under the guidance of lofty Powers obtained insight into the Laws of Nature, after the bandage had been removed from her spiritual eyes.

She had no wish to be consecrated as a priestess; she remained aloof from the pious songs in the temples, and this did not at all endear her to the priests.

She was unassuming and quiet, occasionally diffident, when she perceived in the false conduct of the courtiers anything unnatural, anything in conflict with her nature. Then she would have dearly loved to flee her parents' castle, far away, to the realms into which Apollo permitted her to gaze.

But each of her secret pains, borne in silence, brought ample reward through higher recognitions and personal development. With great love she tried to make use of the fruits of her rich experiencing for the benefit of her fellow-creatures. Yet it appeared that they could not understand what she so generously and blissfully tried to offer them in her opened hands. They did not see the fine working of the Laws, which began to flow radiantly from Cassandra, and would without fail have drawn to themselves the homogeneous species, love unto love.

But human beings were empty and unable to give, nor even to receive anything. This was a bitter pain for Cassandra, and she closed her hands. Only the lowliest of the servants, only the poorest of the poor, who stood begging at the gates, and above all the animals, strove towards her in love.

A vast knowledge of plants was revealed to her spirit. In order to retain everything made known to her through Apollo's power, she learned the art of writing.

A Greek student from Athens, whose ship had been washed up on the shores of Troy and who had been well received there, became her teacher. But she never spoke with him about the actual purpose of her thirst for knowledge.

The rocks also, and the forces of the earth, indeed even the forces of

177

the elements were revealed to her eager spirit, and many mysteries became comprehensible to her.

Often she recognised the causes of all man's inadequacies and weaknesses, and in her great longing to help she also found the means for their recovery.

A radiant weaving of helping spiritual forces began around her. Always she stood in a clear Light, from which all Darkness had to recoil. But it pained her to discover that her surroundings did not change. Not one strove to understand and follow her.

Her sisters and companions withdrew from her. They shrugged their shoulders derisively, and preferred that Cassandra leave them to their empty conversations about men, dresses and jewellery rather than entertain them with music or her lively observations of Nature and life. Giggling merrily they banded together, leaving the Pure Light to burn on a solitary height.

Sometimes Cassandra felt that she was living utterly in vain. Those were her most difficult hours.

ONCE, WHEN SHE WAS resting again in Apollo's grove, he appeared to her in a cloud. He sought to approach her in love, and showed her in alluring pictures what miracles of might she could accomplish in conjunction with his animistic power.

But there was a repelling force within her that startled even herself. With flaming words of anger she resisted his approach. She had no idea whence came the sudden conviction that she belonged to One Who was higher than all. The Power of God streamed through her.

And the Tempter, who had appeared in the guise of Apollo, vanished. – –

Suddenly a raging storm arose; the light of the sun faded, and swirling blackish grey mists scudded over Troy. In an instant everything was enveloped in darkness, and a terrible shaft of lightning struck the trunk of the acacia that stood beside the grotto. The thunder rumbled and roared, the earth quaked. Long after the clouds had drifted away, the sun was still without brilliance: for with the power of her will Artemis,

178

the Goddess of Purity, had overshadowed it. The face of the moon also darkened its lustre.

All of a sudden Cassandra was painfully aware that this darkening signified a bitter warning from the animistic beings, and that the Darkness would cast its shadows over her and her race for a long time to come.

She rose to her feet as though she had awakened from a dream. What was that Light which had shone for her, so familiar and yet so remote from the world? The blood was flowing in her veins as if permeated by liquid fire. She was invigorated by the stream of Light, not dazed, as she had thought at first. –

The stars, large and clear, gazed down gently from the sky which had been swept clean of clouds, as it was freed from the raging of the storm.

The darkened sun had gone down, and a starry night was dreaming quietly.

But today the glorious sky with its myriad shining worlds appeared dull and lacklustre to Cassandra, strange and cold, for she stood in the Ray of the Living Primordial Light which was her Home.

She had risen to a Height whose Radiance far surpassed that of the sun. She had been permitted a glimpse into her Luminous Homeland. –

The concept was still unclear within her soul as she returned to her earthly existence. But she was aware that much hardship still awaited her.

She saw herself treading a steep path, surrounded by people who picked up stones and flung them at her. Horrified, she felt the pain and would fain have fled, but the earth held her fast with a thousand bonds.

WHEN CASSANDRA entered the courtyard, the big watchdog was howling plaintively, and lay down at her feet. There was a dull, oppressive silence in the castle, only the lamenting tones of a flute sounded from the hills.

As soon as she entered, a hush fell over the room where the women sat working. Curious, unkind glances followed her, and foolish, superstitious nonsense was muttered behind her back.

The Darkness was massing.

It was human fear of the one who saw through everything, the fear which became suspicion, even hatred.

It touched Cassandra to the quick. What should she do? If she told them how she pitied them for entangling themselves in their base lies, they would simply deny everything. With bowed head she went into her room.

THAT NIGHT TWO SHEPHERDS stood on the pasture, near Troy's outermost gate. The sky shone deep blue, but above the castle they saw a Light in the form of a Cross.

MASSING EVER MORE, dark clouds drifted across from Greece. A storm had cast a small fleet ashore, thus saving Paris and Helen. Troy was seized with rejoicing as the couple strode through its gates. Dazzling was the radiance of their beauty, and splendid the feast that followed their reception.

But Cassandra could take no interest in it.

CASSANDRA WAS UNABLE to sleep. She saw ships on the high seas and recognised those of her father. They were sailing home, bringing ill tidings, and an ominous weight settled upon Cassandra.

With a lamp she entered her mother's apartment to tell her what she knew. But coldly and doubtfully Hecuba regarded her daughter, and shrugged her shoulders.

"Do not upset the house! Let us wait and see."

Even her mother did not believe her.

More solitary than ever she stood on this earth.

Meanwhile feasts were celebrated and the good things of the earth were squandered. With aching heart Cassandra heard the screaming, bawling revellers emerging from the halls. They were still celebrating the return of Paris.

With a burning torch she went among the drunkards, calling out to them:

"Soon your throats will fall silent, and you will regret not having saved the wine for the lean years!"

Laughter and shouting was the answer.

"The virtuous one should go to bed and sleep!"

Anger and loathing silenced Cassandra. She turned away. But the Flaming Breath of the Word had awakened in her, and worked on; she could now no longer keep silent! She heard a warning voice again and again telling of her people's fate if they would not listen. With upraised hands she begged that the great Light might release her, but she was given the answer:

"You must fulfil!"

AND IT WAS EXACTLY on the thirtieth day of the following month that her father's ships landed on the coast – as Cassandra had seen – and announced the imminent arrival of Menelaus.

Heavy clouds lay on Priam's brow. A discussion with Paris took place in the undisturbed privacy of the father's quiet room. Pale and thoughtful, with a matured expression of manly resolve on his face, the son left the room.

Then Cassandra was at his side. Lovingly, but emphatically, she laid her hand on his shoulder, and as she looked up at him, her shining eyes were ablaze. With words whose sound appeared even to her as the distant pealing of bells, she spoke to her brother. She spoke of the link between guilt and atonement, of man's free will and of his responsibility.

At first the words fell like gentle rain into his soul, understanding and comforting; then, however, she directed her warning out of the Spirit to the spirit. Like pinpricks the exhortations struck the sore spot of his conscience; Cassandra spoke warningly of the reciprocal effect of Eternal Justice. And finally came the demand:

"Recognise your guilt and take Helen back to her husband yourself! Save your people from destruction!"

181

Earnest of countenance, ever more dismayed, her brother listened to Cassandra. Where did she find these words? Whence did she draw the power? Open to everything sublime, pure and great, he at once perceived the Truth in her words, and sensed the Power of the Light-Will.

"Release yourself from the oppressive bonds, release yourself and strive towards the Truth, only then will you grasp what it means to stand free in the Light of God!"

Like a solemn entreaty to her beloved brother the words reverberated and died away in the passages. Covering his head from the Power of her words, he had fled, for he would not part from Helen.

Sadly Cassandra had to learn that the Truth can only gain a foothold where man is prepared to receive It, and where deed follows upon volition.

She wrapped a dark veil round her head as a token of mourning. For now she knew that Troy's fate was sealed.

ENORMOUS PREPARATIONS were being made to receive the enemy. With a watchful eye Priam directed everything. The people subordinated themselves to him willingly; there was diligent activity everywhere. All the store-rooms were well stocked, and the supply-routes were protected, so that the produce of the fields could be brought in.

The reserves of arms were ample, the buildings were strong and the bulwarks and ramparts judiciously laid out. The walls could defy the most powerful enemy, and a dogged will-power as well as trust in the protection of the gods made the defenders confident of victory.

With the courage of enthusiasm and all the flaming will-power of the race at that time, they hurled themselves into this battle against an enormously superior force.

Only Cassandra looked sorrowfully toward the outcome of this conflict. The wise women, who spun the threads of fate, had shown her in the mirror of the spirit what they were spinning, and unspeakable anxiety filled her breast.

The threatening weathers would not end that year; it seemed that Poseidon wanted to set all his storms against the Greeks. Thus Troy had ample time for the final preparations.

Hecuba had much to do, and all the women assisted her. A silent, oppressive sorrow, uncharacteristic of her otherwise so energetic and quick-acting nature, lay over her. It was as though she had to reflect on something beyond her comprehension, which she pushed away out of some inner fear. She divined that she would have to change completely if she were to find the solution to this enigma. For her this enigma was and remained her child, Cassandra.

Often Cassandra assailed her mother's soul with an impetuous insistence. With touching childlikeness she courted understanding from the austere, proud, and matter-of-fact woman. But often she avoided her mother for days, even weeks, and not one word of the most common kindness towards her passed her lips. Then much was spoilt in the taciturn mother who longed for warmth where Cassandra was only full of diffident reserve.

But the less trust evidenced by the mother towards Cassandra, the more uncommunicative did Cassandra become as well, and both these attitudes steadily widened the gulf between the women.

A deep ardour was peculiar to both of them. While Hecuba suppressed it, and thought she could smother it within her, Cassandra let it pour forth from the rich experiencing of her soul, which she brought to ever more glorious flower through the gifts of her spirit. Through the constantly active development of her spirit she had become like a shining vessel that was filled unceasingly and longed to pass on in a steady stream what she received.

But her mother was obstructing this wonderful rhythm of life in her. Instead of opening herself to the overflowing Blessing which sought to pour over her, she erected walls and coverings for herself that separated them for ever.

But the Power of the Omnipotent Light was not to be fettered. It poured out Its Blessing ever more strongly over Cassandra. Yet in her earthly life she lost more and more of the cheerfulness which had been the very essence of her nature. Wherever she went, barriers awaited her, which she had to break down if she was not to allow herself to be obstructed. Slowly life became a burden for her.

Only work afforded her comfort and release; Cassandra was particularly occupied with the preliminaries for the care of the sick. In this connection her extensive knowledge of herbs and the preparation of tinctures were of special help to her, so that she created astonishing things which had never been known before. On her animals she tested what was to bring healing to human beings; trustingly and willingly these animistic friends accepted from her pure hands what human beings would not have understood.

Within the walls of Troy two camps were gradually formed, at first imperceptibly so, but then, with increasing earthly struggles and cares, also manifestly: the one for and the other against Cassandra.

Slowly the news had reached the people about how great and rich was her knowledge of Nature's secret forces, of soul and body. It was also said that sometimes she conversed secretly with invisible beings in the gardens and groves.

The people had grown superstitious ever since the hour when the sun had eclipsed. Cassandra was linked with this celestial event in which they fancied they recognised the wrath of Apollo. No one knew how the people arrived at this conjecture, but there was much whispering about it.

Cassandra was not troubled by what the people said; indeed she herself heard the least of it. But Hecuba was all the more irritated by it, for she abhorred any talk about her daughter's wisdom. Cassandra's warnings became increasingly irksome and upsetting to her mother's existence; increasingly she disturbed the souls of her brothers and sisters, as well as of the others in the palace.

And strange to say, whether she spoke or was silent, every one asked himself quietly: what will Cassandra say about it? Yet they little heeded her advice, which was always judicious, simple and natural. But if they did not follow it, their decisions invariably miscarried. Then, however, they would not admit to the truth of what they had been told.

To Cassandra the people were inscrutable; she hardly felt sorry for them any more when they went astray. Nor was she any longer surprised at their injustices; like a child she only rejoiced when she encountered a human being who was different.

But this joy was granted her less and less, for with the mounting cares, the bad qualities of human beings were likewise aggravated, even to outbreaks of the most violent emotions. It was always Cassandra who released these, often through a word, often simply through her presence. So strongly was the Power of the Light expressed through her that everything ugly and wrong reared up and was exposed as soon as she drew near.

Amazed, Priam observed his daughter's unusual nature. She who appeared so unassuming and pure, so unapproachable in her regal equanimity, who was so touching in her delicate womanliness, she called forth many a storm around him, so that he had much to settle. At times Hecuba behaved like a fury.

THE STORMS HAD abated, and the sea was still, deathly still. Above it shone a great red fiery star: Mars was particularly close to the earth.

Among the highest in the land a quarrel had broken out about whether Paris should hazard the voyage with Helen. Cassandra implored him to set sail, otherwise they would be doomed to destruction. Scorn and reproaches were the only answer.

The sea was so calm that a voyage was unthinkable. It was decided to consult the oracle.

But the oracle was silent; all the seers were silent since Cassandra had spoken.

Hecuba flew into a rage. Openly, in front of the maidservants, she abused her daughter, accusing her of disturbing the oracle. As Hecuba was uttering these words, Cassandra saw a black bitch with bared teeth standing beside Hecuba, and from that hour her mother's face always appeared to her only blindfolded. At first it grieved her, then she bore it in silence. Cassandra strove to become ever more reserved, and to let people do what they would not give up in any case. Her spirit had the connection with the Light, which guided her into ever-increasing and gladdening clarity. She knew her second ego to be there.

185

Powerful streams flowed down to her in moments of holy absorption, and thence, out of the Light of the White Dove, came to her also the Knowledge about all things and the Knowledge of the One God.

These were the hours in which Cassandra was linked with the Source of her Origin and, newly armed, followed her earthly path to further fulfilment.

Her lips spoke less and less, but all the more aptly and unforgettably.

THE SHIPS WERE IN READINESS. Concealed from spies, they lay prepared to put out to sea and to reconnoitre, manned by able warriors and commanded by the bravest heroes. Priam, Hector and Paris however were to remain ashore. The ships were awaiting a favourable wind.

At night the falcons screeched menacingly. Hecuba tossed restlessly on her bed. Since she had reviled her daughter, her soul no longer found peace; melancholy faces with unsteady, glowing eyes stared at her. Shadows approached her, attracted by her thoughts, and would not depart from her. Fearfully, her solicitous love clung to her sons. A foreboding of the danger arose in her. She was dominated by anxiety and passionate maternal love.

The more her love was consumed in fear for her sons, the greater became her secret rancour against Cassandra, and soon she began to fear her clear, knowing eyes. She closed her heart, indeed finally even the door of her room, to her daughter.

But Cassandra did not rest. The more she discerned Hecuba's sorry state, the more faithfully she watched over house and court and over her dear ones. No one was to sense that in the grave time of impending danger the mistress of the house was failing them. Quietly and inconspicuously she did her work, quietly she withdrew when her mother intervened actively.

All perceived the blessing of her diligent hands, but no one endeavoured to find an explanation for the simple greatness of her being. On the contrary, everything was made even more difficult for her through the egotism and obstinacy with which she was opposed. Thus her life had become a cruel struggle.

THE WIND HAD TURNED, the ships set sail. From the high tower they were greeted by a horn, another answered from the sea. Once they came into better winds, they sped along swift as arrows. The oarsmen did not need to exert themselves. Well armed and equipped they set forth with pennants fluttering merrily in the wind.

The shores were guarded, the men were armed and the gates fortified, the weapons glinted brightly in the sun. Troy appeared festively prepared.

There were heavy seas, and the winds carried the ships to Hellas by the shortest route. The waves lashed against the planks, spraying their foam high into the sails. The storm drove the ships apart, but they soon came together again. It felt to them as though they had never before sailed so unitedly. At the top of the swiftest sailing vessel a light, in the form of a flying bird within a luminous circle, sometimes gleamed white and spectral. It always appeared in moments of danger. The warriors were not afraid; they knew that they were under the protection of the eternal ones.

They could hardly discern anything for the waves, mist and spray. Through the raging of the elements a sound resembling the wailing of a horn was heard at times. They were approaching this sound. But they did not want to sail too far out lest their return be cut off.

Towards morning the sea suddenly became calm, and after some hours the visibility cleared. There, in the distance, they sighted ten Greek ships which were grouping. On the swiftest of these was the image of a dragon. They must be huge ships, far superior to those of the Trojans. Therefore they decided not to risk battle on the open seas, but to sail back. They now had a moderate breeze; with their lighter vessels they made more rapid progress than the Greeks. As a result the distance between them increased steadily, and again the gods seemed to favour them.

Cassandra knew how matters stood; she had mounted the tower, which afforded the furthest view across the open sea, and there she recognised the place where her people would await the Greeks. She told Priam, who then prepared the departure of additional ships under Hector's command.

187

Expectant silence lay over the land, and it was as though the sea were gently rumbling. Towards midday the sky became overcast, the air was vibrating, and blackish green waves pressed towards the shores of Troy. Cassandra felt a burning restlessness and impatience within her as she awaited fresh tidings. A small sailing-vessel landed, bringing news of the ships.

It turned out that Cassandra had been right. Her brothers gazed at her in silent admiration. Priam, however, quietly thanked the gods.

Cassandra was moved to joy by the change in her dear ones. She could give them more good news. The Greeks had been dispersed, and the Trojan ships were able to sink a large hostile vessel without difficulty. They had hurled rings of fire at it and thrown spears. It had gone down with everything on board.

This news too was soon brought to Troy by a messenger, and triumphant rejoicing filled the city. Already everyone believed that the Greeks would be repelled with ease. They made great thank-offerings, lit fires, the women bound wreaths of flowers and adorned the statues of their gods and the altars. Animals were slaughtered and presented to the priests. Loud jubilation resounded across Troy; people were in raptures.

On the largest square, where the hall of the elders stood, and praying women walked to the Temple, the exultant crowd thronged. They had caught sight of Cassandra on the tower and hailed her, the herald of their joys; they called her their patroness, the favourite of the gods.

But Cassandra was not pleased.

"As they acclaim me today, so will they stone me tomorrow," she said to the watchman, who was standing beside her. He stared at her dumbstruck.

"I could prove it to you instantly," said she when she saw his disbelief. "I need only go down and tell them that their rejoicing is premature, that it is madness. Instead they should quietly hope, and each fulfil his duty; they should not sacrifice hundreds of animals which they will yet need for food, nor throw the precious bread and grain into the fire. Believe me, the gods delight far more in a genuine sense of gratitude, which unites with them, than in orgies of joy that stem only from base instincts and squander the gifts of God in sinful dissipation."

And she went down to Priam and asked him to forbid these senseless deeds. Hecuba looked at her scornfully. Like venom the words escaped her lips:

"Would you even deprive them of this joy after constantly plunging us into anxiety with your pessimistic visions? You are mad in your conceit!"

But Priam went quietly outside and pondered his daughter's wise words.

ONE NIGHT there was a knock on her door. Cassandra sprang up and was soon standing before the messenger of the watchman.

"Diodoros sends you word that it is time," and he went before her to light the way.

Their steps echoed through the succession of corridors; they mounted the steep flight of stairs to the roof-garden. There a gate led into the tower, up many steps, past the chambers well-stocked with missiles and arrows, past the chests filled with torches and the large oil-casters. Cassandra hurried right up to the watchman's room and on to the platform. All fatigue had left her.

Her keen eyes peered towards the sea. All still seemed calm out there, but far, far away in the north-east the mists had taken on a red glow. Surely that could not be the sun?

The smell of burning was borne through the air; a faint tremor of excitement ran through her, and the cool morning breeze made her shiver.

Was that not the blast of a strange horn far away? For some time she strained her ears. A strong breeze was blowing from the east.

Now she felt as if she were standing on a great ship with huge red sails full-blown. Its masts were dark brown, as was the timber of its hull. Strong ropes secured the sails, and a dragon could be seen on the vessel's prow. On the bridge stood a tall heroic man with shining eyes, facing her. He was very handsome, like an earthly embodiment of Mars. Around him was a glow of heroic courage and unusual strength.

189

A flaming love of adventure shone from his golden brown eyes. His helmet gleamed in the light of a nearby fire. The oars beat time, creaking as they bent. A sharp wind whistled about the masts. The ship shuddered as it caught the impact of the waves.

Suddenly the captain caught sight of Cassandra.

"Hello, you beautiful young maiden, are you one of the naiads?" Thus rang the words from his laughing mouth. "Surely you bring me good portents, you bring tidings of imminent victory!"

This was Odysseus, King of Ithaca, who had vowed his help to Menelaus against Paris, the abductor. Cassandra had seen him, had heard his voice and recognised his nature. She knew that he was the most astute of their enemies, and she dreaded his strength.

Her spirit had hastened in advance of events. Near the enemy, at times even visible to him, she experienced the battle of Odysseus with the Trojan fleet. Flames shot up from a Trojan ship, and one of the Greeks' vessels sank. Her people yielded, and in the distance the helpers of Odysseus came in view.

Awakening, she found herself on the tower. The wind caught up her veil and, leaning far forward, she gazed steadfastly into the distance. Black smoke hung over the sea, which reflected the first rays of the rising sunlight. Around the smoke quivered the hot breath of flames in a ruddy glow. But the burning ships could not be seen.

Yet one thing was clear: before evening her people would have to put out to sea and rush to the aid of the outposts, otherwise it would be too late. In haste Cassandra left the tower.

DURING THESE DAYS the people took a lively interest in all that came to pass. Questions and speculations flew about the city. Above all, however, the people concerned themselves with the rumours about Cassandra's prophecies; this greatly angered the priests. The love and reverence offered her quite naturally by the people were merely the reciprocal effects of the love which she bestowed in such full measure. But the priests did not know this; covertly they accused her of black magic, and became her enemies.

At that time, however, all that opposed Cassandra was restrained by the delicate threads weaving a protection around her. Automatically human beings either excluded themselves from Love's pure weaving, or they opened themselves to It, thereby treading the path to God, according to the Law.

IN WARNING, CASSANDRA had called her father to battle. The heroes followed with rejoicing. Solicitously the women prepared the meal, and aided the final preparations.

The torches illuminating the great hall blazed brightly, and servants brought the gleaming utensils for the meal. Golden vessels filled with exquisite wine were passed round.

The ships were ready and awaited the signal for departure. The city became quiet, all lights had to be extinguished. Darkness was to await the enemy and unsettle him.

The hymns of the priests resounded in the temples; they consulted the oracle, but received no answer. The gods remained dumb and a bleak, dull silence of uneasy suspense lay over Troy. Cassandra had told her father of the battle with Odysseus, but no one else was aware of the situation.

Everyone had long since gone to rest when things began to stir down at the shore. Quietly and in utter darkness ships put out to sea, towards the enemy. Keeping a careful watch, they remained within reasonable distance. Softly they glided over the water, cruising back and forth, pulling their oars silently.

But even before new moon, the ships returned, with the news that they were being followed by Odysseus and other vessels. And no sooner had they reached their home shores than they heard the blast of the horns challenging them.

Thus began the tragic fate of Troy. One battle succeeded another – combats with fire and sword and frightful missiles. Ferocious as lions and full of courage the Trojans fought, but the Greeks were equal opponents of great gallantry.

During the first few years it was a noble trial of strength, a war inspired with genius and shrewdness. Much blood was shed; mothers mourned their sons, wives their husbands. Innumerable ships were lost, and the events impressed their traces deeply in the souls of the people.

Gradually the bitterness grew; the hatred mounted, the furies raged through the lands, fanning rage with torch and whip; seething, the Darkness hissed across the earth. Cassandra was overcome with horror. Again and again the Trojans repulsed the ships; ever more numerous and embittered became the attacks.

Many severely-wounded soldiers were carried inside the walls of Troy. Cassandra nursed them with the assistance of wise doctors and competent women. Healing was in her word, healing in her hand; everyone whom she passed felt strengthened. Her sphere of activity grew ever larger, as did that of her spiritual influence. And the best and purest wanted to serve her helpfully, happy to be allowed in her proximity. Peace radiated from her.

Hecuba's oppressive words could no longer reach her. Cassandra went her own way which was ordained by higher Laws.

THE DIN OF BATTLE HOVERED over the waters: shouting and yelling, the blowing of horns and the shrill whistling of missiles. Axes struck the cracking planks resoundingly, and the steam of the boiling sea mixed with the fumes of smoking, charred beams. Tattered sails, soaked with hot oil, floated on the waves, burning. Eerie lights illuminated terrible scenes of horror. The dense black smoke of the burning ships rolled on for miles, obscuring all visibility.

Great was the anxiety in Troy. The Greeks had received enormous reinforcements – that much was known, but the battle had lasted for days, and still no message had reached the shore. The people were beginning to feel uneasy.

They had gradually abandoned all hope that the enemy would withdraw, and the nearness of the hostile fleet was very oppressive. Horrified, they saw it constantly augmented despite all losses. New reinforcements came repeatedly through the wealthy Agamemnon, who had assumed command of the war.

In unguarded moments Cassandra wrung her hands. She was no longer to intervene with her Knowledge, the Spirit from the Light would not have it. She was silent and sad, full of unrest and anxiety for her dear ones, for the city, for the people. Who was to keep watch, who was to warn? For they were all blind and deaf, full of self-seeking and passion. Fear aroused the evil instincts in human beings. They had isolated themselves from the connection with the Pure Help. The Darkness, ever anew generating horrible forms, lay tenaciously over Troy and Greece.

Full of wrath, Pallas Athene stood over the countries. She held the shield with the terrible serpent-head of Medusa before her radiant countenance, and it leered mercilessly at the people. Cruelty and lewdness increased boundlessly. Women especially degenerated. The savage experience of war, the separation from the men, brought about frightful conditions in the Hellenic cities. Women sank ever lower. The worship of gods became idolatry.

FROM OUT OF THE Eternal Father's Love a veil was placed before Cassandra's seeing eyes. When she suddenly kept silent, and no longer intervened in the actions of human beings, they soon forgot what she had taught them, what she had bestowed upon them. The love and respect formerly shown towards her by many was exhausted, and she became more and more solitary.

She longed for the Light of her Home, and the petition broke forth from her heart:

"Thou Eternal One, All-One, what have I done, why dost Thou smite me? Take this bitter cup from me! – – Yet not my will, but Thy Will be done!"

With that a rushing burst through the walls, the house shook. Light flooded the room; within It a Cross shone forth. A Voice spoke:

"Hear Me, Maria, I AM HE Who calleth thee, endure! Thine is the Realm and the Love, Bearer of Love! I am One with the Father, and thou art Part of Me!"

Out of the Light a Countenance of great purity, severity and, at the same time, goodness gazed upon her. The Eye was aglow with the Light of Life.

Now Cassandra knew why she had been deprived of her clairvoyance: it had been done out of love, for her completion.

This was Cassandra's preparation for the most difficult part of her earthly existence.

TERRIBLE YEARS FOLLOWED for Troy in the Judgment of God!

The defeat at sea had been heavy. More than half of the ships had been destroyed by fire; with them the majority of the warriors had perished. Those who could still be saved either were severely wounded or succumbed to their burns. Fortunately Hector was still able, just in time, to save himself together with his elite band and the remainder of the ships.

Grim and embittered, exhausted from battle, soiled with soot and blood, thus they returned. There was much work and agitation in the castle. But the enemies were unflagging; they continued the war, forced the landing and surrender of the fleet. The noise of battle no longer abated. A gigantic arc of Greek ships encircled the coast of Troy.

After a brief pause the Spartans engaged their men. Foot-soldiers and cavalry took up their positions on the shore, and pitched the tents there. The King's tent shone red among the others; it was well guarded.

Horror-stricken, the Trojans peered out from their walls at the host of their enemies. They had not imagined Agamemnon's assault to be so overwhelming. But bravely and tenaciously they defended every inch of their native soil, and much blood was shed.

Paris fought like a young lion. Wherever he appeared the troops of the Greeks massed. They would have loved to capture him; for he was the object of their greatest wrath, he and Hector, who never let his brother out of sight. Odysseus was his most ferocious opponent.

Soon the encampment of the Greeks extended in a semi-circle along Troy's shores, moving closer to the city each day.

The Trojans had to muster all their forces in order to brave the assault of this superior strength and not lose contact with the hinterland.

Months and years went by in that way and many passed into the Realm of Shadows. Fresh youth grew up. They were evidence of the number of years which elapsed, never-ending, ever the same in the ups and downs of the capricious fortunes of war that had subjugated all. Disease had broken out among the Greeks; it was attributed to a poisoning of the wells. The first signs of epidemic-death – the vultures – moved in circles over the battlefield, screeching.

The gates of the city were firmly shut; they bade defiance with broad strong walls and towers. The armouries bristled with weapons. But below in the depths the treasures of the realm were piled in bales, and the huge stores of choice wine offered comfort against the fear of succumbing to thirst.

Priam led the army and the people with strength and prudence. They all showed him love and respect. Loyally and gratefully they looked up to their ageing ruler.

Hecuba had changed very much. A secret feeling of guilt preyed upon her soul. Restlessness and a terrible fear of the furies tormented her all the time. Her outbursts of rage terrified everyone. Little remained of the once so clear and judicious woman. Cassandra no longer suffered under her mother; so far as she was concerned Hecuba was a sick, indeed a dead, person.

ULTIMATELY THE BESIEGED were forced to retreat inside the walls of Troy. They were now cut off from the rest of the country, of which vast stretches lay bleak and deserted, for fear had driven all those who had once lived there into the city.

The Greeks cherished the hope that the Trojans would soon run out of food, but they did not reckon with the prudent foresight and planning of Priam. They plagued the city in all kinds of ways and challenged the heroes to venture a sortie. Yet the Trojans were as wily as they were courageous, and did not readily allow themselves to be outwitted. They also did much damage to the Greeks.

The walls were heavily assailed, and shuddered dreadfully; the whole city trembled from the thrusts of the assault weapons which, like huge

towers and battering rams, kept pounding the ramparts. Large catapults hurled enormous stones.

Cracking and bursting, many a missile caused great damage, but still
it could not weaken the strong defence of Troy.

The Greeks had not imagined it to be so hard. Moreover they realised that Helen was still within the walls of Troy, and therefore they
did not want to destroy the city completely. Repeatedly Menelaus de-
terred them from doing so. Disgruntled they deliberated at night in
Agamemnon's tent.

The water had been cut off long ago, the wells had been destroyed,
but in Troy neither man nor beast appeared to be suffering from thirst.
Did they have a secret spring?

Food had become scarce, but it was wisely and sparingly distributed.
Priam maintained strict discipline. Whoever did not comply was killed.
Although clandestine agitators arose among the people, they were
quickly silenced by the people themselves.

In their affliction more love was spreading among those who were
good than had been the case in times of prosperity. Cassandra worked
hard for the sick and supervised their care. She never went among
the others, for they shunned her, and that grieved Cassandra. The
priests had spread the rumour that she had become insane, and since
the majority of the people believed the priests, she was anxiously
avoided.

Troubled, Priam regarded the daughter who was such a great support to him. In his eyes she wore a luminous crown on her head; to him
she was like a gift from the Luminous Heights. He did not understand
why people tormented her. In his opinion she had never yet said or
done anything foolish. Had he become too old to understand? She was
never with the others; she was always at work and always silent. But a
serene Light was spreading more and more about Cassandra.

THEN CAME THE GREAT day for the Greeks. They worked tirelessly; no
one knew what they were doing. But one night it was suddenly very
quiet around Troy: no attack, no barking of dogs, no neighing of hor-

196

ses. It was an almost sinister quiet. Yet it was soothing, for the previous weeks had been difficult for Troy. Hunger had now set in after all. Nearly all the animals had to be slaughtered because of the water shortage. Bread was becoming scarce, for two of the large granaries had been destroyed by fire.

The old and the children crept about like ghosts, since the men and the youths had to be provided for first; they were given a larger amount of food, but had nevertheless grown thin and weary.

Increasingly, dirt and disease were rampant. The doctors could hardly cope with the work, and the fires that cremated the dead were burning day and night. Black wings of death spread out over Troy.

The young warriors wanted to undertake a sortie, but Priam strictly forbade it. They had never seen him so furious. What then was he still hoping for? Did he want to condemn them all to death by starvation, to waiting idly until the end came? They clashed angrily.

The outcome was different from what they had all expected. When dawn broke, the watchman blew jubilantly into his horn. What kind of sound was that? It sent a shudder through them all. Was it alarm or joy? Again the trumpet blared forth, loud, ever louder it rang jubilantly across the city. Was there to be an attack after all? What of the enemy's reply to this provocative tone? Everyone rushed on to towers, rooftops and walls, Cassandra being one of the first.

The sea was deserted and calm, smooth as a mirror.

Where were the ships of the Greeks? Where were their camps? They saw only scattered implements: battering-rams, stones and catapults, but these appeared to be useless. And what was that standing below on the shore? A gigantic animal, the replica of a Greek horse, stiff, long-legged and ungainly.

Intuitively Cassandra perceived disquiet and terror at the sight of it, but all the others were full of exultant joy. The gates of the city burst open and the people streamed out into the sunlight. Freedom after the strain of ten years of war, a gift from the gods!

They skipped about with happiness like children and embraced one another. They went to the beach and roamed all through the deserted camps where they found bread and wine in abundance. Happy and grateful, they enjoyed the moment. Only a few cautious ones, Priam and Hector among them, were filled with suspicion.

Suddenly a cry arose in the crowd:

"Let us take the horse into the city!"

And they mounted it with ladders, for it was very tall, made wreaths and decorated it like a sacrificial animal.

Suddenly there was a shrill cry from the tower:

"Woe betide, woe betide you, woe betide Troy! Do not let yourselves be tempted. Be warned, burn it down to ashes and dust!"

There was a hush, then a grumbling, a resentful rumbling arose, a scornful, piercing derision! After that, silence again.

They placed the animal on rollers so that it could be moved, and again the warning call rang out:

"Woe betide Troy! Be warned, burn it down!"

And Priam ordered that they should leave it where it was for the time being. So they went back into the city, grumbling, and cursing Cassandra.

ALL DAY LONG the Trojans ran through the streets rejoicing and shouting in jubilant excitement. A more flagrant contrast between this day and the previous one could hardly be imagined. Adorned with flowers, waving colourful cloths, they danced to the sound of pipes.

In the great square before the temple a fire was lit, into which they cast fruits and flowers, maintaining it until evening. Choruses of gratitude were spoken in the temples. The white-clad priests walked about praying and burning aromatic herbs. Flames shone in bowls before the houses, and flowers were thrown out of the windows. The jubilation was unequalled.

Then night descended. The last glowing streak of the red sun faded away in the west on the edge of the sea; the stars were already shining, and over Troy glimmered the light of festive fires. Disregarding Cassandra's words and Priam's command, the people went out through the great gate.

Dark and ominous, the Greek colossus, the strong battering-rams, still stood by the walls as sombre reminders of past days of horror. They glinted eerily in the colourful glow of the bonfires. The rutted, trampled roads still spoke clearly of the recent years of war. The earth was devastated for a long time to come. Shadowy figures flitted about: the earthbound fallen who were awaiting redemption.

Soldiers, townsmen and farmers staggered out of the gate in a procession. They were joined by the fallen in long rows, dancing around them merrily. But some shook their fists in warning, trying to restrain the crowd.

Thus did the people approach the beach where the decorated horse was awaiting them. They danced around it in a wild frenzy of joy. Then the procession began moving at a snail's pace back towards the city with the colossal beast in their midst.

Loud warning shouts echoed through the passages of the castle, across the rooftops, through the courtyards and walls. Restless, tireless, Cassandra ran to and fro, filled with the consuming fire of terrible knowledge, tear-stained, with large shining eyes and imploring hands raised on high. Thus she roamed the halls and groves, the gardens and streets, not heeding people, some of whom shrank back nervously, while others mocked her in laughing derision.

At a distance the loyal watchman followed her, and by her side trotted the great light-brown watchdog. With a voice that made the walls quake she called again and again the warning "Woe betide" across Troy.

The stones trembled, but human beings paid her no heed. At the gate she pushed back the gaping throng, and stood before it, garbed in white, with her arms wide open. Thus she waited, solitary, aglow with the volition of her conviction, and defied the whole people. The procession drew ever nearer. Now the first of them saw Cassandra; they hesitated, stopped short and conferred. A whip cracked, a voice shouted, horses came galloping towards the scene and dispersed the crowd, and the raging throng of mad people surged towards Cassandra.

"Down with the crazy one who grudges us our joy!" screamed one person.

Howling, the great dog leapt at his throat. The crowd of people rolled on. The strong arm of a soldier pulled Cassandra back, and instantly she was surrounded by warriors under the command of a captain.

"Come with me in the name of Hecuba, Cassandra!"

And they took her into their midst like a criminal and led her up into the castle.

Hecuba did not appear. It was as if no one knew about Cassandra. Like a stranger she was led by the soldiers through the inner courtyard gate. They opened a little room on the ground floor and confined her there. Cassandra was not despondent, rather as though benumbed. She heard only a Voice saying the words:

"Follow Me; for I am in the Father and thou art a Part of Me!"

An indescribable, supernatural Power sustained her.

MANY LONG HOURS must have gone by. The streets had become quiet, and the bonfires had nearly gone out. Everyone enjoyed the relief of sleep in the feeling of liberation. They were all exhausted from the excitement they had gone through. Only the faithful watchman did not sleep, he kept guard before Cassandra's prison. A dim lamp shone beneath the gate, casting a pale gleam through the small barred window. Yet the room was aglow of itself with a white, serene Light.

Deathly silence lay over the city. Only the death-rattle of a large dog, which was crawling painfully along the ground, could be heard at times, and the shrill plaintive hoot of an owl, coming from the sea. By the castle gate the great animal collapsed; it had perished. Blood trickled from a deep wound in its neck.

Suddenly there seemed to be the clashing of arms. In the city? At this hour?

A GLARE OF FIRE blazed on the roof of a stable. Startled birds and bats flew up. A red glow flashed eerily on the roof of a barn. Light steps stole around outside the walls. Wooden bolts creaked, beams broke, there was a thundering sound as of horses' hooves and a clanking as of iron.

Everyone was still asleep in Troy when the gate of the castle burst open with a crash, and Greeks carrying torches stormed into the courtyard. A short blast from the watchman's horn, which was smothered in a death-rattle, was the only warning. The surprise attack had succeeded.

"How right Cassandra was!" Those were the last words of the faithful one.

Achilles rushed past him towards the Trojans who had armed themselves hastily and were hurrying out of their houses. Within minutes the peacefully-sleeping city had become a screaming inferno of despair.

The fire was blazing horribly, the horns were blaring aloud, the people bellowing louder still. The few domestic animals ran through the fire; stray horses raced across the courtyards.

The wooden horse stood in the middle of the square; the black cavity of its barrel, which had served the wily Greeks as a hideaway, gaping wide open.

The Princes were in ferocious hand-to-hand combat. The killing was horrible. Beams collapsed, and the battering rams pounded parts of the walls. The Greeks received fresh reinforcements. On the square around the wooden horse a wild melee was raging; there the Spartans under the command of Menelaus took possession of the temple, believing that they would find Helen there.

Troy defended itself desperately. Priam stood on the platform of his tower and gave orders, but it was difficult to maintain discipline among the utterly confused people. Paris and Hector were at strategic points, but their men were beset by a force of tenfold superior strength. Hector appeared now here, now there. His adroitness and courage spurred his soldiers on.

Suddenly a terrible cry rent the air, anguished, piercing. Was it the cry of an animal hounded to death, or that of a mad woman? Even the savage noise of battle ceased for a moment.

Achilles had come face to face with Hector; he leapt wildly from the chariot which he had driven through the battling foot-soldiers, and his horses trampled underfoot whatever would not give way. In frenzied combat he slew Hector, and the horses' hooves were about to crush

201

him. But Achilles had him tied to his chariot, and at a frantic speed he galloped with him through the gates.

Steaming blood covered the earth. In great numbers the wounded lay on the ground, breathing their last; they were trampled down and crushed by the pitiless wheels. At a furious speed, mad with rage, Achilles drove around the city, with the cruel goddesses of vengeance in swift flight about him. Paris saw what was happening, and vowed not to yield until he had avenged his brother.

The number of Trojan troops diminished steadily; the superior strength of the enemies was becoming overwhelmingly apparent. A short while before, Odysseus had brought Philoctetes with him, and now both hurled themselves into the battle as well. Their appearance and the influx of able archers revived the flagging spirit of combat. The Greeks were already slaughtering women and children, and their ferocity grew with the bloodbath. Constantly the fires multiplied, and the walls collapsed, burying everything beneath them.

The women of the castle cowered together in a small room. They were sore afraid, but most of all they feared Hecuba, who behaved as if she had lost her mind. The only one, the comforter, the helping love, Cassandra, was not with them. Lamenting and weeping, Andromache sat in a corner, holding her son in her arms.

The women had witnessed Hector's death from the balcony, and Hecuba had screamed like an animal. Shaking, with constantly tremulous fingers and apprehensive, restless eyes, she crouched on the floor. The smell of death was in the room. From the noise in the passages it was evident that the castle was already in enemy hands; escape was out of the question.

Now Priam appeared at the door, he prepared them for the worst: death or captivity. It was ashen grey and cold in the room.

A cry, a call echoed through the house:

"Priam!"

It was the voice of Cassandra. Only then did they realise that no one had known where she was, yet they were not ashamed.

Cassandra's prison had opened. With head held high she strode through the warriors, and none of them had touched her. As if by a miracle she had not been injured, but liberated, by the collapsing wall.

Now she stepped before Hecuba.

"Hector has fallen, with Priam I will ask for his body. Paris will also die, Troy must perish; all of you will fall into the hands of the enemy. This is your doing, Hecuba. Do you remember my warnings now?"

Priam gazed at his daughter. Bowed with grief, he offered her his hand:

"Let us go."

But still the battle raged on. Night had given way to day and the day again to night, and still murder howled through the ruins of Troy. The slaughter had become senseless, but it would not end.

Hours later Priam and Cassandra returned with Hector's mutilated body and prepared the funeral pyre. But they could not light it, since the hostilities were renewed. Andromache sat quietly by her husband's remains, weeping.

A yell of rage sounded from the enemy. Paris had slain Achilles. He had been raised up high on his shield by his soldiers. It was then that Paris was struck by the avenging arrow of Odysseus, shot from the bow once used by Hercules. With the quivering arrow in his neck Paris was carried on his shield to Priam, who wept and tore his white hair. He stepped outside before the enemy and presented his breast to the host of his opponents.

Behind him stood Cassandra, who caught sight of Odysseus for the first time. He had also seen her, and vowed to capture her alive. He clearly remembered his vision at sea.

THE GREY MORNING of the third day was approaching. The ruins of Troy, the funeral pyres, lay smouldering. The ashes of the dead had been preserved in great stone vases and placed in the vault. Priam had also been buried.

Troy was dark, it was dark in the souls of the captured women.

The Greeks prepared to leave Troy. In triumph Menelaus had conducted Helen on to his ship, and many followed him. With Agamemnon, Odysseus had designated the ships for the captives. Cassandra was to be taken to Mycenae. This news had struck her like death, indeed worse than that, but she prayed quietly:

"Not my will, but Thy Will be done, Lord!"

The beach was ravaged and drenched with blood. Birds swooped down on the corpses that had not been buried. A storm threatened from the blackish green, wild waters.

The ships left the shores of Troy, and Cassandra cast a final glance at her father's demolished house. The storm howled woefully through the sails.

TROY HAD FALLEN, and the last of its great heroic race were on the high seas, at the mercy of the waves. The noble Priam, father of many sons – among them Hector and Paris and Polydoros, the stars in the ring of Trojan heroes – Priam was no more. Eternal woe to the proud fallen Troy, once so gloriously created by the grace of the gods! Now it was dead, extinguished in ruins and blood; plaintively, the winds carried the lamentation of the forsaken ones, who had died in the ashes of Troy, across the sea.

A storm raged over the sea, and the ships laden with rich treasures were scattered.

The most precious pearl, shining in the Light of Purity, Cassandra, was under the charge of Agamemnon. Her gaze, which reached into the depths of the past and was able to grasp the wide expanse of the future, was alive again.

The days of the voyage and the horrible nights during which her companions anxiously awaited the sinking of the ship were but minutes, seconds for her.

She had gone Home into a Light that shone brightly for her through all Darkness, and she could never lose it.

But she beheld the terrible destiny of mankind, the decline of the nations and the races.

"Agamemnon, listen, be warned! Assassins, dastardly assassins, are lying in wait for you in your own house – beware! A woman, like a venomous viper, beautiful and dangerous, lives in your house, and a man, a weakling in her hand, cowardly and full of vice, is her companion. Oh, would that the winds could do away with us on the high seas, that we would never have to see the end, the end of proud heroes!"

Thus spoke Cassandra, and bleak were the tidings for Agamemnon.

While the other prisoners deep down in the ship suffered grievously, Cassandra was often allowed to be on deck with Agamemnon. He loved to behold her proud, calm, dignified nature. Purity and peace emanated from her, the vanquished, the slave, and passed over to the feared commander, the enemy! There was neither hatred nor love between them, but each showed the other the greatest respect, for they were worthy of it.

Cassandra was filled with anguish when she thought of the future, for she knew what was awaiting her. With horror she saw Mycenae and its inhabitants; she saw that the eternal gods had turned away from this cesspool of corruption. It was like a nest of serpents, of which each wore a crown with many precious stones, and every stone was deadly poison.

The walls were dark, as were the halls, filled with the pain of the forsaken and the lust of the voluptuous. Sin leered from every corner.

This was where Cassandra's way was leading!

At times the thought of her dear ones tore painfully at her heart. Often she sought to probe the destiny of Andromache, who was forced to follow the son of Achilles into captivity, for she had loved Andromache. But that was denied her. Andromache had become too engulfed in her sorrow to be able to make contact with Cassandra. Through her sorrow she forcibly pulled the spirit of her husband down to earth, by calling him to be near her.

Hecuba was dead. Lost, with darkened eyes, she stormed through the gloomy depths of Hades. She had completely forgotten the Luminous Radiance which, emanating from her child, Cassandra, had once wished to show her the way. She too could not connect herself with Cassandra, who like a bright star attracted to herself only light souls, while the Darkness in her proximity hissed up malevolently.

THE GREEK FLEET had been scattered in the great storms. But Agamemnon, with the rest of his ships, rich booty and many slaves, Cassandra also among them, had landed safely in Argolis.

The land looked gloomy and forbidding to Cassandra, covered by a heavy grey shadow which only her eyes perceived. Ugly entities moved within it, revealing to her the condition of the people.

The ships had unexpectedly been driven ashore by the storm, and the seamen were concerned that they might be damaged.

Wading through the water, they reached the shore with difficulty, and tried to find a way of crossing for the women and children.

Disfigured by affliction and grief, wasted by hunger and disease, the slaves presented a lamentable sight. Many of them had died on the voyage and been thrown into the sea.

The procession of slaves gathered with difficulty; they were chained together. The stronger men had to walk under a kind of yoke with their necks bent and their hands tied behind their backs. Yet Agamemnon's men did not deal harshly with the prisoners. They merely followed the dictates of custom at that time.

Slowly the news of the ships' arrival had spread, for the people flocked round. At first they were curious, then gladdened when they realised that their King had returned home victorious. But it struck Agamemnon at once that they almost tried anxiously to avoid him.

Was this the way the people received their lord who had been in danger and need, far from home and country for many long years? Cassandra recalled the jubilation whenever her father and brothers returned home from their voyages. How different it was here. Was this the joy of the victor?

The sight of this strange country, of these withdrawn people with their unsteady gaze, settled upon her heart like a heavy weight.

Agamemnon had returned home, he, of whom many seers had prophesied that he would never set foot on his land again. Everyone acknowledged himself to have been a bad householder, now doubly burdened at having witnessed and tolerated the disaster in the royal house.

The way seemed long and far to Cassandra, the road was stony, and a wild storm was still sweeping in from the sea. They were joined by

206

more and more people who stood together in groups awaiting the procession. Stones were thrown at the captives, injuring some of them severely. The soldiers who accompanied the procession tried to prevent this.

The carts caught up with the procession of slaves, and the latter had to wait by the side until they had gone past. The dust of the street was so dense that it was hardly possible to see the people. Gasping, the prisoners dragged themselves along; their chains weighed heavily on them.

Cassandra walked between two women who had once maligned her a great deal. One of them had been in charge of the maids; she was utterly devoted to the priests and had always feared Cassandra's knowledge, for her conscience was not clean. The other was her granddaughter, a girl of twenty years. Neither left her side and both sought to alleviate her heavy lot as far as possible. Cassandra was pleased to have women from her homeland near her.

Thus weary, slow and mournful, the procession moved towards Mycenae. The hardship of the journey was engraved deeply in the souls of the prisoners. Every single step was painful to the women, as though they were walking barefoot on a thorny path. The groaning of those who collapsed from weakness cut them to the quick.

In the distance, tall and proud, rose the beautiful prosperous city. Its brownish-grey walls looked dark and menacing, but behind it shone white buildings, and splendid clumps of trees told of beautiful gardens.

Yet everything was so strange, so totally different from Troy. Where was the resplendent, charming life so much extolled by the poets? Where the hand of the blessed gods? It did not appear to be a happy land. Here the earth breathed mourning, misery and discontent, and Medusa stood menacingly over the people.

When the procession of slaves finally reached it, the city was in a state of great, joyful excitement. The people were happy, for they hoped for a fresh beginning and better times through the return of their Prince. But the oppressive rule of Clytemnestra was feared.

Gorgeously arrayed, with the crown on her head, adorned with the most exquisite jewels, thus stood Clytemnestra on the steps of her palace, and let the procession of carts and riders move past her in greeting. Not far from her stood Aegistus.

The Queen had perhaps been beautiful at one time. Now she bore the marks of her vices on her painted face. Her tall, once proud figure was like a decayed wreck which meticulous care had adorned with the most precious jewels of the world.

The lustre of her eyes was not the radiance of deep inner joy at the return of her ardently desired husband, but in them glowed the unsteady flicker of approaching madness and a hidden fear. Her body exuded the foul smell of vice, which the costliest of exceeding precious essences could not mask, for it was of a different substance.

The reception of her husband resembled a well-rehearsed play, for she was accomplished in the art of dissimulation and fine words. But Agamemnon was disappointed. He recalled Cassandra's words and all at once understood what she had told him. He had been warned. Great bitterness rose up in him, which however he strove to subdue.

But his daughter, Electra, rejoiced like a child. Sobbing, she fell down at his feet, and with her long hair wiped the dust from his shoes. This one great gesture expressed all her loyal, willing devotion, her joy at the reunion, and the pain over her blighted youth. Not a word passed her lips.

The carts and riders had moved past, as well as the foot-soldiers and the bravest, most experienced archers. Now came the procession of slaves, flanked by the soldiers who thrust themselves between the prisoners and the gates of the castle so that the women were protected.

Cassandra walked among the other women with her head bowed. They were all composed and calm, though deeply affected and quite spent from the arduous journey. When Cassandra stepped through the gate it was as if a light passed through the gloom of the courtyard.

She stopped short as she was about to walk past Clytemnestra. Raising her flaming eyes she scrutinised the Queen. Clytemnestra wavered, growing still paler beneath her make-up and returning Cassandra's gaze with a glassy stare. She was unable to withstand the scrutiny of these flaming, slate-blue eyes. The stones on her breast clinked, so great was the trembling of her body with pent-up agitation.

"Clytemnestra, you are standing before the gate of Hades! Remember that when the hissing serpent of your evil passions whispers alluring pictures into your ears! There is still time, but you are on the edge of the abyss, and a ray of the avenging lightning is about to descend upon you. Look within you, Queen, and ask yourself whether my counsel is right!"

Suddenly there was deathly silence in the courtyard. Only the ringing voice of Cassandra re-echoed from the walls, resonant as a bell.

For an instant Clytemnestra flinched, but her favourite slave steadied her. Those around her were petrified.

Then she raised her arm and pointed imperiously at Cassandra.

"See that this one is securely imprisoned on pain of death, she is worthy of it. Throw her into the tower, alone. I hold you, Kyros, responsible for it."

With that she staggered into the house; she did not even wish to see the booty that followed in the many carts.

The festive rejoicing ceased. The prisoners walked silently through the gates. But Electra left the women to follow Cassandra and Kyros, quietly, with her head bowed and an expression of firm resolve. A ray of Light had touched her soul, and it seemed to her that henceforth to all eternity she had to follow in the footsteps of Cassandra.

The guard Kyros, a giant of a man, led Cassandra. Electra followed at some distance, for she did not wish to irritate Kyros.

They finally reached a round solid tower in which a hundred steps led downwards.

The tower rose far above the castle. But in its depths was a room to which no ray of sunlight had ever penetrated.

Aside from a rough wooden bench and a table on which stood a stone jug and a bowl, it contained nothing. A musty, dank atmosphere overwhelmed them as they entered, and spiders' webs hung from the ceiling. Cassandra shuddered.

As Kyros was about to lock the door behind him without saying a word, he hesitated, for something attracted his notice. Searchingly he looked at Cassandra, then at the ceiling, at the walls, and examined crevices and cracks. Shaking his head, he finally left the room and bolted it from outside with a loud creaking noise. Cassandra was imprisoned.

"A strange thing befell me, Queen, with the foreign Princess from Troy," Kyros said to his Mistress as he rendered his report. "I am indeed thoroughly familiar with the dark tower, in which your enemies have often enough been held captive. But never before has it appeared to me so dark, and then so light after this woman had entered it. I have examined it thoroughly, but have not found the source of this unusual light."

Clytemnestra laughed at him.

"You fool, you are getting old, or has she deluded even you, as she did Agamemnon?"

NOT LONG AFTERWARDS something terrible occurred in Agamemnon's castle in Mycenae.

A piercing scream had followed a gruesome silence. A voice called:

"They have slain him, they have slain Agamemnon!" It resounded from below, through the halls, shaking the house. Clytemnestra and Aegistus, both deathly pale, rushed from the victim's room when they heard this cry. But outside, the Queen, as if horror-stricken, tore her hair and lamented her dead husband.

Electra stood behind a pillar by a dark curtain and watched Clytemnestra with burning eyes.

The night was endless and the day following the night equally dark for Cassandra. Otherwise so active, she suffered under the monotonous silence surrounding her. Feverishly she traced the thread of her life, and looking back to its very beginning, was able to see only sad things, but never anything wrong or impure. Her path of suffering was hard but pure; her spirit did not belong to the spheres in which human beings originated. She remembered the guidance of Apollo and the pure Light which had drawn her upwards to Itself, and she knew that she had suffered for the sake of Love.

She prayed. Then the tower opened upwards, and like a pillar, brilliant White Light came down to her.

"Soon you will have completed your Mission, and come to the Father," the words resounded from Above. "Fear not and wait for Me, for behold I will come quickly!"

Then the locks rattled, and there was a rustling as of silk and gold. With Kyros behind her, Clytemnestra stood in the doorway, pallid and haggard, with staring eyes.

"You can tell wondrous things," said she, "and know of many customs, so Agamemnon tells me. Know that he wants you to help me, slave; for I am sick. You are to drive away the evil spirits from me, which torment me, especially at night. You are to give me your potions and lay your healing fingers upon my aching limbs, and you are to tell me the stars and stones that bestow eternal youth and power, for you know them!"

Calm and composed, Cassandra looked at her.

"I will tell you, Queen, what you should do, in order to be restored to health. What will you give me if I help you?"

"I will give you half of my wardrobe and a tenth of my jewels. I will give you a slave girl, and you will live near me and be honoured as a princess."

"I have no desire for such things, Clytemnestra. I do not covet your treasures, and the honour of your house is repugnant to me. Agamemnon is dead, you have slain him through Aegistus; I know it. Undo your deed, and the furies will depart from you, I cannot accomplish it. Do not treat your children like the lowliest slaves in your house, give them their due, and you will have sufficient. Give them love, and you will receive love. Go within yourself with pure thoughts, and pure thoughts will surround you a thousandfold. Send dishonour and debauchery from the walls of your house, and you will see honour and purity enter. Turn away from evil, seek the Luminous Fields of Eternal Love, and you will attain them. But I believe it is too late, Clytemnestra!"

Moaning, the Queen had collapsed, and was unable to rise.

"You will pay the penalty for that, accursed seeress," she hissed, gasping, "now I will show you who I am!"

She rose to her feet, drew a dagger from her belt and rushed at

Cassandra. But a shining ray stood between her and Cassandra, and she was unable to move her arm.

"Behold, Who I am!" the words rang from Cassandra's lips. "Take what you deserve!"

Clytemnestra rushed away like a madwoman.

After a few hours Cassandra heard noises at the door. Stones were being dragged, and scraping and grating could be heard through the wall. Then she knew that Clytemnestra was having her buried alive out of fear. No despair overcame Cassandra. She had concluded her life, and her spirit had hastened ahead. In devotion to the Father's Will she awaited the hour in which He would call her; then she would follow. Her departure was no struggle as with human beings. In fulfilment of the Divine Will with Which she was one, she left the gross-material vessel as she had once entered it.

The Word formed by her lips was her last promise to mankind. It was the Word: *Imanuel*!

The grey waters, penetrating upwards from below, which were to increase the horrors of her death still further, no longer reached her alive.

Her body fell quietly into oblivion, but her Flaming Spirit is eternal.

A singing and ringing streams out of the Universe. Hearkening, the seer takes up his pen, and in faithful volition renders what his spirit receives:

MARY OF MAGDALA

"BEHOLD, THE KINGDOM OF GOD is at hand; therefore I say unto you: Repent ye, repent ye! Hear my voice, the voice of a preacher from the wilderness."

Thus did the mighty voice ring out on the road, loud and powerful.

The sound of it was profoundly stirring. What was the tone vibrating in that voice? It caused the heart to tremble, and penetrated the deepest depths.

In spite of the sunny noonday heat hanging over the hot, dusty roads, a shiver coursed through the woman resting in the quiet garden, secluded from the stream of life. She rose to her feet and walked towards the broad, low wall, whose upper part formed a balustrade for the raised garden which was supported below, towards the road, by heavy, massive walls and pillars.

She leaned forward and looked in the direction from which the voice was coming. It was the voice and the words that made such a powerful impression on Mary Magdalene: *"Repent!"*

Musing, she inclined her beautiful head, which could barely support the abundance of her blond hair. It was elaborately arranged; the curls that fell down to her shoulders had been carefully pinned by a Roman hair stylist. The clasps and pins glinted in the sunshine falling through the lush, dusty leaves.

Her hands rested lightly on the grey stone of the wall, which was covered by a layer of moss.

Mary Magdalene was reputed to be one of the most sought-after women in the city. She was very beautiful, but was admired even more for her cleverness and intelligence. This made her an influential woman who was very popular in Roman circles, but she enjoyed equally great esteem in Jerusalem.

In her house she offered generous hospitality as one of the great he-

...o in ancient times exerted a strong influence on art, politics
...onomy.

...d in a dense cloud of dust, a crowd of people was approach-
...among them the strange voice rang out again, punctuated by
murmuring and acclamations, shouts of joy and even singing.

It was John the Prophet, who was proclaiming the Kingdom of the
Lord, who was gaining ever greater popular influence, and who spoke
with the power of love, vanquishing people with his pure volition.

Mary was afraid of him. She heaved a faint sigh. She was still young,
but when she reviewed the unsettled extravagance and wealth of her
life, a desolate emptiness confronted her!

As she suddenly perceived the emptiness, she felt in like measure the
oppressive weight of the years thus far spent.

Mary was powerful and sought-after, but not happy. Her soul, capable of enthusiasm, was in quest of truly great experiencing, not of
enthralling hours. She was neither frivolous, nor bad, nor superficial,
but filled with longing to help and truly to love. But not with *that
kind of* love which had been expected of her, and which had given her
an insight into the depravity of the world; *that* was not love as she
perceived it.

The love for which she longed was probably no longer to be found
on this earth. It had become a dream for the world, it belonged to the
gods.

The trees were rustling, and below her the passing crowd whispered
and murmured. Suddenly she saw John, whom they called the Baptist,
come into view from the cloud of dust in the road. With his flashing,
deep-set eyes, he looked up into Mary's face. For a moment he paused,
and raised his hand as though in greeting.

Mary stepped back startled. She, who was usually so sure and sophis-
ticated, was at a loss to know what to do. The gaze of these blazing,
deep-set eyes was at the same time like a reproach and a question.

Deeply shaken, Mary walked through the garden into her house. She
moved nervously from room to room, grappling with the decision to
send for the strange Prophet. It gave her no peace until she had discussed it with her most trusted servant.

218

"He will not come," he said, "he speaks only among the multitude, and declines invitations to private homes. He refuses to be questioned. His manner is totally different from that of other speakers, Mistress, and therefore he will not respond to your summons either. He knows only his will, he is like a blazing fire, both consuming and illuminating, but he will do nothing to oblige a beautiful woman."

"Do as you have been told; then we shall see! Moreover, what you say is unseemly. Who tells you that I am asking a favour? Obey my command."

Her beautiful eyes flashed in anger; lines of bitterness were etched around her mouth. The fact that a servant answered her in this way, and presumed to give such a reply, was another sign of how she was regarded.

She immersed herself in music. The solace and purity for which her soul longed she always found in the music of strings. She had no wish to receive any of her visitors or friends. Neither did she go into the city, but remained in her country-house. An unfamiliar heaviness settled upon her soul; she anticipated a fateful turning-point. Anxiously she awaited John's reply. And it came: "He who would approach the Kingdom of God must go to meet it. It will not pursue him."

These words were a hard blow to Mary.

DARKNESS HUNG OVER Jerusalem. The sin of the great city was shameful. Yet her glistening Temple shone like an exquisite treasure in the earthly sun – promising, obscuring the inner decay. Jerusalem, the holy, the glorified and the celebrated city of cities – the rich, the great, the powerful, how did she actually look! The mighty castle in which Herod Antipas reigned with Herodias, his terrible wife, rose up menacingly – an accursed place.

It was dominated by vice. Often Herodias put the golden goblet with poisoned wine to the lips of her victims. It was as if she herself was filled with the most venomous poison. Her presence made the atmosphere dense and heavy.

Already groaning under the oppression of Rome, the people were still further enslaved by Jerusalem. Like an abscess that bursts open, contaminating everything around it that is still healthy, thus did disaster emanate from this centre of vice.

And into its very midst came the threatening voice of John! For days and nights! It drove Herodias to the verge of madness. Finally she had John arrested lest he incite the people to rebellion with the power of his words proclaiming the Kingdom of God on earth.

"I baptise you with water, but He Who is to come after me will baptise you with the Holy Spirit!"

Those were his words.

Already the people were speaking about the miracles of the Nazarene. The most incredible rumours came from afar, fanning the anger and fear of Herodias into such hatred that she demanded the death of John.

Yet when Herod had given his consent he collapsed from fear, and was struck down by a terrible illness.

When the dreadful deed had been carried out, total silence descended upon the normally-so-active city. A howling storm swept across the country, carrying with it frightful masses of sand. People were alarmed.

In the Temple the flagstones of the great courtyard cracked while muffled thunder rolled underground.

The atmosphere was charged with imminent disaster. People went about nervously, fearful; discontent was everywhere, but also a dull, oppressive silence. No one spoke freely. Empty phrases were the rule in the circles of scholars, courtiers and others in high positions of the country as well as of Rome. All of them concealed their true nature in order to reveal nothing of what took place within them.

In this Mary Magdalene excelled. But since she had taken the enormous step, since she had overcome the pride within her and appeared before John to hear his word about the Kingdom of God, since then she loathed this life of falsehood. It was as though the eyes of the Prophet had read deep within her soul. He must indeed have known how much she was suffering.

Yet he had behaved as if she did not exist. He spoke at that time for everyone; no one took any notice of her. What would normally have seemed to her embarrassing and annoying, even offensive, at that moment suited her – to go unnoticed. Moreover, she was dressed quite plainly and wore a grey veil over her head and shoulders.

It had been the last time that John the Baptist was heard speaking freely to the masses. Late that night he was arrested.

But the people stood at a distance as though spellbound, listening to his voice which still resounded from the depths of his prison. The listeners were unable to force their way into the courtyard of the castle. The gates were too heavily and rigorously guarded. Nor was there any need, for this voice seemed to grow wings which bore it out over all obstacles into the souls that opened themselves to it. But in these souls it caused indescribable upheavals within a few hours. This was also the case with Mary Magdalene.

Once more her whole life up to that time passed in review before her.

She had never before been truly shaken. Proudly she went her own way, which had been laid upon her like a burden. She had been drawn into everything which in her heart of hearts she would gladly have avoided, above all the constant association with people in high society.

She had intuitively perceived the emptiness of this life as increasingly burdensome; she longed for some priceless treasure that seemed to her to be buried somewhere. She had been seeking, but she did not really know what. Wherever she went, no matter how brilliant the external circumstances, she encountered a vacuum from the very first moment.

Therefore she sought the company of wise men in order to learn from them. She learned easily, but the knowledge of these men seemed to be dead as well. Her quest for the meaning of life, that was to revive her spirit like a bubbling spring, was in vain.

The knowledge of the learned scholars she valued, within its limits, but she aspired beyond these limits. She sought among the women, she courted their friendship, to learn what a woman's soul developing to maturity should be like. Deep within she seemed to remember that she had already known and loved pure women. Her heart swelled when she thought about it.

But here too she actually experienced only disappointments now. At first she believed that she must seek the fault within herself; later she kept the great longing concealed within her. Through her wealth, her education, through connections with great artists and scholars she gained increasing access to a circle remote from women of the higher classes.

Through her love for a rich Roman artist she had been tied to this circle for years, and when he left her she was surrounded by admirers and friends who were only too willing to comfort her. With dread Mary Magdalene remembered this time of her inner despair and her outer triumphs. The longing for the unknown bliss was completely buried, and it had become dark around her.

While she sought distraction in the whirlpool of the world, things did not improve. Without parents and lonely as she was, she began to realise that people only sought her out in order to get something from her: her beauty, her wealth or her stimulating company. She longed to give. But she wanted to help human beings by lovingly giving to them; she wanted to give people happiness and solace, not just to while away spare time as a plaything.

She visited the poor. But there she was met with such a wave of hatred, suspicion, bitterness and lack of understanding that she hesitated at the threshold of compassion, and did not dare to take the step. It was shortly afterwards that she had seen John the Prophet. From that moment she was totally convinced:

"If anyone can do it, this man alone can advise you."

And with the one short sentence that he had conveyed to her, he had prepared the way within her. With those few words he had demolished walls of a false conception regarding earthly ties:

"He who would approach the Kingdom of God must go to meet it, it will not pursue him!"

How much had he given her with that alone. And now Herodias had had him put to death.

On hearing this news, Mary experienced the first truly and deeply perceived sorrow.

From the hour when she learned of John's death she looked back upon her earth-life as though it had been lived by someone else. She felt as if she were now moving towards another life and discarding everything that was burdensome. The words of the Prophet preoccupied her increasingly each day. She was seeking the Kingdom of God! It became a firm concept within her that was linked with the Nazarene of whom the Baptist had spoken.

She looked for people who could tell her where he was. And she would do what John had said. She would go to meet him who was bringing the Kingdom of God.

When she had made this resolve she suddenly felt light and free. Her eyes filled with tears, and a warm feeling of gratitude rose up in her, which moved her deeply. This is how it must be on returning home after a long journey, she thought. Her active intellect drew this comparison without realising that it was indeed a similar process.

IT WAS A LONG TIME before she learned where she could find Jesus. Now nothing could restrain her any longer. She must go to him.

At first she had herself carried in a litter, but then, after a rest in an inn, she sent the servants back.

They shook their heads. What new adventures might she be planning now? And those who entertained such thoughts were not to be censured on that account, for they did not know her soul. They thought her capable of only the most fantastic things, but certainly not of a step of such momentous gravity.

It was striking that Mary Magdalene suddenly spurned all finery. A long, grey garment enveloped her tall figure. Her veil was of the same colour. Her shoes were solid, suitable for walking, and she joyfully followed the road that had been described to her.

Light, and as if liberated, she walked along the dusty street in the burning sun. For Mary the hours passed swiftly. Within her a buoyancy awakened that was new to her. The desire to reach the goal of her spiritual longing made her forget everything which, in her comfortable life of idleness, would hitherto have seemed a great insurmountable effort.

She found it natural to be treading this hot, arduous road. It did not surprise her, but she noticed how easy it was for her. With every step she drew nearer to her goal.

223

Would the Nazarene really establish the Kingdom of God on earth as John the Baptist had said?

There were quite vague, yet rather earthly notions of it in the world which Mary Magdalene had lived in hitherto. Most people smiled, regarding these ideas as delusions. Others suspected some clandestine political organisation behind it, and ambitious persons believed in an earthly tyranny. But all of them saw in it an impossible welter of intellectual conceptions. Scarcely anyone had understood John and grasped his clear words.

To Mary Magdalene it seemed that she had already experienced something similar long, long ago. But each time she was gripped by a feeling at once of pain and joy which she could neither explain nor describe. She had been accustomed to observing herself and everything around her. She experienced herself and her surroundings like a spectator at a play. Sometimes she also had a part in it, but only when she was confident of success.

But now she was like a child, timorous and apprehensive. Whenever she was overcome by this blissful, melancholy ache which seemed like homesickness, there was nothing left of the proud, calculating, passionate woman, rather only a great shyness.

Thus musing, she moved steadily onward. Of what concern to her were the oncoming troops of soldiers, the many wagons, the merchants and beggars? She saw only the small market place emerging, of which she had heard, where there was a house to which disciples of the Prophet from Nazareth were said to be frequent visitors.

Gradually Mary Magdalene began to feel thirsty and weary. Her pace slowed down, and her feet ached. She did not notice people gazing after her in surprise.

The landscape was becoming more beautiful and verdant, and a gentle cool breeze came from the lake. But Mary Magdalene would not rest for fear of missing the best time. Then a great throng was approaching, presumably from the direction of the lake. All of them seemed to come from afar, and looked like pilgrims – women, children and old people among them, but also vigorous men. They were mainly Jews, but Romans from distinguished wealthy families were also in the procession.

Mary Magdalene was struck by one thing above all: the impression of fellowship emanating from these people. It was as if every individual volition had been effaced by one great, common felicity.

A thrill, a slight tremor, coursed through Mary. Filled with the great things they had experienced, the people were speaking of miracles that had taken place recently. One person told another, each adding more to it, and many things were understood altogether differently from the way in which they had been recounted.

Mary Magdalene listened, and a slight disappointment entered her soul. Did humanity once again bring their small ego into this great spiritual experience that it might be reflected there? Now they were indeed all shaken by a Power of which she had become conscious at once, and still en masse they remained so unchanged! But she would not judge; she had first to examine herself.

The throng went past her. Involuntarily she had stopped, because she did not want to be swept along by the multitude of which she was not yet a part. She would follow behind the very last ones. But then a second procession came. The people seemed to cluster round a focal point. Slowly this procession too was approaching the waiting woman.

A few young men were in front. Among them were handsome, imposing figures. But she noticed that they were very abrupt and by no means forthcoming with people. Mary felt a deep sense of shame. The men made a good impression, for an aura of purity emanated from them. But why the severity? Where was the love that offers solace to seeking souls?

Could these be the disciples of the Prophet?

Then she heard a voice, kindly yet firmly reproving them for being so severe.

"Remember the hour when you stood by the lake and asked, 'Lord, may we come with you?'"

Mary Magdalene fell to her knees; she raised her hands and looked up. He who had spoken was walking past just then.

They were such simple words, and yet they reflected a world of love, warning, reprimand, and so much encouragement for the seekers.

225

"If this man is filled with such goodness, then you too may approach, Mary Magdalene!"

Thus spoke her inner voice. But he had already gone past, ere she was fully aware of his presence. One glance, however, had touched her! And it had penetrated her soul like a flash of lightning. She felt as though with this glance he had seen through her entire life. And something else had caught her attention. He looked like a Roman, but yet another, much more radiant countenance had looked at her from out of him.

She was still kneeling by the wayside. A small troop of stragglers approached. Two women went up to her. They also had the clear radiance on their foreheads; a quiet peace, solicitude and goodness emanated from them.

Kindly they lifted up the deeply moved woman, and took her into their midst. An invigorating wave of power flowed through Mary Magdalene. These women had what she had always so longed for – they had love and purity, and the simplicity of their being gave them great charm. Mary Magdalene felt safe.

With the natural intuitive perception bestowed on them by Jesus they sensed that this woman had had a difficult life. Joyfully they offered her counsel and help.

Mary Magdalene did not say much; she was incapable of doing so. Her soul was filled with confusion and horror when she compared herself with these women, and she now knew that she herself lacked the best, the most precious possession of woman: purity.

Now she was tormented by the thought that Jesus would reject her. The more she subjected the nature of the two women to close scrutiny, the more she felt herself to be lost.

Finally, when they had reached an inn, and Mary Magdalene had been accommodated in a small, clean room, one of the women brought her food; then they left, suggesting that she rest first of all. They promised that they would soon look in on her.

But after a short rest Mary Magdalene felt that she must rise. She left the house and hurried through the streets. Evening had fallen already. Mary Magdalene walked along a narrow lane bordered by high walls.

She stopped at an iron gate and inclined her ear to the flowering garden. From the open hall of the house at the other end of the garden appeared to come a voice that made her heart tremble. There was but One who spoke like that.

He who has once heard the Voice of God, and opened his soul to It, knows It, and never forgets It. So it was with Mary. Again she felt the faint trembling in her heart, again her knees seemed to give way, and again she felt this warm wave of bliss flooding through her, followed by the bitter pain at her unworthiness. Mary Magdalene was experiencing an inner upheaval; she forgot everything; only her yearning spirit spoke, urging her to the feet of the Lord just as in times long past it had already knelt before His Power. The spirit remembered the petition and the vow, of which the intellect knew nothing any more.

These were the days before Passover, and Jesus was to go to Jerusalem with His disciples. They were guests in the house of Simon, and were sitting in the open hall, which afforded a view of the garden and on to the houses of the market. Night had fallen, the branches of the tall pines rustled. Numerous flowers sent their fragrances into the hall.

Jesus was very quiet. He was sitting in the circle of His disciples, and over them all seemed to lie a slight tension, like the foreboding of some evil turn of events which they were unable to avert.

Then hurried footsteps and the voice of the guard were heard in the garden. But the woman who now appeared would not be restrained. With light, hasty steps, as though fearful of losing her courage even at the last moment, she hurried up the stairs, and approached Jesus. She bowed low before Him and kissed His feet. The soft veil which had almost entirely covered her slipped down, and a flood of golden hair fell over her face. The tears flowed unceasingly from her large eyes which were directed imploringly at the Lord. Jesus had turned a little, and looked down at her patiently and very earnestly.

But the disciples, and in particular the master of the house, regarded it as unseemly that this woman should disturb them, and Simon said to Jesus:

"I know that she is a wayward sinner! Will you not send her off?"

227

Simon was a Pharisee. But Jesus looked at him, then searchingly round the circle of all those who were with Him, and gently He shook His head.

"Listen, Simon, I have something to say to you: a creditor had two debtors; one owed him five hundred pence, and the other fifty. But because *neither* had *anything* to pay he frankly forgave them both.

"Do you see this woman? She has washed me with tears and anointed my feet, and you, have you done likewise?

"Many sins are forgiven her; for she has given much love. But to whom little is forgiven, the same loves little.

"Mary Magdalene, your sins are forgiven. Your faith has helped you. Go forth in peace!"

And Mary Magdalene rose to her feet and went away. She felt as though a heavy burden had been taken from her.

But those who were sitting at the table were greatly surprised that Jesus forgave sins.

AROUND MARY MAGDALENE a luminous cloak had been laid, which illumined her. She was happy. As in a dream, she walked along, not knowing how she had come back. Soon she was with the other women again; she felt literally drawn to be near them, and perceived that she could now speak openly and enquire about anything that moved her.

Again and again she was struck by the simple and natural way in which they took everything that happened in the course of the day, and by the joyful manner in which they seized upon anything that in some way could benefit themselves and others.

She observed every one of their emotions; she perceived their intentions and thoughts and listened with opened soul to their words; she wanted to learn from them, for she knew that Jesus Himself had guided and blessed them.

They spoke to her of Jesus, and their loyalty, their love and devotion to the Lord shone out of every word.

Mary Magdalene was becoming more quiet and unassuming; she listened inwardly and no longer recognised herself. Where were the many impulses and thoughts which used to move her constantly, which at times had made her so restless, overbearing and hot-tempered? It was quiet within her, only a pure sound like a clear bell vibrated in her soul. A light had begun to glow within her, and she prayed without seeking words.

At night she often lay awake on her narrow, hard bed, but these sleepless nights brought her more strength and refreshment than the deepest slumber had ever given her. She knew when she rose in the morning that her whole life must become new. Therefore she wished to ask Jesus to allow her to serve Him as the other women did.

She would sever herself from her past life, would sell her possessions, her jewellery, and emulate the women in humility, loyalty and purity, that like them she might bear a shining light in her soul. She was guided in wondrous ways. At times it seemed to her that a helping spirit stood beside her, advising her.

Full of trust and completely relaxed, she yielded to the stirrings of her soul, and learned much in the process. When Jesus spoke, she was always present, and absorbed His Word like one dying of thirst.

For the time being she did not return to her home but followed the Lord. She knew that His pathway would lead to Jerusalem, and that knowledge made her feel strangely oppressed. Therefore she asked Jesus as He stood alone in the garden before Simon's house:

"Lord, may I go with you?"

He looked at her gravely and said:

"Your request is granted. Come and follow me."

Then He continued, speaking kindly:

"Mary Magdalene, you will be witness to the God-Happenings on earth. But you will grasp and proclaim only a small part now. Your path is not a beginning, as you imagine, but a continuation. You will come back.

"Whenever Divine Light sets foot on earth, you Chosen ones will be present, unless you go astray.

"Not until the Son of Man comes will you understand the complete cycle. You do not yet have the requisite maturity. I would like to tell you so many things, but you do not yet comprehend that which you are now experiencing. How are you to grasp that which is to come?

"I want to help you to gain life; see to it that you preserve it for yourselves!

"I do not bring the Judgment; I lead you on the way into the Kingdom of God. But when the Son of Man comes, you will also see me again. For I and the Father are One, and He is in Him!"

Mary Magdalene was intelligent and more mature than the other women. All the suffering she had experienced had advanced her quickly. Therefore she could understand the words of Jesus with wonderful ease, and every time He spoke with her she made great progress in her development. She absorbed His Word with her spirit; she was able to experience It visually within, and it seemed to her that she was imbued with more Light each day. Thus she was being prepared gradually to recognise the whole of life.

But with that she intuitively perceived as well the thorny path which none of them could be spared on this earth. She saw the glaring sunlight which made the dust-laden road into an ordeal when she walked on it – mostly in a dense mass of people who wanted to follow Jesus.

But she also saw how a black cloud, delicate as a mist, was spreading in the blazing sun.

"You must warn the Lord about Jerusalem," said something in her. And so she did. But He looked at her lovingly.

"I must fulfil the pathway if I am to go into My Own."

At that Mary Magdalene saw a radiant White Light in the form of a Cross emerging from the figure of the Lord. But she did not tell the others, for He forbade it.

ONE OF THE DISCIPLES lurked stealthily around Mary Magdalene, as if regarding her with envy and suspicion. It was Judas Iscariot. She avoided him whenever she could, for from the first meeting she knew that nothing good could come from this man. Repeatedly she reproached herself for it; he was, after all, a disciple of Jesus, and the Lord was especially kind to him.

At first she avoided him because he always spoilt her most beautiful hours with some question. Then she forced herself to tolerate him. She did so out of love for Jesus, but at the same time she suffered, for now she perceived clearly that Judas was plotting evil. With each day he grew more presumptuous and sullen.

A great unrest came upon Mary Magdalene. She went about observing everything. If she wished to rest, she felt driven to rise again. A state of fear and anxiety befell her, which became unbearable. She was not concerned for herself, but for Jesus.

She told the disciples about it, and Peter explained that they had long since formed a protective ring around the Lord, and that the gifts which He had placed in them would work through them and bear fruit. He also told her that Jesus was sending forth the disciples that they might recognise what they could accomplish in His Will. She could put her mind at rest when she knew that one of them was near Jesus.

But her mind was not at rest until she had grasped that now she must not follow the Lord, who was indeed surrounded by those closest to Him, but rather go before Him. She went to Jesus, told Him about it, and asked if she might be permitted to go to Jerusalem. She gave Him no reason.

But Jesus was well aware of the reason, and answered:

"Go forth in peace. Put your affairs in order, and prepare the bridge to your friends."

This time she did not quite understand the words of the Lord. But when she thought of the people whom she would see again now after her own inner transformation, she saw a stream of luminous threads flowing before her, attracting or repelling the others. It was as if she were moving in the centre of active radiation-forces and as if she herself were sending these forth. Now that of her own volition she had taken the step of working for Jesus, the Power which He had bestowed upon her poured out of her. And she went forth filled with new life, and was no longer afraid.

She had become a stranger in her own house. She walked through the beautiful, luxurious rooms and the magnificent garden in the manner of a guest who, whilst having made grateful use of the beauty and com-

231

fort, wanted now to journey on and was happily leaving everything behind.

The servants reacted to her in totally different ways. Some, who had formerly been shy and reserved, now felt drawn to their mistress. But the others, who had once eagerly served her, adopted an almost hostile, partly provocative attitude when Mary Magdalene spoke to them. They were extremely annoyed that they did not know where their mistress, who had come back so altered, had been.

Scornfully they looked down at her simple, unadorned attire; shrugging their shoulders, some even turned their backs on her, for they realised that here there was no more to be gained for them. The golden times seemed to be over. To them Mary Magdalene appeared pitiable.

They laughed at her and no longer recalled how kind she had always been to them.

Mary Magdalene asked them to leave. They were dismissed by the guardian of the house with ample wages and gifts. But the others continued in her service.

As with the servants in her own house, she fared similarly with her acquaintances and friends. Many did not even recognise her or did not wish to remember her.

She herself regarded them all with different eyes. She discovered many values under a quite modest exterior, and much emptiness and conceit where she had once looked up in admiration. During the short time of her absence she had learned to recognise the value of a human being with the eyes of the spirit, and not to judge by earthly concepts.

The number of those whom she could lead to Jesus was small! But it now seemed more important to her to observe them and to make use of her connections. So she sought to pick up the threads that afforded her an insight into the behaviour of the Pharisees, the Romans and the Jews.

It was not easy in these turbulent days. Some of her old friends looked upon her with diffidence. They did not dare to speak near her; they felt ill at ease.

The tense excitement in the great city weighed upon the people more heavily and oppressively than ever. To her it seemed that an indescribable force of the Darkness was massing here. Lurking, it lay concealed while a wonderful, clear Light was approaching this hideous swamp with radiant Power. Again she was overcome with fear and anxiety.

Neither by day nor by night could she find peace, and she explored the nature of this calamitous city. Friends of the disciples received her, and she was able to benefit them in many ways. One of them, Joseph of Arimathea, was greatly looking forward to the coming of Jesus. He prepared his house to receive Him.

And Mary Magdalene went to see Joseph of Arimathea; she told him of her anxiety for Jesus, which left her no peace of mind, and she described the dark nature of Judas.

But Joseph set her mind at rest, and promised to keep his eyes open. To him it was apparent that Jerusalem was longingly awaiting the Lord, of Whose deeds the whole city was speaking.

THUS CAME THE GREAT fateful hour when, amid acclamations and merrymaking, celebrated by tumultuous shouts of Hosannah, the Son of God in the circle of His disciples made His entry into Jerusalem. The whole city resembled one enormous anthill.

In feverish agitation the multitudes crowded through all the streets and across the squares. For hours they stood on the roads, awaiting the Lord.

It was impossible for Mary Magdalene to make her way to Jesus. Too dense was the crowd that filled the narrow streets. She only heard the indescribable jubilation, and what the people were saying. It was as though the city was in a state of euphoria.

By a roundabout route she struggled against the human tide until she reached the gate opening on the road leading to Bethany; there she hoped to find some of the women.

"Mary Magdalene, give ear! Now your work begins!"

Was it not the voice of her Lord, or was it that of a celestial being, an angel?

"Upon the Rays of Purity this voice floats down to you from Above, for through your volition to serve God you have opened yourself to it.

233

You have matured through much suffering; the Lord has richly endowed you through great Love and through His Grace. Take care of the women. Wherever there are women who, like you, bear the ardent desire for the celestial crown of Purity, my Power will work through you. So that you may recognise who is speaking to you, behold me, myself!"

Heavenly Radiance seemed to pour down upon Mary Magdalene. It had come upon her while she was on her way through the steep, walled lanes of the old Jerusalem. Overwhelmed by the Radiance of the Light, she leaned against a wall and closed her eyes. She was alone. The Radiance remained before her inner being even with her eyelids shut; indeed it even intensified, and a luminous countenance looked down upon her.

"I myself am not now able to descend to your earth. Only my Power touches you so long as the Son of God still dwells on earth. It is bestowed upon you for the blessing of many who thirst for it. Take care of the maidens, the orphans and those who are forsaken. The understanding was granted to you, to you alone will the Power also be granted."

Word upon word these tidings came to Mary Magdalene from eternity. Thus was she blessed, while people still called her a penitent sinner.

The lovely figure before her wore a Crown of Lilies. Pervaded with Light, the large eyes shone in radiant blue. In a long white robe, surrounded by the flowing Mantle of Light, the Prototype of Purity, Irmingard, stood before Mary Magdalene's spirit. Trembling, Mary bowed her head, hiding it in her hands. Worship and gratitude filled her soul.

Musing over this wonderful experience, Mary Magdalene passed through the gate leading on to the narrow road to Bethany. There in the distance she could already see the gleam of the small houses. Behind them extended the gently-sloping gardens of the Mount of Olives.

This journey was unusually difficult for her. By the time she reached the house of Lazarus her legs would barely carry her any longer. While sitting on the bench before the house, and awaiting the return of its dwellers, she beheld strange pictures.

Before the pillars of the great Temple-hall she saw a closely-packed crowd of people in the yard. Expectantly they were looking up at the Temple entrance, from which the vendors in wild confusion were scattering in all directions. This event had the appearance of panic.

In the background of the wild scene Mary Magdalene saw Jesus coming out of the Temple. He shone white in the light-coloured robe that He was wearing today.

And now she also heard Him speaking. His voice touched her heart. The people were listening spell-bound.

But a group of scribes pressed in noticeably upon Him, and among them Mary Magdalene, full of trepidation, saw a lurking snake rise up. From this hour she knew that these men intended to destroy the Lord.

MARY AND MARTHA returned, and had much to tell. They went into the house to prepare a simple meal, and considered how to go about arranging the Passover for the Lord. Mary Magdalene spoke with them and forced herself to be outwardly calm. But with her ever-present sensitivity, Mary discerned the true situation and said to her:

"Greatest joy and grievous fear are dwelling in your soul side by side. Take care that the Lord perceives only your joy when He comes. It is good to be vigilant, but do not be troubled!"

"Where is Judas?"

The question evidenced their mutual suspicion. Mary Magdalene, however, resolved to return to the city shortly.

That evening Jesus spoke with them for a long time.

MARY MAGDALENE was aghast as she approached Jerusalem again. The entire atmosphere seemed fraught with disaster.

But she, whose heart was so filled with bliss that, as one richly endowed, she wanted to give of it joyfully and gratefully to all who were athirst for it, she who had come from the radiant, harmoniously swinging circle of the disciples of Jesus and who was still awe-struck by the life-giving Divine Breath that wove around Him, she wanted to work, to watch, to make use of her connections and exert her influence to protect the path of the Lord. And in accordance with the Command of the Luminous Woman she wished to give helping love to all those who were in need of it.

What had Jesus said when she told Him of her experience?

"Keep the Power that streams into you from the Luminous Realms of My Father, and make use of it. It is given to you to help many who would otherwise not attain to it. You are the bridge to human beings! Keep to yourself, deep within, what you have experienced. It is not for the knowledge of the world, which does not value this jewel, for the world cannot understand it. Transform for humanity what you have gained from it, only then will the fruits from the seed of the spirit be made manifest!"

Once again, as always when the Lord addressed personal words to her, they continued to work on with vital power, and were fulfilled. Within her a living knowledge and recognition grew, and Mary Magdalene was linked in spirit with all the happenings, with everything that now came to pass.

For that reason too she was horrified by the wild, exaggerated behaviour of the people who now, during the days of Passover, were gathering in ever greater numbers in the capital. She was glad that Jesus did not dwell within these walls.

Constantly thoughts of anxiety for Jesus assailed her! They weighed heavily upon the joyful, quiet bliss of her soul.

From totally different quarters she often heard remarks intimating that an army was being rallied for Jesus. She was alarmed, and contradicted some who spoke of it; but on realising that this angered people and made them suspicious of her she soon kept silent. Suddenly her soul was suffering extreme anguish.

"They are harming Him! They will bring ruin upon Him with their delusions and personal lust for power! What am I to do? Warn Him again? But He would only say: 'I must go the pathway into My Own!' And the disciples? They do not believe me, but call me a frightened woman and reproach me with lack of faith!

"Indeed they do not know how He is misunderstood by people when He speaks of His Kingdom. Even they themselves form wrong ideas, and believe in earthly power. How often already has Jesus told them: 'My Kingdom is not of this world!' But how do His disciples interpret these words?

"Perhaps Peter understands it best of all; so does John, and yet even John cannot quite free himself of false ideas."

With these thoughts her anxiety was growing steadily. Again she experienced the loathsome impression which Judas had once more made on her last night. Like a thief caught unawares he had stood in the doorway when Jesus asked him:

"Where have you been?"

His lies had struck her like arrows, and she knew that Jesus was seeing through him. Horror and disgust overcame all of them, and deep sorrow was reflected in the face of the Lord.

Again she thought of Joseph of Arimathea as the only help. She went home and prepared to visit him. An hour later the litter carried her to his residence.

Again evening had fallen. Her heart ached, and in spirit she sought Jesus. She felt as though she were connected in a wondrous way with Him, as by a luminous thread, through which tidings about His state of being were transmitted to her.

The feeling of loneliness grew into the agonising pain of abandonment. But suddenly a clear Light was spreading about her.

She saw Jesus sitting at a long table covered with a white cloth. Around Him pulsated a rotating Halo of Light. He broke the bread and offered the chalice with the wine to His disciples. All of them looked different that night. Jesus was suffused with radiant Light. The picture she beheld showed Him in a brilliance that was not of this earth.

And again she felt that with her human faculty she could not understand what was taking place there, that behind the radiant event of this Meal was a great Act and a Fulfilment of Divine Love. What she was permitted to witness in spirit she did not comprehend but she felt strengthened by it. –

Meanwhile she had arrived at the estate of Joseph of Arimathea.

The litter was carried through a tall gate into a courtyard surrounded by a garden wall. A fountain plashed softly and monotonously.

It was already dark. But the air of the hot day still lay warm beneath the mighty trees. Heavy shadows enveloped the tall house in which hardly a light was burning.

But a torch had been mounted at the entrance-archway leading into the open hall. A white-clad Roman was standing here, and bowed politely before the late visitor. He was the caretaker of the great house, who represented its master in his absence. Mary Magdalene was disappointed at seeing him, because to her it signalled that she would not find Joseph of Arimathea at home.

Her voice betrayed agitation when she asked for the master of the house. But she was informed that Joseph of Arimathea had gone away a few days ago; no one knew his present whereabouts.

Utter dejection and disappointment were reflected in Mary Magdalene's face. Moved by compassion, the Roman invited her to enter and to rest. At first she was about to decline, but then she had the feeling that nevertheless she must follow him into the low room, which had the appearance of a guard-room on ground floor level. She accepted the invitation, hoping to find out more about Joseph of Arimathea.

But the man was reticent. He was reluctant to speak even though he perceived that Mary Magdalene was much troubled. He must assume that this woman had not come at such an unusual hour without good reason. Silent, he stood facing her. Disappointed and exhausted, she reclined her head and closed her eyes. All at once the sentence came involuntarily from her lips:

"I have come because of Jesus of Nazareth!"

The name had the effect of a password. The impassive, restrained countenance of the Roman was illumined by a light of inner bliss.

"I see that you are one of His followers," said Mary Magdalene, "and you can trust me."

"Yes, I love Jesus and would like to serve Him," was his reply. "I know that I can speak openly with Mary of Magdala. The Prince has spoken to me of her. He has set off with Mark, the Roman. Political unrest was the reason. The Lord has been implicated in it. I must keep watch here. Shall I send a message?"

And Mary Magdalene told of her observations and anxieties.

"Fear nothing. What could be done has been done already." The words came clear, firm and comforting from the lips of the Roman.

After this utterance he was again formal and reserved. He bowed low and ceremoniously before the woman, with greater respect than was normally the Romans' way.

Mary set out on the return journey through the dark night. Her body was weary unto death; exhausted, she leaned back against the cushions in her litter. As darkness shrouded her completely, as the gentle swaying of the litter soothed her nerves, and the light of the torches carried by her escort shone dimly along the edge of the road, great calm and strength came over Mary Magdalene. It seemed to her that a Power close at hand was protecting, guiding and invigorating her. And yet she was sad.

Desperately sad and forsaken, remote from everything earthly. What could it be?

Slowly remembrance awakened within her. She recalled the hours since the awakening of her spirit, when she had opened herself to the Light. She recalled the experience on the way to Bethany and the blissful visions she had been granted.

But suddenly she now perceived the anguish of death. She experienced indescribable fear, loneliness and desolation, the struggle of a soul severing itself from its body in unspeakable agony. Human suffering, experienced from a lofty vantage point, so it appeared to her. And yet not her suffering. But whose then?

Her heart was burning, her eyes filled with tears, cold sweat ran from her forehead. Her hands were icy, and clasped as in prayer. In spirit she beheld a picture. Darkness enveloped a figure which had sunk down in pain upon a rock. There was solitude all around; only the rustling of the olive trees could be heard. Heavy clouds drifted across an ominous sky, barely permitting the pale moonlight to filter through from time to time.

The atmosphere was oppressive and sultry. A leaden weariness weighed upon the creatures of the earth. It was like an imminent death of Nature.

In Mary Magdalene this suffering became a certainty. She suffered

239

for a long time, and felt as though she must leave this earth. Her body consciously endured unspeakable agonies, and she was no longer able to think of her own person. Where was she? Like a stream, dazzling clarity entered this darkness.

"Father, Father!" she heard the voice of Jesus. This sound vibrated through all the Heavens.

Powerfully a dazzling pair of wings spread out in the Radiance, and a Hand, blazing white and clear, offered a Chalice from out of the Light. Beyond this, Mary Magdalene saw no more.

She was carried into the house as if dead, when they stopped before the gate at daybreak, at the time of the first cock-crow.

MARY MAGDALENE was aware that she was being carried into the house and laid down to rest. Bethsabe, her faithful maidservant, was at her side. Solicitous, motherly love emanated from her. Bethsabe was probably the only one of her maidservants who really knew Mary Magdalene, who saw shining within the withdrawn soul of this imperious, seemingly cold woman the luminosity of the jewels placed there by God, which until recently had been buried. The awakening of Mary Magdalene had also enkindled the love for Jesus in her servant.

After she had tended the completely exhausted body of her mistress, Bethsabe lit the small hanging lamp, whose tranquil light Mary Magdalene loved. Then she went quietly into the ante-room where she kept watch. Her thoughts were sad and filled with distress, for a messenger had come in the night and announced:

"I have come from Bethany. Tell Mary of Magdala that they have arrested the Lord and taken Him before Caiaphas."

Bethsabe felt as though she was losing her foothold. The message struck her like a bolt from the blue, and she was greatly concerned that she could not pass it on. Now Mary Magdalene had come back. How was she to give the message to the deeply shaken woman, who could hardly open her eyes? Fear and pain raged in the faithful soul; she too suffered for the Lord, Who was most precious to her.

She had spent all day in extreme and grievous anguish, seeking to drown her worries in work.

The light flickered in her mistress's bedchamber, a deep sigh was heard, then all was quiet again. Bethsabe stood up and listened. She drew the curtain aside and gazed at Mary Magdalene. Was she not lying there as if dead? Her eyes, otherwise so sparkling and alert, appeared extinguished. Her features were still and gaunt; beads of perspiration trickled down over her brow from her luxuriant hair.

Bethsabe washed her, and Mary Magdalene stirred. Bethsabe dreaded the moment when she would have to break the terrible news to her mistress. But then Mary Magdalene raised her head from the pillows; she sat up and gazed into the distance.

"Bethsabe, something frightful has happened, they have arrested our Lord, Judas has betrayed Him! Jesus is innocent, but they want to harm Him, and we will be unable to do anything unless we receive help from His Father. I know everything, but ask no questions and speak not of what you hear from my lips, for it is not mine to pass on to others. What I experience is for the Light alone."

Bethsabe did not understand her mistress, and was afraid. Mary Magdalene was speaking as if she were delirious. Suddenly she said:

"I want to go to Bethany!" She tried to get up, but invisible forces seemed to push her on to her bed, and a hand appeared to hold a clear mirror before her eyes. The pictures she saw emerging in it made such a powerful impression as to cause her severe pain.

She saw Jesus sitting on a bundle of straw in a courtyard. His hands were tied, and a spray of thorns was wound around His head. A stick had been thrust into His hand. The courtyard was dark. A cock crowed in the distance. A slight painful shudder coursed through Jesus; He sat quietly looking into space, but His eyes were vacant.

Where was He? The pain had almost been removed from Him; He was as if extinguished. Whatever was yet to come passed Him by.

Mary Magdalene was occupied solely with the one wish to be able to help, to avert the terrible thing which she felt with virtual certainty to

241

be approaching. If only she could do something, if only she did not have to wait idly until the end was upon them.

Then, as though on delicate strings, the voice of the Lord floated towards her:

"Do you think that I could not ask My Father to send Me His angelic hosts? Only when I am no longer with you, and the Help comes to you, will you understand Me. Have I not often told you that My hour is nigh?"

Mary Magdalene trembled when she heard the voice of Jesus. It seemed to her as though luminous rays were flowing through her.

Exhausted, she fell back and went to sleep. Weeping quietly, her maidservant knelt at the foot of her bed and waited lest she be needed. She did not dare to stir.

Towards morning, Mary Magdalene rose from her bed. Her body was invigorated, and her soul, which had undergone such extreme suffering, was still and comforted.

She had but one thought: she would go to Pilate. Therefore speed was essential; and she was given the strength for this errand.

PONTIUS PILATE stood musing in the atrium of his house. It was still early morning; but he was already prepared, for a heavy grey day lay before him. The night's rest had not released him from the pressure which had increased since the previous evening to a state of strained, uneasy distress.

Nervously he had paced up and down the terrace in the evening twilight. He felt as though a broad, scorching ray of sunlight were standing over his head today, striking him oppressively from out of cosmic, incomprehensible Laws. He wanted to resist this fateful Power which weighed upon him, the mighty, the incorruptible, the great one of Rome, like a nightmare. But the Power was so compelling; it followed him at every turn.

Uncertain, he pondered over something indefinable that had never before happened to him, and was suddenly entering his life. He, the man of well-considered quick decisions, who was otherwise never afraid, who possessed a clear intellect and a heart full of austere kindness, he stood and pondered, was benign and thoughtful, oppressed by the Power which seemed to him to be not of this earth.

Thus did Mary Magdalene find the governor, Rome's foremost official, to whom she wished to speak. When the servant announced the early visitor to him, the Roman's cold superiority became instantly apparent in the features which had just at that moment been dominated by uncertainty.

Shrugging his shoulders, his impulse was to send the visitor away. But Mary Magdalene's will was imbued with strength and free of doubt, trusting that the longing to work for the Lord must move mountains and soften stones. Then why not the heart of a most honourable, aristocratic Roman such as Pilate? She knew neither fear nor indecision, and Pilate received her.

Dignified and confident, yet with utter courtesy, Mary Magdalene stood before the powerful man.

She spoke of Jesus. She was not the penitent, not the fallen woman. She was the convinced servant of the great Redeemer of mankind. Pilate listened attentively. He had long followed with interest the course of development of the Jewish religious movement. He himself was a philosopher who was seeking God. What had been prepared by John seemed to be crowned by this Jesus.

But he did not deny that the number of his followers was growing too large. He was a Roman – of what concern to him were the affairs of the Jews! He governed for Rome! What was the religion of this people to him? And yet there was more than religion here; there was something here for which the soul yearned. That was what Pilate felt.

Mary Magdalene told what she knew about Jesus' work and life, so that Pontius Pilate might know the truth. She did not plead for the Lord; she could not intercede with a human being for Him, for she still heard within herself the admonishing voice of Jesus:

"Do you think I could not ask My Father to send His angelic hosts to help Me?"

After a long discussion the Roman dismissed Mary Magdalene. He would see to the Prophet.

As if liberated from the pressure of the night, Pontius Pilate walked back into the atrium. There he found a written message from his wife to him.

She had had a dream. He should have nothing to do with the righteous Prophet. These words of his astute, noble wife were a warning to him.

Thus the hour was impending in which Pontius Pilate was to be confronted with the decision of his life.

THE MURMURING OF THE CROWD came closer. Here and there shouts could be heard, and the guards had trouble restraining the people before the courtyard. A small troop of armed soldiers conducted the prisoner before the governor.

Pilate had stepped on to the staircase under the pillars of the house. With calm, cold objectivity he regarded the man opposite him.

The simple nobility surrounding him inspired Pilate with reverence. A faint awareness of Power neither identified nor understood stirred within Pilate. Here something other than the power of the stronger was perceptible; here was the Power of the Spirit.

At first glance, Rome's experienced official knew:

"This man is innocent!"

And he voiced it.

Jesus raised His eyes and made a movement with His bound right hand, as though He were lifting up Pilate's spirit. With that the Roman breathed a sigh of relief. Jesus had given him more than Pilate could suspect.

But he was unable to exceed the letter of his regulations, and had to put to the Jews, shouting impatiently and already storming the gate, the question laid down by the law: which of the accused they wished to have released at Passover. He expected them to choose Jesus, for the others were common criminals.

Therefore he could not believe his ears when they shouted the name "Barabbas". An ominous, oppressive silence followed. No bird-call, no sound was to be heard. The world was numb, as though dead. Everyone's breath and pulse seemed to stop.

Pilate stood as if thunderstruck. Once again the unpredictable soul of the people had revealed its abject inferiority. This dastardly, perfidious rabble filled him with loathing. He would have preferred to have them all annihilated.

Why did they hate this Pure One? The spiritual pressure intensified to the utmost in these brief moments of decision which were like hours. What became perceptible to him in quest of the Truth as an oppressive but furthering Power, drove the Darkness to frenzy, to bloodthirstiness and rage. And it shrieked as with one voice from countless throats: "Crucify him!"

Then the same twice over.

And Pilate washed his hands to symbolise that he was innocent of this murder.

Thereupon the servants of the Roman gathered round Jesus. The soldiers led Him away and guarded Him. The large iron gate removed Him from the people's view.

Like a red glow, the radiation of their thoughts lay almost visibly over the mob, finding dreadful expression in the words:

"His blood be upon us and upon our children!"

A FRENZIED TUMULT had now also broken out in the city. For days reports of conflicts and disturbances had already been coming in from the country. But with relentless severity the Romans soon restored order. Only the soul of the people, the atmosphere of the whole city, was saturated with suppressed rage, blood and turmoil.

The women hardly ventured on to the streets. Nervous and apprehensive, they stood in a narrow steep lane leading up to the road to Golgotha, and awaited the sorrowful procession which, accompanied by soldiers, came slowly from the court-house. They joined it.

With leaden heaviness the terrible happening moved past them. It was as though they were no longer alive.

The rhythmic tread of the soldiers mingled with the shuffling footsteps of those following, who yielded apathetically to the weight of sorrow that paralysed the whole of the city.

These were horrible hours. Suppressed sobbing came from the crowd that lined the streets.

With the other women Mary Magdalene stood not far from the place of execution. She suffered unspeakable torment of body and soul, agonies which she would never have considered possible. Although she was present, she saw nothing of what was happening on earth. It was only Mary, the mother of Jesus, who was conducted by John and who stood near the foot of the Cross, who attracted Mary Magdalene's attention. She felt how her heart tightened in grievous pain, and she thought: how great must be the suffering of His mother!

It was so terrible on earth that words could not express it: as though the sky was falling, and covering the city with a shroud.

Jesus's hour of death was nearing its end.

Softly, only faintly perceptible, the words came down from the cross: *"It is finished!"*

At that moment everything around Jesus shone forth in brilliant Light, and Mary Magdalene's eyes were opened still further. What she saw was so pure, so sublime, so remote from the earth as to be inconceivable to the human spirit.

The Cross stood on the dark ground of Calvary. But the wood of the Cross was no longer visible. Everything below it was enveloped in jet-black clouds. But above, where the body of Jesus hung, was so much Light that the earthly forms remained completely hidden.

Magdalene saw only the bleeding wound at the side, the gleaming marks on His feet and hands and the radiant Countenance, over whose brow drops of blood were trickling. The crown of thorns was as of liquid gold and glowed as though in the fire of agony. But it was a pain totally different from the earthly, for that had already been suffered in advance by Jesus.

The blood shone red as ruby. Face, hands and feet as well as the side of the heart were suffused with radiant Light. Where the arms were spread out extended mighty, gold-flaming wings of Light. And this whole picture, which was merging into a holy glow, ascended slowly through a Light-gateway surrounded by Knights. Steps leading to infinite Heights became visible. This shaft of Divine Light pierced the darkness of the earth's gloom at the brief moment of passing, when the words were uttered:

"Father, into Thy Hands I commend My Spirit!"

It was the blazing up of the Divine Ray, and the Return into the Light!

But mankind perceived nothing of it.

Once more there was a flash of dazzling Light. Flaming wings were spreading over the Cross.

Then from the throng the voice of a man rang out in conviction:

"Truly, this was the Son of God!"

The earth had become dark; the ground was quaking. Full of fear and terror, men were trembling. Transfixed, their eyes glassy, they stared at one another. Horror, fear of an ineffable woe weighed upon them.

Thus did the responsibility surge over the human spirit.

THE MESSAGE of Mary Magdalene had reached Joseph of Arimathea too late. Despite his immediate departure from his country-house outside the city, he was unable to be in Jerusalem so quickly.

When he reached the place of execution, the Lord had passed on. Deeply shaken, those closest to Him were still standing about in small groups.

The soldiers of Pontius Pilate established order among the people, and sent them away.

Then Joseph of Arimathea had the body of the Lord taken down. They laid it on the Prince's outspread mantle and wrapped it in white cloths.

The women from Bethany had approached timidly, Mary Magdalene among them.

The governor Pilate granted the request of Prince Joseph of Arimathea to inter the body of Jesus in a grave hewn out of rock.

Nature was dead, as were the things that normally were filled with radiance. Like empty shells, people moved in the direction of the grave.

The disciples carried the body of the Lord. The others followed. They laid it in the grave and closed it with a large rock.

Mary Magdalene could hardly part from the grave. A narrow path ran along the slope, level with the top of the rock. Deeply absorbed, she followed this path. She had to be alone. Her eyes were smarting, her forehead pained her, and she was hardly able to lift her feet any longer. She seated herself on a boulder, looked silently at the sepulchre for a long time, and wept.

Gradually her pain changed. The terrible numbness within her was dissolved in a prayer. Pure and light, a clear stream rose up from her, quite slow and timorous at first, then increasing in strength, and reciprocally an abundance of Power came to Mary Magdalene from Above. Again she felt life within her; it seemed to her that she was being granted sublime help. A voice said earnestly and sorrowfully, yet comfortingly:

"The Holy Grail has been veiled until the third day. Then you will see the Lord again in the circle of His followers. Come and pray at this place in the morning."

A light shone forth in Mary Magdalene, and it appeared to her that this light was moving through the cold stone into the closed grave.

She rose and walked slowly through the dusk. There was peace in her soul.

THE NEXT MORNING while it was still dark, Mary Magdalene went again to the grave of the Lord. She felt as though she were following the Lord, longingly absorbing within her the Light that still flowed to her from Above, and moved further and further away.

Occasionally when her spirit suddenly grew conscious of itself in the physical body, Mary Magdalene was overcome with a pain of being forsaken and lost; it was so great that she thought she would perish.

She suffered the agony of the whole world, but the world did not comprehend what it had burdened itself with and evoked through the death of Jesus, through the murder of the Son of God. She suffered, but she had to suffer in order to mature for her service, to which the Son of God had appointed her.

How should she vividly impress their guilt on human beings, how should she plant the germ of womanly virtue in the fallen earth-woman if she herself did not mature through suffering to the highest recognition?

During that night each of the disciples had to mature in his own way through suffering. It was the lawful fulfilment of this Happening.

It was a holy night in which the disciples carried the body of their Lord from the sepulchre to the place which was to conceal Him for thousands of years.

Mary Magdalene was walking in silent prayer to the grave, carrying a basket of flowers under which she had hidden crucibles with precious balsam. With it she wanted to prepare the body of the Lord for its long rest according to Jewish tradition.

When she reached the tomb, she was enveloped by a great Power. It seemed to her that she was stepping beyond herself and seeing everything: the night-grey mist still on the plain, the faint glow on the ranges of hills, and the dense gardens extending in a wide arc over the ridges, all in a white, supra-earthly Radiance.

Mary Magdalene came to a halt; she was standing at the vault of the sepulchre in the rock, on either side of which a clear Radiance shone forth. Her eyes were dazzled; but with the Power given her she was able to bear the Radiance.

In the bright Light figures could be discerned which stood out more and more clearly the less frightened Magdalene was by the extraordinary nature of her perception.

So distinct did their form become that they appeared like earthly bodies, and yet they were transparent and emitted a silvery shimmer.

"Fear not!" said one of the figures, "and hear what we tell you: Jesus, the Son of God, has risen with His Divine Part, Which was in Him. He will abide with you and walk among you another forty days. Here and there you will recognise Him, and receive of His Power for the blessing of Subsequent Creation. But His body will be preserved in testimony for the Judgment which must now inevitably come upon Creation, and for the time of the Son of Man here on earth."

As if a chisel were engraving the words in stone, so were they engraved in the spirit of Mary Magdalene for eternity. Her spirit absorbed, understood and preserved them. But to the women who had followed her quietly her lips declared:

"Behold, when I came I found the stone removed, and two luminous figures were within the tomb. Let us go to the disciples and tell them that we found the grave empty."

But as they were returning on the road, trembling and sobbing with emotion, and the rosy colour of the sun was tingeing the fine mists, a form appeared before Mary Magdalene out of the cloud layer drifting across the hills. A radiant Countenance, transfigured by the White Light of God, gazed at her. Hands were extended towards her, as though raised in blessing; in them glowed like ruby the marks of the nails, and the voice of the Lord spoke with the radiant resonance and the soft tone uniquely its own:

"Do not touch Me, Mary! You would not be able to bear the Power. It is I! Go forth, and tell My disciples."

Mary was deeply shaken; yet she was animated by a great vigour, and the pain was taken from her. She saw clearly that it was the Lord. But she also knew that it was not His earthly body that had stood before her, for she could only behold it with *that* eye with which she apprehended the luminous pictures from Above. Jesus had often sought to explain her visions to her, but now it had become still clearer and more intelligible; she was almost alarmed by the vast magnitude of such grace.

And human beings knew nothing of it! But she herself had indeed perceived the terrible shuddering of Nature at the hour of Jesus' death, and almost forgotten it even the second day after.

On the way to the disciples she let the women walk a little ahead of her, for she wanted to be alone. And the Lord appeared to her again and said:

"I am. I shall go before you to Galilee. Three of you will see Me and still not believe or comprehend it, for they do not yet understand the working of the Laws of My Father; in their imagination they confuse form and effects of the Divine Radiation-processes.

"Therefore I also said to you: 'Do not touch Me!'

"Because hitherto they knew only My outer cloak, they will not recognise Me immediately now. Only you have already beheld Me with your spiritual eye and can therefore see Me now as well.

"You are beholding Me as I come from the Father, but no one is able to see Me as I am in Him.

"You will wish to explain it to them with a thousand words, and they will neither understand nor believe. Therefore tell them only this:

"'I go before you to Galilee' said the Lord, for He is risen and has told me so, that I may make it known to you!"

AND IT CAME TO PASS as Jesus had said. They could not believe it. Peter went out to the tomb and found it empty. He did not see the Lord there.

But it was quite different with the women. Their deeply-grieved souls were thirsting for every ray of hope, for every glimmer of light that fell into the desolate days. They missed Jesus ever more and sought Him with longing. Through Mary Magdalene they experienced the meeting with Jesus and thus saw the Lord themselves.

They went to the disciples and confirmed what they had been told by Magdalene. But the men did not believe them. This caused the women to form a closer bond among themselves.

Just in these days of the most grievous pain there was a wondrous weaving full of power and love among the women. When they went to the disciples these felt as if a greeting came with them, a greeting from the happy time when Jesus had dwelt among them.

When the disciples were alone, they were overcome with grief, and each one felt a particular sting. It was the weakness not yet conquered by their human nature at the time the Son of God was murdered. This sting in the soul of every one of them left them no peace when the hour of suffering began, until each had recognised and overcome his weakness.

But in their deep sorrow the women sought help in faith; they did not abandon what had been engraved upon their souls by the holy words of Jesus. They clung to it with the tenacity of that spirit which never leaves its Home once it has found it. Therefore they were also the first to be allowed to behold the Lord. They called Him by the words which He himself had given them: The Risen One.

Only one of the women had to suffer as did the disciples; and this suffering weighed her down even more. That was Mary, the mother of Jesus.

John, who had promised Jesus to take care of His mother, stood faithfully by her. And it was also given to John to comfort and understand her, for Jesus had told him what He had not voiced to anyone else: His grief over Mary, who had never quite understood Him, and who had become increasingly the *earthly* mother the more she worried about Him. But she in particular should never have needed to worry had she but truly understood and believed. She had been caught in the prejudices of her people, only half freeing herself from them. That became her destiny and her guilt.

But the death of her Son, the grief over Him, brought her recognition. With terrible force the weight of her self-chosen path descended upon her. Intuitively she perceived herself to be a stranger, a homeless one among the disciples, to whom her Son was home. But now she recognised and knew that she could live only among them, in the circle of their thoughts and their living love, in which she hourly recognised anew the seed sown by her Divine Son.

Yet her suffering and her recognition beneath the Cross had also bestowed upon her a help whose spiritual effect she was not yet able to understand. John, who with the eye of his Master, through his knowledge of the Divine Laws, was learning more and more to look behind the happenings of earthly life, recognised it, and observed Mary with inner joy.

Mary Magdalene was drawn irresistibly to her. It had always been given to her to guide with love those in need of comfort, those with cares, and the oppressed, more so than the others who thought themselves so secure, and who in their self-satisfaction were mostly bringing about severe problems that determined their fate.

The Lord had endowed Mary Magdalene with the gift that in these days of sorrow she would be able to see with open eyes the consequences of all deeds in herself and others.

But at the same time she remained like a closed book and made sure that it was solely the fruits of her experiences that she offered to help others in loving solicitude, without revealing her knowledge, for that is how it was meant to be.

She was often near Mary and soon won her trust. With fervent joy Mary Magdalene saw how the Light was spreading about the mother of Jesus, enveloping her like a mantle. And she too it was who, together with John, was able to restore self-confidence to that severely dejected one who was suffering in body and soul. They awakened the sense of duty and confidence in the quailing soul who imagined that the Lord would now no longer accept her services. And slowly Mary began to live again.

Then her Divine Son appeared also to her. She perceived the Power of His Living Light as if in blessing over her hair, which had become white.

"Have you seen the Lord, Mother Mary?" asked John, trembling, and Mary whispered softly:

"Yes, my Son lives and is with us!"

To MARY MAGDALENE IT SEEMED that the Spirit of the Lord urged her to stay near His mother to help her. She herself found comfort in it, and was receiving added strength and help in everything she did. In the circle of the women who were dear to her she consciously prepared herself for the task of which Jesus had spoken to her.

She became ever lighter within. In spirit she witnessed all the appearances of the Lord, even when she was not with the disciples. They had not believed her at the time when she had brought them tidings of the risen Lord, but soon they too had met the Lord and, filled with joy, they had told her of it. But she knew that they would never fully grasp His appearance, the nature of His Light-risen body.

So she was sitting again one day among the women. While they attended to the household chores, she was hemming a cloth for Mother Mary. Then suddenly she perceived the women's voices as if from a distance. She leaned her head back against the bare wooden wall of the alcove. The small oil-lamp flickered erratically, spreading light and shade in the low room. A strong fire was still burning under the great cauldron of the open hearth in the corner.

A quiet, clear light began to fill Mary Magdalene's spirit, and she gazed into a white, unadorned room, in which she discerned the disciples of Jesus. They were sitting round a table, but not all of them were present.

She heard them speaking about the Lord. And between John and Peter she saw a luminous haze begin to glow, which presently took on the radiant form of the Lord. In their animated conversation the disciples did not perceive it until Jesus touched them gently. Then at last they saw Him standing there and were startled.

But He pointed to His wounds and said:

"I bear these wounds for you to recognise Me readily, and in remembrance, for you would otherwise not know Who I am, until I offer you the bread and the wine."

The sound of the familiar, beloved voice penetrated the spirit of them all deeply as once it had when Jesus had given them the Last Supper.

"I bless this bread which I offer you, as I offered My body – as I offer Myself to all who long for the Heavenly Bread. And I bless this wine for you, which begins to glow at the hour when My time is coming to a close and when in the Heavenly Ray I return into the Father.

"Do you now understand what I said to you then with the words: 'I come from out of the Light and return into the Light when the Hour of the Renewal of Power begins. On the Waves of Light I will be borne back into the Realm of My Father. And if My earthly body were taken from Me before the Hour of the Outpouring had arrived, I would have to wait until I could re-connect Myself with the Divine Ray, until the Father opens Himself to Me!'

"I am preparing you for this hour; for you shall experience it, you my disciples. Peace be with you. As the Father has sent me, so do I send you!"

As He spoke these words there shone from His figure a brilliance like a white flash of lightning, and rays flowed across the room from His uplifted hands. They spread in delicate waves, and the disciples felt them penetrate head and heart like the Breath of God. Holy silence, peace and bliss lay like a Light-Radiance above them and strengthened them.

"Take the Power of the Holy Spirit!" thus the voice of the Son of God rang through these luminous waves, and every word was like a living seed-grain springing up. White rays reached higher and higher. The ceiling of the room could no longer be seen for the glowing Light. White pillars and arches seemed to rise like a dome above the Son of God. In infinite distances it appeared like a sea of glass, lofty, white and clear as crystal. Within it hovered the Holy Dove, the Holy Spirit of God, Whom the Son promised His disciples.

The Divine Voice penetrated deep into Mary Magdalene's soul. She gazed into a sea of movement and radiance and was not able to grasp the working and creating of Divine Power. But that which she and the disciples had been promised at this hour by the Divine Voice was fulfilled.

Each day brought them fresh experiences and progress in their recognition. Jesus still appeared to them frequently; He spoke to them and filled them with the Power of His Holy Word. He commanded them to remain in the city of Jerusalem until the Day of Transfiguration.

NATURE BLAZED upwards radiantly to the heavens; the hot light of the sun quivered golden. Jubilant voices rang in the vast garden, on the hills, across the fields.

And in the blue heavenly peace, in the Light-pervaded Divine Blessing, amid the singing of insects and birds the Son of God walked for the last time over the earth before His disciples.

With that living vision which was bestowed on her, Mary Magdalene saw the disciples following their Lord, Who was walking ahead of them, to Bethany.

And He spoke to them in love. And they asked Him about the Millennium. But He reproved them, saying:

"It is not for you to know the time and the hour which the Father has reserved for His Power. You will receive the Power of His Holy Spirit and be My witnesses in Jerusalem."

255

They were standing on a hill and the figure of the Lord was in radiant contrast to the pale blue sky. A White Light surrounded it in a wide circle, and Rays broke forth from it in the form of the Cross. Flaming white, the Light-stream revolved around His figure which, becoming ever clearer and more luminous, rose up gently from the earth.

A white, radiant band of Light reached down from the infinite blue of the firmament and united with the Light of the Son of God on Its Living Waves, which came from the Primordial Power of His Father and touched the earth, bringing renewal. The Ray out of the Divine Light raised Him up and bore Him back into the Fountain-head. The myriad sparks of Light which quickened the Cosmos at this hour still enveloped like glimmering flakes the spirit of the gazing woman who was permitted to witness this Divine Happening; then it fell into a deep sleep.

And two Light-figures bòre the sleeping spirit back down into its earthly body. On awakening it was told by them:

"Await the Holy Spirit Which will come like Jesus, the Son of God!"

A sacred fire was burning in her spirit, and blazed up high so that she beheld its brilliance. At the same time a Power flooded the earth, as though the Light were pouring all Its Might from Heaven over sinful mankind.

A WHITE, PURE LIGHT was shining around the disciples of the Lord. Joy swung in their circle, a love and harmony that could no longer be clouded by anything earthly. They were all imbued with the thought that Jesus had promised them the Power of the Holy Spirit, and their spirits were awaiting It.

They were little affected by the hatred of the people who had slowly begun to persecute the disciples of the Nazarene again. It had been assumed that with the murder of Jesus an end had been put to this movement, and there was hope that the irksome Galileans who were leading the people astray would separate in disunity and be scattered to the four winds.

But anger, disappointment and fear crept into the ranks of the

Pharisees and scribes when they heard about the Risen Christ. They therefore disseminated calumnies against the disciples and stirred up trouble wherever they could.

The small community which banded together was maliciously shadowed to see whether a charge could be preferred against its members that must destroy it.

The disciples, however, were quiet, unassuming and reserved. Yet the lustre that appeared to flow from their heads was intensifying in those days. Whoever sought to attack them lost heart or missed the opportunity when near them. But the disciples themselves attacked no one. Their confidence was great. Whoever came with a request for help or advice always went away strengthened and comforted.

No one was able to penetrate their firmly-knit circle when they were together. Often there were over a hundred people.

The nearer the Day of the Outpouring of the Holy Spirit came, the more strongly did the pure Power vibrate in their circle. The women too were now often with them. Mary, the mother of Jesus, Martha and Mary, the sisters of Lazarus, and Mary Magdalene, who was living in eager expectation. Her spiritual eyes had been more widely opened, and she perceived the approach of a Sacred Fulfilment of the Law in Creation, which she did not yet understand.

For her the awakening and the renewal in Nature had always been a festival. She perceived it intuitively as a gift from God, which is bestowed upon the world every year.

Once she had made thank-offerings to the gods of spring, had celebrated the festival of the Jews in memory of the exodus from Egypt. Mother Nature always bestowed her most beautiful gifts at that time. There was abundance, joy, jubilation and fervent gratitude to the Most High in Magdalene's soul, but at the same time there was always that painful longing which she could never dispel or comprehend.

Year after year, from her childhood days to the time of her most severe suffering, this period had always been the most festive but also the most difficult, compelling her to deep reflection and longing. It weighed fatefully upon her throughout her earth-life. Now it had become the moment of rebirth of her spirit.

Often the Luminous Spirit from Supreme Heights, who had become her guide, brought her warnings or messages to be conveyed to the disciples.

So he also announced to her the hour of the day when they should all be together in harmony. Mary Magdalene felt as if her feet were walking on clouds. The air was filled with mild, lovely scents, and the flowers and grasses shone as though reflecting the light of heaven.

She went to Mother Mary, bringing her and John the tidings. Joy and peace was with them.

AND THE HOUR OF FULFILMENT CAME. They were all gathered in a beautiful circular hall afforded them by Mark, the Roman, for their joint Hours of Worship. The tiles of the floor gleamed, as did the bright walls. The women had placed many flowers and blossoms in tall earthenware vessels in the niches of the hall.

Above, it arched into a small dome surrounded by a flat roof-garden. The house lay in a garden enclosed by high walls. It was completely unused and almost unknown.

It was so still all about that the blossoms could be heard dropping from the branches. Not a breeze stirred. Midday calm had settled over the roofs of the otherwise-so-restless Jerusalem.

When they were all gathered and sitting in a wide circle around the disciples, a rushing sound came from Heaven. It roared about the house like a mighty wind. The lights on the walls and the blossoms that adorned the room moved fitfully to and fro.

Those assembled were sitting in silent expectation, devoutly lifting their spirits, all seeking the Lord and worshipping God.

Radiant Power surrounded them palpably. In circles of Light, which widened as they approached, the shimmering Light-Dove was inclining towards Subsequent Creation. Joyfully the disciples opened their spirits, and on the path of Divine Streams of Rays the Power of the Holy Spirit came upon them.

The whole room was flaming gold; at its highest point shone the White Circle of Rays, in it the Will of God become form: the Holy Dove.

And Mother Mary remembered with gratitude the day when Jesus was announced to her. She now perceived intuitively again the Power and Love of God as in that Holy Hour. At the same time a flaming Radiance rose above all heads and the people began to praise the Lord, to thank Him!

The Light of God had penetrated them; It had illumined and called them. They were now prepared to proclaim the Word of their God and Lord to the world.

It was quiet again around the house and in the mighty expanse of heaven. The roaring sound had faded away. The deeply-shaken, spiritually so richly-endowed human children stood in prayer before their God and Lord.

When they opened the gates to go home, many strangers were standing around the house. Near and far people had heard the rushing of the mighty wind, and seen the dazzling Light streaming from the sky.

They were much surprised when they heard the disciples speaking and loudly proclaiming the Glory of Jesus with radiant eyes, and filled with the Power and Authority of the Word.

They shook their heads and said:

"They are full of new wine."

But Peter was seized by the power of love and joy. He proclaimed the Message of the Lord to the people for the first time, and promised them enlightenment through the Power of the Holy Spirit in baptism. And many opened themselves to the Word and followed the disciples. –

Mother Mary, however, went home with John. She wanted to begin her life anew in the service of God.

So the time came when the disciples parted. Each was driven by the Power of the Spirit to the place appointed for him by the Lord, and they spread the Light of God among the peoples.

THE POWER OF THE HOLY SPIRIT raised Mary Magdalene into Luminous Heights. To her it seemed that she was awakening to new life on a different plane.

On a lucid stream, which in clarity and power can be likened to the purest water, living germs of Light were rippling down into the World of Matter which she had left behind far, far below her.

Dazzling were the terraces on which she ascended higher and higher, step by step.

From the clusters of magnificent plants which shone in paradisal colours, from the pathways lined with tall sturdy trees forming vaulted leafy domes of light and gold, luminous figures were coming towards her and leading her.

She herself was Mary Magdalene no longer, but had become a flame, radiant, blue-white and calm; another name floated about her, a name which was written in the Golden Book. She had the impression of being a child; she was free, all earthly heaviness had fallen away from her; the sin which drew mankind into its reciprocal circles had also remained behind.

In her shone the Power of the Holy Spirit, the liberation from hereditary sin, and the purity of spiritual rebirth.

She felt a hand on her arm; following its gentle pressure she moved on. She knew not who was walking by her side, nor did she wish to find out; too great was the bliss within her. She mounted upwards; in this was embodied her whole aspiration, rising upwards in worship and gratitude with the knowledge of the Love of Jesus and of the Outpouring of the Holy Spirit.

At the same time she perceived that this Creation ended only where she had believed she would already find God, and that she herself had hitherto traversed a realm of denser material substance, which was a reflection of what her marvelling, exultant intuitive perception recognised here as Primordial Creation. And with that a remembrance came to her as though she had already known this glory and merely forgotten it in a long dream.

The spheres through which she moved upwards became ever larger, ever wider, ever more luminous; finally she saw herself amid flowers, surrounded by flames of her species.

Radiant white male and female light-giants were approaching her. Their expression alone permitted recognition of their nature in the most perfect form. Also, what they wanted to convey, what was brought forth by their volition, everything was immediately visible as a matter of course.

Thus Mary Magdalene knew that they were inviting her to walk with them through the lofty portal whence golden streams filled with life were flowing. They did not speak, and yet she knew their will, their intent. She also knew that she herself could only follow them because she had received the living spirit-spark of this sphere through the Son of God.

She gazed into a huge hall, whose mighty cupolas were supported by luminous pillars. Light flowed in broad streams from the highest point. Steps led upwards to a White Table behind which stood a Golden Throne.

"I am from Eternity, the Beginning and the End!" so it resounded and roared in the surging Light.

What was it? Was it the Voice of the Divine Son, which she had heard so often in supreme delight? Was it another Voice heard once before by her spirit? But where?

Distant memories of earthly pilgrimage and changing worlds arose and pervaded the swinging of her spirit like a breath. Like a remote dream-experience the land of Egypt, the golden light of a Temple, the face of a child appeared before her. Orbits of stars, cosmic streams separated her quickly from the sight. Again she looked heavenwards:

"Lord, help me to remember, if it is Thy Will!" thus spoke her spirit.

"I am the Will of God!" the Voice resounded from Above. "I scatter my seed into the World of Matter. To you, spirit-flame, I gave the Power for ascent. Make use of it, that you may proclaim the Magnitude of God's Glory to the world."

Ever more swiftly, as if floating, she approached the Throne of that Light-flaming Cross Which sent forth Its sheaves of rays. At Its side shone a Rose and a Lily.

But this was not yet the end of the Glory that she was permitted to behold. Again resonant words sounded forth:

"Sphere of the Primordial Spiritual, thou highest boundary for the human spirit, open out!"

These words came from the stream of the Living Cross of Light,

261

Whose form condensed into the human prototype. Holy mystery of the Light surged around the Flame on Whom the Primordial Spiritual spark was bestowed out of immeasurable Love.

"For the fulfilment of your mission, human spirit, go forth and experience what was ordained for you from the very beginning. Behold the rotating of the Living Power."

Circles of rays formed a Chalice through which the Power descended. Shining figures guarded it and surrounded the Column of Power through which the Divine ascended and descended.

There was the Holy Dove! It came down into the Holy Castle. There also was the Light of the Son of God Jesus; It ascended ever higher, ever further, and was finally immersed in the Sea of Clarity which extended, became circular and deepened.

Without beginning, without end, the Light revolved, more radiant, more powerful than a sun.

"I and the Father are One!" the Voice of Jesus resounded above the human spirit.

Then a powerful Voice reverberated thunderously into the Universe:

"Behold My Will, Whom I send as Judge over the righteous and the unrighteous: *He* is called *Imanuel*!"

Flaming white, He stepped from the Fountain-head of Light, dazzling like a flash of lightning, keen as a sword, mighty as an angel of wrath, the Holy Dove above His head. Roseate light spread out before Him. From His right a Rose emerged, the Lily blossomed at His feet, and He Himself was like a King to behold.

Rose-coloured, luminous veils flowed over the radiant Castle, and in everything swung the Name: Parsifal.

SINKING DOWNWARDS, the blessed human spirit began its return to the World of Matter, in prayer and thanksgiving. The memory remained behind like a dream.

Such was Mary Magdalene's experience. –

When she awakened again on earth, she was unable to move at first. Full of anxiety Mary and Martha stood by her in these days, and

Bethsabe had not left the bedside of her mistress, who lay among her cushions motionless, as if dead. She did not understand what had happened to Mary Magdalene, but the other women guided Bethsabe, giving her strength and calm.

But soon the will reawakened in Mary Magdalene, and she was able to rise from her bed. A feeling of great strength pulsated through her, which she determined to use for deeds.

Her spirit urged her to the poor and outcasts. Her path was difficult, but she followed it in the knowledge that the Lord had sent her forth.

Thus passed a considerable time. Mary Magdalene no longer saw the Lord. She now stood in her earthly activity. For this she received strong spiritual help the moment she was in need of it. The women felt drawn to her, especially young girls. Mary Magdalene herself was unaware of the great effect of the Power of Attraction flowing to her from Above.

She perceived a growing connection with that Maiden Who had once appeared to her in a light-green mantle adorned with lilies. It was Irmingard, the Pure Lily, Who passed Her guiding Power into the bridge upon earth for earthly womanhood to find a firm support when they sought it. And all who had opened themselves to the Word of Jesus, and followed the disciples, found help and strength in the recognition of true Purity.

Many women from wealthy houses were now drawn by the Teaching of the Son of God, which His disciples proclaimed in public. They asked to be baptised, and placed themselves and their belongings in the service of the Light.

But the greater the number of followers, the more the serpent once more began to rear its head. Especially the hatred of the Jews was mounting; they suffered terribly from the consequences of their deed perpetrated against Jesus.

Since Jesus had left the earth, evil had beset the people in the Jewish realm. A dark fist weighed upon many of them with relentless determination.

But the uproar in their spirits was all the greater. At first secretly, then openly, they began to persecute the followers of Jesus.

263

One night, a brilliant ray like a flash of lightning illumined Mary Magdalene's room. But it was followed by neither thunder nor storm. On the contrary, there was utter calm all around, and such clarity and bliss in Mary Magdalene as she had not perceived since Jesus had departed from them.

She was fully awake and saw everything brightly illumined. From the highest Height a Voice like a trumpet rang out:

"Go out at daybreak to the sepulchre of your Lord and wait there. You have one more task to fulfil here in this dark city. Then seek out Mother Mary, for it is time, high time to do so. You are not to return to Jerusalem once you have fulfilled your task.

"Hand over your work to others who will administer it well, and entrust yourself to the guidance of your spirit. You are not to know where you will rest at night. You are to follow the Word of your Lord and drive His sheep into His folds. Remember always that you are walking in the Power of the Lord, and act accordingly."

Magdalene rose from her bed, prepared for a journey and saw to the absolute necessities. She also gave a few instructions for the early stages of her absence. Then she departed.

SHE WALKED BRISKLY through the garden and the gate which were still in darkness, and hurried out into the open. She chose quiet lanes, for the streets were already busy in the early morning. There was a medley of jarring, haggling voices and various languages. Donkey-drivers shouted, and camels with their peculiar wail moved through the gates.

Mary Magdalene sighed with relief when she reached the ridgeway upon which she had walked so often to the Lord's tomb during the most arduous days. There they had laid Him to rest, but His earthly body had already been removed when His luminous body appeared to her.

Suddenly Mary Magdalene was seized with the fervent longing to find the place where the body of the Lord had truly been given refuge. So she hurried along the narrow path and was soon standing at the sepulchre.

It had changed very much. It was no longer the grave of the Lord.

Mary Magdalene sensed what a place of obsessive worship and greed would arise here. All at once she knew why it was not in the Father's Will that the Vessel which had sheltered His Son should fall into the hands of posterity.

What had at the time appeared inconceivable, inscrutable and dreadful to her, that the body of Jesus had been taken away, she now perceived intuitively as being right, willed by God, and comforted, she rejoiced over it.

She was no longer able to pray at this place, and she walked on. By the densely-overgrown slope she turned left into a small, recently-trodden path.

Greyish green foliage surrounded her; the bushes arched like vines so low above her head that she had to stoop. Half-way up the mountain she reached a clump of rocks, and found herself before a cave, over whose right arch three crosses had been engraved.

She entered this cave, and had the impression that it was used by shepherds to shelter from inclement weather. The opening which appeared far down on the right side was quite narrow, yet a body was able to squeeze through.

With a single-mindedness which surprised Mary Magdalene herself she ventured to push through the constricted opening, and found what she had expected: a narrow, low passage.

Like a reflection she saw the figures of Joseph of Arimathea and John carrying the body of the Lord, wrapped in shrouds, before her.

Mary Magdalene knew that these pictures which, clear as crystal and in colour, as if alive, unrolled before her, were meant to tell her about the resting-place of the earthly cloak of the Son of God. She was seized by a holy reverential awe, and the pain that had been gnawing at her soul when the Lord died made itself felt again. It seemed to her that she was actually walking quietly, bowed down, and step by step through the dark confined passage with these two faithful ones, in order to protect and shelter the beloved body of the Lord according to the Command of the Light.

She experienced the moment when the passageway widened, and a small cave admitted the men, who laid the body of Jesus upon a stone bench, anointed it as prescribed and wrapped it in white shrouds. A small open niche in the cave afforded a view of the wide, greenish-grey misty country still asleep in the half-light of early morning.

Joseph of Arimathea closed this gap with his own hands using a rock that fitted precisely yet naturally. Every crevice was carefully filled in with clay and dry creepers, and made into a solid airtight wall.

In this burial-chamber, at which the two disciples worked diligently and secretly for two nights, rested the body of the Lord, its head bathed in White Light.

When Mary Magdalene returned to clear consciousness she was standing bent at the end of the small passage and pressing her face against the cold, damp wall of a natural rock. It was rough, loamy and a little damp. She could go no further, and knew that this was the entrance to the cave in which the disciples had interred the Lord.

A White Light, the same as had given her the Command at night to go to the tomb, flared up beside her, and it seemed that its Radiance was shining through the thick wall before her.

She saw the white sunken covering of the shrouds which had protected the body of the Lord, and she saw His skull; it was of a wonderfully noble form, especially the forehead and the round, symmetrical curvature of the head.

An eyetooth was missing in the dazzling white row of the upper teeth. This small dark spot was deeply engrained like a special mark in her memory.

As swiftly as it had come, the Light and with It the picture It had given her – a picture for the future, so it seemed to her – was gone.

Mary Magdalene could go no further; she turned and in silent, fervent prayer walked back the way she had come.

Now she sought the nearest path by which to reach Mother Mary's dwelling-place.

MARY WAS LIVING in the house of John by the Sea of Galilee. She had changed almost beyond recognition. All the old had fallen away from her since she was imbued with the Power of the Holy Spirit, since she had opened herself to the Light in trusting recognition.

Her face shone; the careworn, sharp features had softened. Love and peace filled her being. Alert and active, she moved energetically about the house and knew how to deal with its occupants and the servants.

Mary felt urged to compensate for the past. She worked with great joy at the redemption of her guilt. Luminous, high guidance approached her, filling her ever anew with strength and that cheerful attitude which was reflected in her face like a celestial radiance.

John was happy about it. But he was concerned that her delicate body was already too weakened by a great deal of psychic suffering, and that Mary would not be with them much longer.

She had the appearance of a pure light which, blazing ever higher, consumes itself all the while. But in her was a petition: "Father in Heaven, grant me once more that I may serve! Allow me still to continue this life!"

But her physical body was no longer equal to it. – Thus did Mary Magdalene find her, and she shared John's view that Mary would soon have completed her life.

Was there not about her a light that could not be of this earth, the pure light of the rosy rays sent forth by the Power of Purity when Mary Magdalene had beheld Her? Did not the fragrance of lilies come to them on delicate clouds, so clearly that Mary raised her weary head from the soft pillows and breathing deeply, listened in that direction? With that a faint smile passed over her face.

Everyone strove to make her last days on earth beautiful. She was surrounded by love. A swinging permeated her room, which of itself bade the others approach her but quietly.

With great solicitude and love the spirit of the mother of Jesus was released from the earthly body.

Helping spirit-figures descended slowly, step by step. Their rays prepared the earthly surroundings and made the cloak ever finer.

Mary Magdalene remained by Mary's bedside. Such clear streams of Light as these here had not enveloped her since the Day of the Outpouring of Power. But whereas at that time the event had come upon the spirits with the force of a storm, Mary's departure was, in comparison, like a delicate breath of spring, touching also Magdalene with its blessing.

Lights were burning in the lucent room; the glimmer of their unsteady flames darted across the radiation of the departing spirit.

It was a few hours before Mary's death. A light figure came from Above, holding out her hands to Mary. She inclined towards her to lift her up.

Jubilant voices, full of warmth and radiance, rang out.

Mary smiled. Her eyes took on an expression as though they were gazing enraptured into the luminous world of the spirit. Irmingard's Power went before her. Upon Its rays her spirit mounted upwards into the Fields of Eternal Peace, in which it sought the Kingdom of her Son.

A shadow crept over her eyes, then they were without life.

No lamentation was heard in the room. Only fervent entreaties and ardent gratitude rose up to accompany the liberated spirit of the mother of Jesus.

WEEKS LATER Mary Magdalene was able to see the ascended one spiritually once more. She appeared more luminous and radiant. From a white veil draped round her head flowed fine golden rays that were like a cool breeze. Mary spoke:

"I have been borne aloft through my longing and the fervent petition for service. The faithful, strict, uncompromising love of John has been of great help to me.

"The gate to the Realm of Peace has opened resoundingly. I ascended upon the golden stream of rays sent forth by the Lily in crystal-clear Purity.

"I recognised that I was meant to mature through earthly suffering, for I was destined to be near the Saviour. I fulfilled this task only during the first part of His youth, then no longer. I did not surrender myself, nor did I renounce the old. Yet I was permitted to ascend when suffering had opened my spirit to the Light again. Only a little remains for me yet to redeem.

268

"But a picture of the future is also shown to me: the erroneous ways of the human spirits who cling to me through their veneration would hinder me.

"But I am already protected from the evil effects. Lilies and roses blossom in golden Light. Far off in the highest Heights I see the gleaming pinnacles of a golden Castle. The Primordial Spiritual Beings have laid a protective mantle around me. Thus I stand untouched, awaiting the last hour of my redemption, for I was given tidings from the Light:

"'Mary of Nazareth is permitted to be redeemed through service yet another time!'"

Such were the tidings received spiritually by Mary Magdalene through Mary, the mother of Jesus. Then the rush of events led her into the world as she had been promised.

She was walking alone through the deep dust of the narrow paths in blinding sunlight, as she had done repeatedly before.

She avoided the wide roads of the Romans and the paths busy with people. She set out early in the morning and rested at the first opportunity while the sun was at its highest. Her wants had become few; she carried very little with her and stayed in the homes of people who were happy to accommodate her.

Magdalene had become free; nothing earthly burdened her any longer. The times when she had still been concerned over some possession were a distant memory to her. Only the will for the Light, the love for Jesus and the sublime task of bringing His Word to human beings lived in her spirit.

A Light went before her, and Mary Magdalene followed it trustingly, for she remembered what she had been told:

"You shall follow the spirit and are not to know where you will rest at night!"

Like a child following its father's guidance, so she allowed herself to be led by this Ray. Nevertheless she remained alert and active in the earthly sense, which was necessary, for times were becoming ever more dangerous and restless.

269

The disciples of Jesus, who were spreading the Teaching of the Son of God in the surrounding provinces, rapidly increased in number. They baptised with the Power of the Holy Spirit and accomplished many good deeds, which convinced people of the Might and Power of their God. The number of believers increased, but this fanned the hatred of the Jews. In the schools and temples where the disciples proclaimed the Word and Life of the Lord to the silently listening throng, they set all kinds of traps for them through questions and accusations. But they also began to incite the people, and then asserted that the followers of Jesus, whom they called Christians, were causing the disturbances. They deliberately sowed doubt and disbelief among people and, seething with hatred, they agitated wherever they could.

Already they had sacrificed a few disciples to the rabble, already Stephen had been murdered by the stones hurled from the raging crowd. Sultry and menacing, the Darkness spread over the spirits, inciting like people to like deeds.

When Mary Magdalene entered the small villages or market-towns, she could tell immediately by the pressure coming towards her whether she should avoid the place or whether she could stay there. Frequently she turned away even though she was already tired.

FROM FAR OFF Mary Magdalene saw a cloud of dust on the great road leading from Jerusalem to Damascus. Flashing weapons glinted in the sun. She felt a compulsion to walk towards this cavalcade of Roman soldiers.

An evil presentiment oppressed the heart of the wanderer, who was coming from a small field-path and now had to cross the main road. She would have liked to hesitate, to hide, or to enter a hut, but there was no such possibility. As far as the eye could see there were only sun-lit low pastures – no shrub, no hill, no bush that could have offered protection.

Mary Magdalene knew no fear. She walked on and was nearing the troop of soldiers; she already heard their horses trotting now. They had to meet at the crossroads. Involuntarily Mary Magdalene covered her head with her scarf as though fearful that her shining golden hair might attract the attention of the riders. The staff she was carrying trembled slightly in her hand. Then she heard clearly the words:

"Mary Magdalene, listen: Whatever comes must take place! Fear not, for through you I would awaken a human being who shall become a torch for seekers. Your path is prepared. Though rough stones bloody your feet, tread upon their sharpest edges and do not flinch. Remember that you are Mine and not your own!"

And her tall figure straightened. With great firm strides she walked towards the road. The Roman in front had already caught sight of her. He was a Pharisee, but he was bearing arms like a soldier and looked like an artist. He sat his steed, tall and powerful, with glowing eyes, wild yet noble and proud. Now he raised his hand in greeting.

"It is rare to see a woman walking unaccompanied here. I think you could lose your way, beautiful Christian. We had better take care of you."

The words sounded courteous, yet an undertone of mockery was discernible which at one time would have roused Mary Magdalene's indignation.

"Not all women need the protection of men, especially when they are already advanced in years and independent. My protection and my escort are greater and mightier than the armies of the Emperor. Stand clear, Roman, and leave me in peace."

The face of the rider flushed crimson. His pride refused to accept the cool rebuff of this Christian woman. She irritated him. He did not know why, but an uncontrollable rage filled his violent soul whenever he perceived the quiet strength of this sect. Was it not as though they stood bathed in Light, which neither worldly authority nor hatred, neither envy nor scorn could penetrate?

How often he had felt inferior in the raging zealotry of his faith! And this feeling of impotence, in association with the earthly power at his disposal from Rome, unleashed all the acts of violence against the courageous followers of that hated Jesus, whom they called the King of the Jews, the Risen Son of God.

All the erudition, all the Pharisee's proficiency in the law, all the

271

knowledge of the Roman who had been a philosopher, balked at that simple greatness of these primitive fishermen who called themselves Apostles, promulgated fairy tales, and worked in silence, quietly and unassumingly, where others were helpless.

A struggle, an agonising conflict had been going on for months within Saul, and the longer it continued the more severe became the sufferings inflicted upon the disciples and followers of Jesus, for his hatred and his determination to destroy grew from day to day.

But the more he raged, the greater, purer and simpler those martyred Christians arose before his spirit. As if in defiance, his keen intellect became aware of the declining power of Judaism, of the Roman dominion and of the arrogance of the Pharisees.

Saul was suffering. He suffered infinite torments until he came to the realisation that the power of the intellect, of renown, of money, contained no values compared with the power of this spirit which filled the hated Christians! When he felt this recognition rising like a shadow within him, he subdued it with the desperate conceit of Rome and the Pharisees.

Now a woman stood in his way in the open road to Damascus where he intended to deal the Christians a decisive blow. And she conducted herself with the dignity of a woman and the strength of a man, with the pride and determination of one superior. She had spoken only a few insignificant words, but these had struck the inflexible man like the crushing blow from a giant.

He reached out his arm for her with the words: "Seize her! She shall accompany us to Damascus! See that this cantankerous individual comes to no harm until she is placed with her brethren who are awaiting our judgment."

In silent obedience the soldiers closed in like a solid wall about Mary Magdalene.

A few riders joined Saul and rode ahead. Magdalene was lifted on to a horse and had to follow them.

She was very frightened. But she remained silent, and in her trusting heart arose a prayer that blazed luminous trails and, in imploring trust, called down radiant streams upon Saul, the Roman.

The cavalcade trotted into fertile regions which indicated that now they were near Damascus. A mild evening fell, turning quickly into a cool night.

It was becoming cloudy; the first wintry rain showers of the year began, making a sharp contrast to the sunny hours of noon. Everyone looked forward to a lodging. They sat shivering on their horses, beginning to feel weary. Only Saul disregarded hardship. He was tenacious in his volition. Inexorably he felt driven onward.

He was a true Hebrew who, once a goal had been set, pursued it to the end with perseverance and an adamantine determination. With diligence and ambition he had acquired a wealth of knowledge, and a mighty flame was burning within him: the true longing for God.

Apparently he was still satisfied with the erudition of the Pharisees from whose schools he had emerged; he continued to bask in the wisdom of the Greek teachings he had studied. His was a brilliant intellect which had to get to the root of everything he undertook, and at heart he was deeply religious.

But his upbringing and his conduct he owed to Roman influence, which was much akin to his desire for self-improvement and his thirst for knowledge. Therefore he was called "Saul, the Roman" by his friends – with a touch of irony and resentment by the Jews but with respect by the others.

He was liked and feared, for he was strict and inexorably just. His speech was true and simple, but to the point. His censure struck home razor-sharp. He had an infallible sense of everything that was good, genuine and pure; and he hated hypocrisy and servility. That is why the soldiers loved him like a father. But weaklings and the underhanded hated him like poison and tried to malign him.

Unerringly he touched the sore points and stirred up all the evil; no matter where he found it, a concealed slough was intolerable to him. He obstinately pursued everything that gave rise to confusion, that caused unrest, and anything which he did not deem right.

With this same obstinacy and preconceived would-be-knowledge he had also involved himself in the struggle against the Christians. Now his fanatical determination to destroy was raging, and he had resolved

273

to deal a heavy blow in Damascus. Full of impatience he strained to get there.

But then at the crossroads this woman stepped before him. What had she said?

"My protection and my escort are greater and mightier than the armies of the Emperor!"

From the moment this utterance was made he respected the woman. Whence came her strength, whence the calm and whence that power which he did not like to acknowledge and yet felt? From her God?

Never before had Saul been so preoccupied, so dazed and so uncommunicative towards his companions. They rode silently beside him. Saul's horse grew restive, perhaps sensing the agitation and tension of its rider. But Mary Magdalene had become tranquil; no anxiety oppressed her spirit. She saw above her the clear, guiding Flame and knew that she was not forsaken.

But above Saul's head a Power was gathering which appeared to her like a glowing sword. She saw that this man was standing at his fateful turning-point, as she had at the time when she heard John's voice. She would have liked to say a helpful word to him. But she was his prisoner, and he seemed to pay no attention to her at all.

When night fell they arrived at a small fortress on the road. There the cavalcade stopped. Brief orders were given. A few Romans received sealed letters from the hand of the commander, words were hastily exchanged in low voices. Then they moved on. Saul rode in front.

Some of the escort rode into the courtyard of the small fortress with Mary Magdalene. She sensed trouble, but her soul remained calm all the same.

Saul had turned over to the Romans custody of Mary Magdalene. He did not want to enter Damascus with this woman.

The riders came into a dark courtyard sparsely lit by flickering torches. Where the walls met at the corner was a massive square tower apparently meant for the watchmen.

Into this tower Mary Magdalene was conducted. The small room which admitted her was then firmly shut. An icy chill rose to her heart when the door was locked several times with a rattling and creaking noise. But the comforting tranquillity did not leave her soul.

She sat down on a small bench and prayed. She closed her eyes; her spirit left her body and walked through the rooms of the fortress. It was as if the doors opened before her will.

Her soul made its way through the solid walls into square, austere and bleak rooms furnished with the bare essentials, and serving as quarters, sleeping accommodation, stable and utility rooms for the constantly changing garrisons.

Everyone was fast asleep; only a few guards were pacing up and down with their armour and weaponry clanking. The horses neighed softly in their sleep. Moths and bats fluttered about; the night was pitch-dark.

A fine drizzle made everything wet, slippery and shiny. Flickering torches were reflected in the puddles. Moaning softly, the wind soughed over the tower and was caught in a creaking wooden shutter in the corner of the yard. Monotonously, it beat like a warning rap against a gate in the entrance-wall.

The guards, no doubt sleepy from the wine, raised their heads and reached for their weapons. These gleamed brightly, but suddenly fell to the ground with a clatter. A muffled cry had escaped a hoarse throat. Dazzled, the men held their hands before their eyes. A shout dispelled any fatigue.

"Make haste, there goes the Christian woman handed over to us! How could she possibly have escaped?"

The commander of the guards gasped the words as though overwhelmed by the shameful fact of being outwitted. But the soldiers were as if paralysed. Their eyes were riveted to a spot in the middle of the courtyard where Mary Magdalene was standing surrounded by a luminous ring.

"Seize her, bind her! She must not escape from us before Saul summons her – that was his instruction. If not otherwise, better dead than alive."

Three distraught figures rushed at the defenceless woman. But – what was that? They clutched at her clothing; they thought they were seizing hold of her, but reached into empty space!

Yet she stood right before them, only stepped aside a little and addressed them. All three of them heard her voice when she said:

"What are you afraid of? Do you think I would escape from you? After all, you are holding me firmly locked away behind these walls. You have not neglected your duty. But believe and see: My Lord Jesus Christ is with me! He allows not a hair on the head of one of His children to be touched prematurely, for I still have work to do in His Name.

"Therefore do not fear; I will not run away from you. I shall bear witness to the Power of our God, Who sets the prisoners free according to His Will and Law, and Who will give help when we trustingly ask for it!

"Follow me into my cell and bind me, for I say to you in His Name: Before long Mary Magdalene will be free. Saul will change his mind even before he enters Damascus. But take this as a sign of the Power of Christ!"

The soldiers were as if spellbound. Never had they experienced anything like it. Never had such an abundance of strength and calm passed to them from a prisoner. Never before had they seen a human being shine like this. They did not understand what was happening, and were utterly confused. They were seized with fear of the God of the Christians, and in great suspense over how it would all end. Hesitant and curious, they therefore followed at some distance the woman who walked before them.

Trumpet-calls had been sounded, and meanwhile many soldiers had gathered at the scene. They had opened the prison and now looked at each other petrified, for the doors had been firmly locked and remained intact.

Mary Magdalene was standing in the centre of the room, which she had not left in the physical-earthly sense. A radiance lay upon her face. The soldiers pressed curiously around her and listened to the words streaming from her lips. She told them about Jesus, spoke of His life, His teaching and His death. Then she gave an account of the resurrection of His Divine Part and of His Union with the Father. She spoke of the Power of the Holy Spirit, in which His disciples were now permitted to work, and of the Might of His Will which they had just experienced for themselves. And one of the group came forward, knelt down and said:

"Is it possible for us also to receive the Power and the Blessing of your Christ? For I believe that HE is the Living GOD."

And Mary Magdalene laid her hand upon his bowed head and blessed him. He felt the Power of the Light and told his companions.

Morning was breaking. Mary Magdalene remained calmly in her cell and awaited news of Saul, for she knew that the Lord had illumined him.

SAUL AND HIS FRIENDS had moved on, escorted by the Roman soldiers; the small rearguard left behind with the Christian woman was to follow. Suddenly the sky darkened. A heavy, oppressive weight seemed to settle upon the riders. They went on their way weary, quiet and morose.

Scowling, the commander stared into space, and could not bring himself to exchange a word with his escorts. A tension was evident that seemed to become ever greater and more awesome. Gradually a feeling of dread took possession of the men, but none of them wished to betray himself. Inwardly they resisted the force of this pressure which was incomprehensible to them, though they clearly sensed it.

A tremendous Radiation-Power was gathering above the commander. But Saul fought like a lion against the voice of his spirit, which was about to arouse him. He feared the inevitable moment and would willingly have postponed it. Anger seized his violent nature because he felt as helpless as a little child.

He perceived that he was standing under a Higher Power. His keen intellect sought out the beginning of this singular condition, and he was forced to acknowledge that it all had to do with the arrest of the Christian woman.

Repeatedly Saul had to think of the moment when this woman had said a few words to him. They had been words of the coolest rebuff, yet they were charged with such faith and trust in her God as to evoke a spiritual upheaval in Saul.

He pondered how it was possible for a few simple words to make such a deep impression. Like a blind man he groped about in the confusion of his soul, seeking connections and logical explanations. But he could not find them. This made him ever more testy and irascible.

Oh, to ride faster, ever faster, to get to Damascus soon! That was his only thought.

Suddenly a rushing gust of wind lashed clouds along overhead, and a glaring white light spread over the figure of Saul, apparently flowing from the cloud rent by a spectral storm.

The horses stood as if turned to stone, some collapsed. Saul lay face down on the ground. He could not endure the stream of Light passing into his eyes from the Radiant Cross, to the very depths of his soul. He lay on the ground as if dead. At the same time he heard a Voice which, coming from infinite Heights, reverberated in his spirit:

"Saul, why do you persecute Me, and those who proclaim My Word for the blessing of the world? It will avail you little if you work against the Power of your God, for you are Mine!"

A feeble breath raised his shoulders slightly, a shudder coursed through his body, but he was unable to straighten himself. The Light still burned in his eyes and caused him unutterable pain. In spite of it he felt a blissful joy within. He seemed to be free of a burden, free of the pressure of his imagined human greatness, and in him who was unable to think, to act or to will anything, the Word came to life and was reality:

"It will avail you nothing if you go against the Power of your God."

He felt: God had revealed His Power to him. He was still blinded by the Light of this Divine Power.

His companions were afraid. They had stood up with difficulty, and wanted to assist him. They lifted him up. When they set him on his feet, and he was slowly able to move the muscles of his great, heavy body again, they noticed that his horse was dead. Carefully they led him to the roadside.

Then he told them in a strange and distant voice that the mighty Flame had taken away his sight, and that they would have to lead him.

He recounted how God had spoken to him. They were greatly

amazed, for they had heard nothing, although they had seen the great Light, which had overwhelmed them all.

"And now," said Saul, "let us ride on to Damascus. But you, Lucius, ride back with some of the men and bring the Christian woman to Damascus. There you will receive further instructions.

Then his men lifted him onto a horse and conducted him with care and respect.

A NIGHT and half a day had passed. A bleak, sultry midday had followed the heavy morning rains. Dark clouds, often rent by dazzling glints of sunshine, hung low down and moved swiftly past the range of hills in the subsiding storm.

It was stuffy in the cell of the little citadel. The many people still remained there, for they did not want to part from the place of their great spiritual experience. In the gloom of the stormy night the Light of Life had dawned upon them through what had happened with the woman prisoner.

Like trusting children they sat at the feet of the Christian woman and listened to the story of her life. And while they were still listening in astonishment, half surprised that a human life could change in so short a time, most of them were themselves already on the way to becoming different. But this they did not yet know.

Magdalene saw with heartfelt joy that her words took root in these simple minds. Only a few stood aside and looked at the others derisively.

"The entertainment with the mad Christian woman helps to dispel the boredom of their guard-duty," they whispered to each other.

To them too the experience of the night was inconceivable. But they soon found words to silence the uncomfortable admonition of their souls in the sleep of spiritual indolence.

Then at midday the noise of galloping horses fell upon their ears. The signal rang out from the tower. They all hurried to their posts; the old discipline and order characteristic of the Roman troops was quickly restored within the small company. The gates admitted those who had conducted Magdalene there the day before. The commander, Lucius, delivered Saul's written order to the captain of the fortress.

Immediately the gates were open for Magdalene's release. Amazed, Saul's men heard of what had taken place in the night, and in whispers they told of Saul's wonderful transformation near Damascus, and of the great Light that had appeared to all of them.

Totally convinced through the pronouncement of the Truth from Magdalene's lips and the swift fulfilment of her words, glowing enthusiasm burst forth among the Romans. These human beings were deeply shaken and astonished, and would all have loved to journey to Damascus with Mary Magdalene. But they were not allowed to leave the fortress. They asked, however, for Magdalene's blessing and the grace of baptism, and she promised to send a disciple of the Lord to them from Damascus.

WHEN SAUL entered Damascus he was already expected by the Christians, for the disciple Ananias had received a message from the Light. They knew that Saul was an enemy of the Lord and had been given authority and permission from the Pharisees and High Priests to capture all Christians and to pass sentence on them. Hence they believed that their hour had come, and assembled every evening at a secret place in an old catacomb to pray. At this time the spirit of Ananias detached itself from its body. It was borne up into a bright clear Light, at whose highest, most radiant point the Cross shone forth.

From this torrent of Light, however, he kept hearing his name. And his earthly lips formed clearly and distinctly the words that penetrated to him from the luminous flood:

"Go forth, and ask for Saul of Tarsus! Do not hide but seek the lion in its den. The Lord changes the ways, remember this, and do not fear. Behold, he is praying, for he has seen you in spirit, and I have told him your name. He is My chosen instrument for conversion, and I will show him how much he is to suffer for My Name's sake. Lay your hands upon him so that he may see, for the earthly condition of his eyes has not been damaged; he has been blinded solely by the spirit. Awaken him with the Power of the Holy Spirit!"

Ananias stood up and, led by the Spirit, went at once to the lane which they called the "straight one". In a house indicated to him by the Light of the Lord he asked for Saul and found him, blind and in prayer.

Saul heard steps approaching him, and turned his head in the direction whence the sound came. He had become a different person. From the strong head, which now appeared slightly bowed, a clear radiance was gleaming. He groped for the place where Ananias stood, and seemed to absorb gratefully a wave of love, for a glimmer of joy stole over his quiet, grief-stricken face, as he said:

"Are you the one whose help the Lord has promised me?"

"Yes, I am Ananias, the disciple of Jesus, and come to you in His Name so that you may regain your sight and be filled with the Holy Spirit." And he laid his hands upon Saul's head and eyes.

Saul went on his knees, tears flowed down his cheeks from his Light-blinded eyes, and he felt as though veil upon veil was falling away from his soul as well. Full of strength he rose to his feet and asked to be permitted to stay in the circle of the disciples of Christ. They admitted him and taught him the Word of the Lord.

A time of joyful activity began such as Saul had not known before. The Light shone in his spirit, and his great gifts were set aglow and quickened by his strong volition.

Before long Saul, as Paul, was proclaiming the Word of the Lord aloud, and refuting the attacks of the Pharisees with their own weapons. A fierce struggle broke out in the schools of Damascus, and now the hatred of the Jews was above all directed against Paul. But he was filled with the Spirit and hardly perceived it.

THE NUMBER of followers grew considerably when the deeds and speeches of the disciples and the transformation of Saul became known. Mary Magdalene too, whose story spread among the people, attracted many to the community in Damascus, for she had begun to teach the women. Here she also established a home for girls, which was named after her, and gave the first instruction to all who offered their help.

She was active day and night, and won many grateful friends. A great power filled Mary Magdalene, always inspiring her to fresh activity. All her work achieved rapid success, and it bore fruit. It seemed that a peaceful existence was about to blossom anew for Mary Magdalene, a beautiful circle of activity among the women. But the insidious efforts of the Jews who were in pursuit of Paul would allow the community no peace of mind. A regular persecution began.

Mary Magdalene was warned. Again the great Light blazed up before her and she heard a voice:

"Soon you will have completed your path, handmaiden of the Lord; make haste lest the murderer's hand cut it short. Be an instrument once more, for Paul is in imminent danger. Yet he is only at the beginning of his work, and his activity will extend far and away across the nations.

"Speed is essential – go to the gate towards midnight and summon Paul to the place with three helpers. From there they should let you down over the wall, so that you may reach the temples in the rocks even before dawn, for they are well on the way to capturing you and delivering you up to be tortured."

Again it was a blustery night when Mary Magdalene set out hurriedly to the disciples. She would deliver the message at once. All of them were gathered in a room in which the lights had diffused a fine, bitter-sweet fragrance. They were just saying a prayer when Mary Magdalene quietly entered the house through a back door.

She waited until the voice of Paul, audible a long way off, had ended; only then did she knock at the low two-piece door. A narrow crack in the upper half was opened. The landlady peered out cautiously, almost nervously. When she recognised Mary Magdalene, her furrowed face smoothed out, and her black eyes assumed a happy gleam. Bowing low, she stepped aside to let Mary Magdalene enter.

Meanwhile many of the assembled had left the room through the front door. The few armchairs and the dark wooden benches stood in disarray along the four rough, bare walls of the large room which must have served formerly as a stable.

In the centre of the room a group of men still stood in animated conversation, Paul and Ananias among them. The others were young pupils who were eagerly discussing Paul's propositions. Now and then the latter interposed a few words in Greek.

In their zeal they had not noticed Mary Magdalene enter. Suddenly they discovered the woman who had joined them. With the word "Peace!" Paul raised his hands as if in blessing.

Suddenly a heavy blow boomed against the gate of the outer courtyard, making everyone start back.

Now the news flew from Mary Magdalene's lips. She stressed emphatically the warning given to her. She had instantly grasped that the pursuers were even then at work. She signalled quickly, and the five people followed Mary Magdalene silently the way she had come.

It was quiet in the rear courtyard; wet from the rain, the lanes through which they were hurrying were deserted and gloomy. They did not know the way, and only followed the direction leading to the mountains.

So they came to a small barred door which was not locked. It led to an old tower whose platform could be approached at floor level, while on the other side it went down into a deep but dry ditch.

The enormous stone-structure was dark grey and rough, covered with dense tufts of grass. It was pitch-dark and deathly silent below. Mary Magdalene looked down horrified, but noticed at once the huge winch designed to convey large baskets of fodder into the city's granaries. She remembered the words she had heard:

"Have yourselves let down there – – –"
and she asked the strong young men to make ready a basket. Into it they bundled the large heavy Paul, who only reluctantly agreed to this plan of escape. Ananias reminded him of obedience. Then the winch screeched under the powerful fists of the three young men.

Magdalene watched the basket descend slowly and ponderously into the depth, her heart pounding with fear. Trembling, she leaned over the parapet of the tower. Would the flight be successful? The shuddering and easing of the rope indicated that the basket had struck firm ground. And soon the men were able to pull it up again.

Ananias and Magdalene were waiting, every nerve strained, for behind them they could see a glimmer of light slowly approaching from the streets of the city. In their overwrought state they imagined that they already heard voices through the moaning of the night-wind. Full of anxiety, the three young pupils assisting their escape urged and advised them to get into the basket together.

"It can easily carry two adult persons, and we will gain time, otherwise it could happen that Paul will be seized below."

This drove them to take the ultimate risk. They entrusted themselves to the basket, which could easily accommodate them. The jolt with which they hurtled into the depth, before the winch began to function properly and evenly again, was terrible. Mary Magdalene was horror-stricken by the swift descent. Would the ropes hold? But then they were gradually suspended once more, moving slowly and surely.

When the basket had nearly reached the ground, the rope suddenly plunged down from above with a swish; they landed with a strong impact. Shaken, they both crawled from the basket. Paul was no longer there, having presumably gone on ahead.

Shouting resounded from above; heavy stones were dropped into the ditch. Both fugitives hugged the wall of the tower, and under cover of its stone walls crept cautiously away towards the mountains.

But they could still hear the clamour of the Jews and the din; sorrowfully they thought of the poor victims who had fallen into the hands of their pursuers. Who was the quick-witted one who had promptly severed the rope of the basket?

Only now did Magdalene feel how much her body ached from the sudden fall, but she walked on bravely in the thought that she had carried out the Lord's Command. The way led through dark, damp bushes, upwards to the first hills, where small, square houses with flat roofs still hugged the rocks like birds' nests. They were uninhabited – remnants of an old shepherd settlement.

Early morning mist began to rise with the faint gleam that announced the sun. Night still lay upon the earth, only the sky was already lighter. The low clouds had been swept off by the storm which had now given way to a mild wind.

Drenched and weary, the two disciples were walking along the upper slopes, looking for a path to the temples in the caves.

"Paul will give us a signal when we are at the place," offered Mary Magdalene in consolation.

But the consolation was for herself more than for Ananias, who was walking erect in front of her.

"We need no other signals than those which the Lord gives us. I know we are on the right path!"

But the journey became very difficult for Mary Magdalene. She was no longer able to step out as vigorously as usual.

"Be still and without anxiety, soon you will have reached your destination. Your life is coming to its close. You will then be permitted to experience the joys of the Light!"

Thus did the voices whisper solicitously around her. Rays of Light were swinging in fine, colourful circles before her; cool hands were leading and supporting her, so that she could walk safely. Yet her brow was covered with cold sweat. A stabbing pain on her left side necessitated frequent rests. She was hardly able to walk on.

"Ananias, you follow Paul, I cannot make such rapid progress."

"If they search for us they will seize you, Mary Magdalene."

"If so, it is the Will of the Lord that they must walk over me before reaching His Chosen one. I will do my duty to the very end!"

Her strength had found expression once more. But it was only the inner psychic strength that sustained her. The strength of her body was exhausted; its hour had come.

Ananias took her to a cave off the beaten track, which offered shelter from harsh winds and was in a glorious sunny spot. The view from the rising hills of the Anti-Lebanon over the endless distances was enchanting in its beauty.

But Mary Magdalene saw no more of this.

Her head drooped on to her breast; dry heat alternated with chills. She longed for rest and a cool drink. For the first time in a long while, she herself needed a gentle word from someone, a helping hand. For a long time her life had been dedicated only to the service of others, with never a thought of herself. But why did the Lord now send her this weakness, this extinguishing? Where had she failed? This question troubled her soul.

Ananias prepared a resting-place. He arranged everything as best he could, and promised to bring food and a jug of water soon, as he wanted to return to Damascus for help.

"Ananias, think of Paul, not me! My hour will soon come. But his task still lies before him!"

Ananias nodded. He laid his hand on her head, her body relaxed, and great calm filled her. Luminous radiance flooded the cave; the face of a shining messenger of God bent over the sick woman. Fine rays were coming from the Light. They sank ever deeper, assuming the shape of an ascending flight of stairs, a luminous ladder, which reached into the highest, Light-filled distances.

Joyful, exultant voices were ringing out from Above, and bright faces were shining forth, which appeared dear and familiar, yet distant and holy to her.

Again the fragrance of white orange-blossoms wafted over her, awakening memories of a distant, hot land, in whose sparkling sands a child was playing at her feet. There was so much earthly felicity in this scene, a remembrance of a wonderful youth. Then the blossoms fell from the golden branches, and a river carried them upon its silvery-green waves in a golden boat to a land in which the hand of a dark power held sway, and again this radiant child was with her.

A fine desert-wind was murmuring and whispering. She stood before the gates of a golden-white city. Above it a Light glowed, more radiant than the light of a sun, from which a white countenance gazed at her.

"I, Is-ma-el, am guiding you!" were his words.

And she looked into the radiant suite of white rooms, undulating palm gardens, golden halls. Before her opened wonderful grottoes, in which dwelt blissful human beings. There were seven sacred grottoes, each in a different colour, but always those wonderful figures with the shining, mature faces were present as well. Among these was only one woman, enveloped in veils, the most radiant, purest of the figures, who was like a flower that had just burst into bloom.*

* Beside Abd-ru-shin she saw Nahome, whose earthly mother she had once been.

286

In the seventh grotto was white, dazzling Light. Only *one* Figure shone forth from this White Radiance. A Man garbed in white with a sword and a sparkling ring, on Whose robe was the image of the Dove. The Light of His eyes was golden. He pointed upwards and said in a ringing, melodious voice: "We will meet again."

A ring of Light began to glow before Magdalene's eyes; then she saw the Radiant One no more. –

Mary Magdalene fell into a long, refreshing sleep. Ananias had left her in order to fetch help and sustenance.

But it was ordained that she should complete this journey alone, as she had also begun it alone, seeking the Lord.

The fever subsided, the pain of the broken rib was taken from her. Again she beheld pictures. Her spirit united with the Light. Now she was no longer by herself. Light-women came to her, and refreshed her with spiritual food.

Again the Power of Purity streamed over her. But not in the form of the lovely Maiden Irmingard as It did at the time when Jesus, the Light of God, still sojourned on earth; this time the Lily glowed white, shining and secure in the heart of the Holy Grail, and sent forth only Her Light-rays across the spheres down into the Gardens of the Pure Spirits, into the light blue silvery grotto in which the mother of Jesus was awaiting her mission. And it was her light-figure which descended to Magdalene.

"As you were with me, so am I now with you," she said.

"From the Fountain of Life I bring you the Power of Purity which you have longed for as the most sublime treasure. It will help you in your ascent. Leave the world freely, for the joys of the higher realms await you!

"Everything swings in the cycle of Divine Happening and Development. Everything is so different, so much more beautiful, richer and holier than human beings imagine. As great and above human comprehension as is the abundance of what has been created in Primordial Creation, so great does the threshold of the subsequently-created planes appear to the spirit emerging from material substance. These planes are inhabited by the blessed human spirits, together with

287

many other Light-forms that you neither yet know at all nor are able to name.

"Only when you have stepped into Eternity will you become conscious of the distant road to GOD!"

And the soul of Mary Magdalene loosened and detached itself from its earthly covering, rising towards Mary of Nazareth. Her feet walked on dainty rose-paths, her slender head inclined a little, and a wreath of Light shone above her white raiment.

"You shall behold Jesus," she said, "and Him Who is yet to come. It is He Whom you will also serve later on earth. Only then will the cycle of your wandering close, just as your present death closes the cycle of your present earth-life, for the spirit journeys on distant paths."

It was as though a Light-thread were stretching upwards, about to break, and it broke.

The soul of Mary Magdalene swung up freely into ever greater, clearer Light until in the Light-Radiance of the Golden Gate it beheld Jesus, the Transfigured Son of God, as He had appeared to her after His death. Streams of Light received her and bore her to a Luminous Isle, where she was to abide for a long time.

THE WONDROUS RINGING

IN THE UNIVERSE HAS DIED AWAY.

THE SEER LAYS DOWN HIS PEN

UNTIL A FRESH CALL FROM THE LIGHT
REACHES HIM!

CONTENTS

Volume I

The Millennium Series

From Past Millennia	374 pages, paperback ISBN 3-87860-222-7
Ephesus	222 pages, hardback ISBN 3-87860-163-8
Zoroaster	254 pages, paperback ISBN 3-87860-221-9
Lao-Tse	283 pages, hardback ISBN 1-898853-00-2 paperback ISBN 1-898853-01-0
Buddha	276 pages, hardback ISBN 3-87860-153-0
Mohammed	240 pages, hardback ISBN 3-87860-080-1

Further works from our publishers:

In the Light of Truth
The Grail Message of Abd-ru-shin

Volume I   "Free yourself from all darkness!"
                212 pages

Volume II   "Now stride upwards vigorously!"
                416 pages

Volume III   "Expand your knowledge!"
                460 pages

Edition in
one volume
(unabridged)   1062 pages

Special edition
in one volume   1062 pages
(India paper, leather)

A special book which clearly answers the unsolved problems of human existence. Through the vast knowledge mediated in its pages, the earnestly-seeking reader who weighs and examines objectively is led out of all the chaos of the present-day confusion and distortion to clear recognitions.
This book commands attention by its carefully-considered language, the clarity of its thoughts, and the setting right of distorted concepts, unmistakably and sometimes severely but irrefutably explained.
The Laws through which the entire Creation came into being and exists are plainly set forth, world events are interpreted in their true significance, and man's responsibility before God and his fellow-men is revealed and explained. Thus to him who opens himself to these recognitions is restored the indestructible inner security of his personality.